Oxford Revise

In par

Edexcel GCSE (9-1) Maths

Higher

Revision Workbook

Authors: Jemma Sherwood and Paul Hunt

Series Editor: Naomi Bartholomew-Millar

The Oxford Revise GCSE Maths Series: Our approach

Our no-fuss approach lets you dive straight into the practice you need for the exam. GCSE Grades help you monitor your own progress on every page, and 'Guided answers' at the back help you mark your own solutions. The practice exam papers come with guidance too: for every question we let you know which page to turn to for extra practice. And you'll find perfectly matched support on the exact same page in the revision guide.

OXFORD
UNIVERSITY PRESS

1-to-1
Page Match with
Edexcel Higher
Revision Guide

Contents

Guided practice papers

For every question in the Practice exam papers, we've provided a note of what page to turn to for more practice on that topic.

Further practice & support: Q1 p.60; Q2 p.17

You'll also find 'Guided answers' at the back of the book, so you can mark your own solutions.

Use of calculators

This book provides support with both how and when to use your calculator. Look for these symbols against questions:

Make sure to use your calculator – it's good practice for the exam.

Make sure not to use your calculator – this question would only appear in the non-calculator paper.

If there's no symbol, then the question could appear on either the calculator or the non-calculator paper.

Calculations

1. Work out

    a)   25.043 − 17.82

.... **[I got ___ / 2 marks]**

    b)   7.4 × 0.26

.... **[___ / 2 marks]**

    c)   17.12 ÷ 0.8

.... **[___ / 2 marks]**

2. Work out

    a) $(12 - 4 \times 2)^3$

.... **[___ / 1 mark]**

    b) $\dfrac{4 \times 5^2}{4 \times 5 \div 2}$

.... **[___ / 1 mark]**

    c) $5\sqrt{50 - 1} + 6 \times 3$

.... **[___ / 1 mark]**

    d) $5 + (-3.2) \times 4$

.... **[___ / 1 mark]**

    e) $(1 - 0.1) \times 4 - (-10)$

.... **[___ / 2 marks]**

    f) $\dfrac{(-0.2) \times (-6)}{-1 + 0.7}$

.... **[___ / 2 marks]**

3. Supermarket A sells a pack of six vegan burgers for £4.65

    Supermarket B sells a pack of eight for £6.59

    Which supermarket is better value? Show your working.

.... **[___ / 3 marks]**

4. Marina's fence measures 1.4 m by 10.5 m. It costs £0.60 to paint the fence per square metre. How much does it cost to paint the fence in total?

£.. **[___ / 3 marks]**

Rounding & truncation

Grade 3

1. Round 20 193 to

    a) 4 significant figures

    .... **[I got ___ / 1 mark]**

    b) 3 significant figures

    .... **[___ / 1 mark]**

    c) 2 significant figures

    .... **[___ / 1 mark]**

    d) 1 significant figure.

    .... **[___ / 1 mark]**

Grade 3

2. Round 0.006 802 to

    a) 1 significant figure

> **Hint**
> Where do significant figures start?

    .... **[___ / 1 mark]**

    b) 2 significant figures

    .... **[___ / 1 mark]**

    c) 3 significant figures.

    .... **[___ / 1 mark]**

Grade 3

3. a) Calculate $\frac{1}{3}(0.02 \times 11.9)^2$. Write all the figures on your calculator display.

    .... **[___ / 1 mark]**

    b) Write your answer to part **a**

        i) truncated to 2 decimal places

    .... **[___ / 1 mark]**

        ii) rounded to 2 significant figures.

    .... **[___ / 1 mark]**

Grade 3

4. One bag of grass seed covers an area of 3.66 m² and costs £4.99. Fabio needs grass seed for a lawn of 32 m². How much will the grass seed cost Fabio? Give your answer to the nearest pound.

    £.. **[___ / 3 marks]**

Grade 4

5. Shirley rounds 0.065 29 to 2 significant figures and gives the answer 0.07. Shirley is wrong. Explain why.

> **Hint**
> Think about the difference between significant figures and decimal places.

.... **[___ / 1 mark]**

Estimation

1. Estimate the value of $\dfrac{317 + 48.6}{9.683}$. Show your working.

> **Hint**
> *Always round numbers before calculating.*

.... **[I got ___ / 2 marks]**

2. Estimate the value of $\dfrac{2.67 \times 1.36}{0.11 + 0.42}$. Show your working.

.... **[___ / 2 marks]**

3. A biologist visits a lake at the start of January and works out that the number of fish in the lake is approximately 1000. She thinks that the population is growing at a rate of 17 fish per day. Estimate how many fish there will be in the lake five months later.

.... **[___ / 3 marks]**

4. In one week, an Italian restaurant sells 96 portions of lasagne. The restaurant sells a portion of lasagne for £8.95 and each portion costs £3.20 to make. Estimate the profit the restaurant makes from lasagne in the week.

£.. **[___ / 3 marks]**

5. James is driving to visit his Gran who lives 405 km away. He leaves at 8.30 am and drives at an average speed of 77 km/h, stopping for a 25-minute lunch break on the way. Estimate the time he arrives at his Gran's.

.... **[___ / 3 marks]**

6. Giving your answers to 1 decimal place, estimate the value of

    a) $\sqrt{47}$

.... **[___ / 1 mark]**

    b) $\sqrt{200}$

.... **[___ / 1 mark]**

Error intervals & bounds

Grade 5 **1.** The length, p m, of a football pitch is given as 110 m.
Write the error interval for p if this value is rounded to

    a) the nearest 10 metres

.... $\leq p <$ .... **[I got ___ / 2 marks]**

    b) the nearest 5 metres.

.... $\leq p <$ .... **[___ / 2 marks]**

Grade 5 **2.** A number, x, is given rounded to a particular degree of accuracy.
Write the error interval for x in each case.

    a) $x = 4.67$ to 2 decimal places

.... $\leq x <$ .... **[___ / 2 marks]**

    b) $x = 5000$ to 1 significant figure

.... $\leq x <$ .... **[___ / 2 marks]**

Grade 5 **3.** A number, y, is given truncated. Write the error interval for y

    a) $y = 9$ truncated to an integer

.... $\leq y <$ .... **[___ / 2 marks]**

    b) $y = 2.5$ truncated to 1 decimal place

.... $\leq y <$ .... **[___ / 2 marks]**

Grade 5 **4.** Sienna uses her calculator to answer a question. The display breaks and she can only see 1.8 at the start of her answer. Let x be the unknown number on the display and write the range of possible values for x as an error interval.

> **Hint**
> Remember your inequalities.

.... **[___ / 2 marks]**

Grade 7 **5.** The side length of a square is given as 15 cm to the nearest centimetre. Work out the error interval for the area, x cm², of the square.

.... **[___ / 3 marks]**

Grade 7 **6.** A car travels on the motorway at a speed of 110 km/h to 3 significant figures, for a distance of 45 km, correct to the nearest kilometre. By considering bounds, work out the time taken in hours to travel this distance to an appropriate degree of accuracy. Give a reason for your answer.

.... **[___ / 5 marks]**

Adding & subtracting fractions

Grade 3

1. Work out and simplify where possible

a) $\frac{2}{9} + \frac{5}{6}$

.... [I got ___ / 2 marks]

b) $3\frac{1}{6} - 2\frac{3}{4}$

.... [___ / 3 marks]

Grade 4

2. $\frac{1}{8}$ of the students in a class drive to school. $\frac{2}{3}$ of the students walk to school. The rest take the bus. What fraction of the students take the bus?

Hint
The whole class is represented by the number 1

.... [___ / 3 marks]

Grade 4

3. Daisy is building a model train track. Her track is $2\frac{4}{5}$ m long. She then takes out a piece of track which is $\frac{7}{8}$ m long and replaces it with a piece which is $1\frac{1}{20}$ m long. Work out the length of her track now.

....m   [___ / 3 marks]

Grade 4

4. Maxwell is reading a book on his e-reader. When he picks it up one day, it tells him he is $\frac{1}{3}$ of the way through the book. He reads some and when he puts it down he is $\frac{3}{4}$ of the way through. What fraction of the book did he read?

.... [___ / 2 marks]

Grade 5

5. Work out the perimeter of the shape shown.

Hint
Add together the whole number parts and then add together the fraction parts.

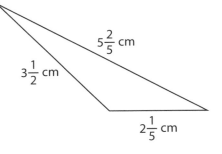

$5\frac{2}{5}$ cm

$3\frac{1}{2}$ cm

$2\frac{1}{5}$ cm

....cm   [___ / 3 marks]

Multiplying & dividing fractions

1. A café uses up $\frac{2}{3}$ of a box of coffee beans every day. How many days will it take for it to use up 16 boxes of coffee beans?

.... **[I got ___ / 2 marks]**

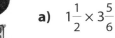

2. Work out and simplify where possible

a) $1\frac{1}{2} \times 3\frac{5}{6}$

.... **[___ / 3 marks]**

b) $4\frac{4}{9} \div 2\frac{2}{3}$

.... **[___ / 3 marks]**

3. Rafael reserves $\frac{3}{10}$ of his monthly wage to pay his bills. $\frac{1}{4}$ of this amount is spent on his electricity bill.

What fraction of his monthly wage does Rafael spend on his electricity bill?

> **Hint**
> What calculation does the word 'of' represent?

.... **[___ / 2 marks]**

4. A triangle has base $1\frac{1}{5}$ cm and height $\frac{6}{5}$ cm. A rectangle has the same area as the triangle. If the width of the rectangle is $\frac{2}{5}$ cm, what is its length, x cm? Give your answer in its simplest form.

> **Hint**
> This question combines fractions and geometry. Find the area of the triangle. What is the same about both shapes?

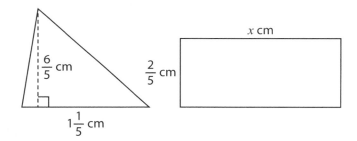

.... cm **[___ / 3 marks]**

5. Vasiliki has a piece of material $3\frac{3}{4}$ m long.

She is cutting it into smaller pieces of length $\frac{5}{6}$ m.

How many smaller pieces can she get, and what fraction of a metre will be left over?

> **Hint**
> You need to divide fractions here.

Number of small pieces = ... Fraction left = ... m **[___ / 3 marks]**

6

Fractions, decimals & percentages

Grade 4 🖩

1. In Lin's class, 6 out of 25 children read fantasy books. In Jay's class, 8 out of 32 children read fantasy books. Lin says the proportion of children who read fantasy books is greater in her class than in Jay's. Is Lin correct? Explain your answer.

....

.... **[I got ___ / 2 marks]**

Grade 5 🖩

2. Sally says that multiplying by 0.01 is the same as dividing by 100. Is Sally correct? Explain your reasoning.

.... **[___ / 1 mark]**

Grade 6 🖩

3. Explain, using prime factors, why $\frac{11}{28}$ is a recurring decimal.

....

.... **[___ / 2 marks]**

Grade 6 🖩

4. Jonathan ran some park races last year. 15% of his races were 5 km runs, $\frac{7}{10}$ of his races were 10 km runs and the rest were half marathons. If he ran 20 races in total, how many were half marathons?

.... **[___ / 3 marks]**

Grade 6

5. In a city, 5.5 out of every 22 square metres are used for housing and services. If housing takes up $\frac{5}{8}$ of this space, what percentage of the total area is used for services?

.... **[___ / 3 marks]**

7

Recurring decimals

1. Express these fractions as decimals.

a) $\dfrac{1}{18}$

.... **[I got ___ / 2 marks]**

b) $\dfrac{20}{33}$

.... **[___ / 2 marks]**

c) $\dfrac{3}{7}$

.... **[___ / 2 marks]**

2. Prove algebraically that $0.\dot{5} = \dfrac{5}{9}$

> **Hint**
> Let $x = 0.\dot{5}$ and find $10x$

[___ / 2 marks]

3. Write $0.8\dot{4}$ as a fraction in its simplest form.

[___ / 3 marks]

4. Prove algebraically that $0.0\dot{5}\dot{6} = \dfrac{28}{495}$

[___ / 3 marks]

Surds

1. Write these expressions in the form $a\sqrt{2}$, where a is an integer.

    a) $\sqrt{18} - \sqrt{8}$

.... **[I got ___ / 2 marks]**

    b) $\sqrt{200} + \sqrt{72} - \sqrt{98}$

.... **[___ / 2 marks]**

    c) $3\sqrt{2} + 7\sqrt{32}$

.... **[___ / 2 marks]**

    d) $\dfrac{14}{\sqrt{2}}$

.... **[___ / 2 marks]**

2. Write these expressions in the form $a + b\sqrt{3}$, where a and b are integers.

    a) $(1 + \sqrt{3})^2$

.... **[___ / 2 marks]**

    b) $\dfrac{8}{2 - \sqrt{3}}$

> **Hint**
> Multiply numerator and denominator by the
> denominator with a changed sign.

.... **[___ / 3 marks]**

    c) $\dfrac{\sqrt{3} - 1}{\sqrt{3} + 1}$

.... **[___ / 3 marks]**

3. Show that $(\sqrt{11} - \sqrt{8})(\sqrt{11} + \sqrt{8}) = 3$

.... **[___ / 3 marks]**

Index notation

Grade 4

1. Peter says that $2^3 \times 5^2$ simplifies to 10^5. Peter is wrong. Explain why.

.... [I got ___ / 1 mark]

Grade 5

2. Simplify $\dfrac{(2^7 \times 2^4)^{-1}}{2}$ fully and leave your answer in index form.

> **Hint**
> A power of −1 gives the reciprocal and a power of $\frac{1}{n}$ gives the nth root.
>

.... [___ / 2 marks]

Grade 6

3. Write in simplified index form

a) $\left(3^{\frac{1}{4}}\right)^{\frac{1}{4}}$ .... [___ / 1 mark]

b) $\sqrt[3]{5^2}$ .... [___ / 2 marks]

Grade 7

4. Work out

a) $\left(\dfrac{2}{5}\right)^3$ .... [___ / 1 mark]

b) $25^{\frac{1}{2}}$ .... [___ / 1 mark]

c) $8^{\frac{2}{3}}$ .... [___ / 2 marks]

d) $\left(\dfrac{16}{9}\right)^{-\frac{3}{2}}$ .... [___ / 3 marks]

Grade 8

5. $3 \times \sqrt{27} = 3^n$

Find the value of n

.... [___ / 3 marks]

Grade 9

6. $2^x \times 2^y = 64$ and $2^x \div 2^y = 4$

Find the values of x and y

> **Hint**
> Start by finding two simultaneous equations.

$x =$ .... $y =$ .... [___ / 4 marks]

Prime factor decomposition

1. Write 110 as a product of its prime factors.

.... **[I got ___ / 2 marks]**

2. a) Write 540 as a product of powers of its prime factors.

.... **[___ / 2 marks]**

b) By looking at its prime factors, explain why 540 is divisible by 15

> **Hint**
> What are the prime factors of 15?

.... **[___ / 1 mark]**

3. a) Write 750 as a product of its prime factors. Give your answer in index notation.

.... **[___ / 2 marks]**

b) By looking at its prime factors, explain why 750 is not divisible by 4

.... **[___ / 1 mark]**

4. The prime factor decomposition of a number, x, is $2 \times 3^2 \times 7 \times 13$

a) Is x even or odd? Explain your reasoning.

.... **[___ / 1 mark]**

b) What is the prime factor decomposition of a number twice as big as x?

.... **[___ / 1 mark]**

5. A number is a multiple of 4, 5 and 6. Write the prime factor decomposition of the smallest number it could be.

.... **[___ / 2 marks]**

Finding HCF and LCM

Grade 4

1. a) Write 160 as a product of prime factors.

.... **[I got ___ / 2 marks]**

b) Find the highest common factor of 160 and 280

.... **[___ / 2 marks]**

c) Find the lowest common multiple of 160 and 280

.... **[___ / 2 marks]**

Grade 5

2. Two numbers have prime factor decompositions $2^3 \times 5 \times 11$ and $2 \times 3^2 \times 5$

Find

a) the highest common factor of the two numbers

.... **[___ / 2 marks]**

b) the lowest common multiple of the two numbers.

.... **[___ / 1 mark]**

Grade 5

3. Fran is sorting her books into piles. She has 225 yellow books and 324 orange books. She does not want to mix the colours and wants every pile to contain the same number of books. Work out the biggest number of books she can put in each pile.

.... **[___ / 3 marks]**

Grade 6

4. Two numbers, A and B, have prime factor decompositions $A = 2 \times 3 \times 7 \times x$ and $B = 2^2 \times 5^2$

The highest common factor of the two numbers is 4

a) Work out the value of x

> **Hint**
> How does the HCF relate to the prime factor decomposition?

.... **[___ / 1 mark]**

b) Work out the value of the number A

.... **[___ / 1 mark]**

Standard form

Grade 3

1. Write these as ordinary numbers.

    a) 1.56×10^8

    .... **[I got ___ / 1 mark]**

    b) 8.02×10^{-3}

    .... **[___ / 1 mark]**

Grade 3

2. Write these numbers in standard form.

    a) 48 000 000 000

    .... **[___ / 1 mark]**

    b) 0.000 0703

    .... **[___ / 1 mark]**

    c) 95×10^6

    .... **[___ / 1 mark]**

    d) 0.68×10^{-4}

    .... **[___ / 1 mark]**

Grade 3

3. The distance from the Sun to Earth is approximately 150 000 000 km. Write this number in standard form.

    ....km **[___ / 1 mark]**

Grade 4

4. Put these numbers in order of size, starting with the biggest.

    2.1×10^4 2.3×10^5 0.21×10^4 2200

> **Hint**
> Write all the numbers in the same form.

    .... **[___ / 3 marks]**

Grade 4

5. The size of a bacteria cell is 4×10^{-7} m and the size of a virus is 0.000 000 05 m. Which is smaller, the bacteria cell or the virus? Show your working.

    .... **[___ / 2 marks]**

Grade 4

6. Here are the populations of four countries.

    Angola: 31.8×10^6 Uzbekistan: 3.29×10^7 Malaysia: 31.9 million   Mongolia: 3.2×10^6

    Which country has the largest population? Show your working.

    .... **[___ / 2 marks]**

Calculating with standard form

Grade 5

1. Work out the value of each expression, giving your answers in standard form.

   a) $(5 \times 10^4) + (6 \times 10^5)$

   .... **[I got ___ / 2 marks]**

   b) $(9 \times 10^{-3}) - (3 \times 10^{-4})$

   .... **[___ / 2 marks]**

   c) $(2.1 \times 10^8) \times (3 \times 10^{-5})$

   .... **[___ / 2 marks]**

   d) $(8.2 \times 10^3) \div (4.1 \times 10^7)$

   .... **[___ / 2 marks]**

Grade 6

2. The MiG 25 fighter jet can fly at 4×10^3 km/h. How long would it take to travel a distance of 3000 km? Give your answer in minutes.

   > **Hint**
   > Remember that
   > $speed = \dfrac{distance}{time}$

   .... minutes   **[___ / 3 marks]**

Grade 6

3. A region on a map forms the shape of a rectangle with width 1.2×10^2 km and length 7×10^3 km. Work out the area of this region in standard form.

   ....km²   **[___ / 3 marks]**

Grade 7

4. The circumference of Earth is 4.0075×10^9 cm. The circumference of another planet is 0.2 times the circumference of Earth.

   > **Hint**
   > Start by rounding the circumference of Earth.

   a) Work out an estimate for the circumference of this planet. Give your answer in standard form.

   ....cm   **[___ / 3 marks]**

   b) Is your answer in part **a** an underestimate or an overestimate? Explain your answer.

   ....   **[___ / 1 mark]**

Simplifying expressions

1. Simplify

  a) $3p - 5q + 3p^2 + 2q + 2q^2 - 9p^2$

.... **[I got ___ / 2 marks]**

  b) $5x^3 - 2xy - 6 + 6x^3 - 2 - 7xy + 8$

.... **[___ / 2 marks]**

2. Write an expression in its simplest form for

  a) the perimeter of the parallelogram

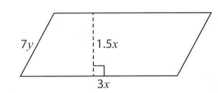

.... **[___ / 2 marks]**

  b) the area of the parallelogram.

.... **[___ / 2 marks]**

3. Simplify

  a) $(2a)^3$

.... **[___ / 2 marks]**

  b) $(5a^2b^3)^2$

.... **[___ / 2 marks]**

  c) $\dfrac{6x^2y^{-3}}{18yx^{-1}}$

.... **[___ / 2 marks]**

  d) $\sqrt{x^4y^6}$

> **Hint**
> How can you write a square root in index form?

.... **[___ / 2 marks]**

4. Find the value of x

  a) $\dfrac{3^{-2} \times 3^8}{3^7} = 3^x$

.... **[___ / 3 marks]**

  b) $2^5 \times 4^2 = 8^x$

.... **[___ / 3 marks]**

Solving linear equations

1. Solve

    a) $\dfrac{5-x}{2} = 12$

.... **[I got __ / 2 marks]**

    b) $\dfrac{2}{y} = 5$

.... **[__ / 2 marks]**

    c) $3 + p = 4p - 6$

.... **[__ / 2 marks]**

    d) $3(3 - 2p) = 4 - 11p$

.... **[__ / 2 marks]**

2. In a golf game, Sarah plays n holes, Ewan plays five fewer than Sarah and Cameron plays twice as many as Sarah. If they play 35 holes all together, form and solve an equation to find out how many holes Sarah plays.

.... **[__ / 3 marks]**

3. Rosalind thinks of a number. She multiplies her number by two, adds three and then writes the answer. Next she multiplies her original number by three, subtracts four and writes the answer. Rosalind realises she has written the same answer both times. What is Rosalind's number?

> **Hint**
> Form and solve an equation using x for the unknown number.

.... **[__ / 3 marks]**

4. This shape is a rectangle.

    y cm

    $(2x - 1)$ cm $(x + 3)$ cm

    a) Form and solve an equation to find the value of x

.... **[__ / 3 marks]**

    b) If the perimeter of the rectangle is 34 cm, find the area of the rectangle.

.... cm^2 **[__ / 4 marks]**

Linear graphs

1. Draw the graph of $x + y = 5$ on the grid.

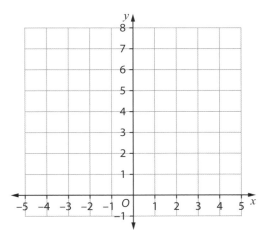

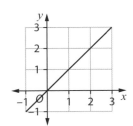

Hint
Work out some points that lie on the line first.

[I got ___ / 3 marks]

2. On the grid, draw the graph of $y = 3 - 2x$

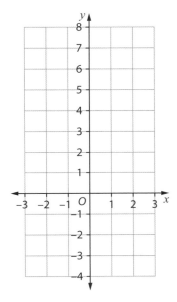

[___ / 3 marks]

3. For each part, work out the gradient of the line and write the equation of the line.

a)

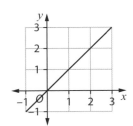

b)

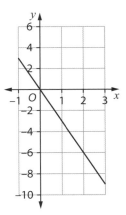

Gradient ....

Equation ....

[___ / 3 marks]

Gradient ....

Equation ....

[___ / 3 marks]

Equations of linear graphs

1. Work out the gradient and y-intercept of each of these lines.

a) $y = 5x + 1$

Gradient ....

y-intercept .... **[I got ___ / 2 marks]**

b) $y = 3 - 2x$

Gradient ....

y-intercept .... **[___ / 2 marks]**

c) $2y = x + 6$

> **Hint**
> Rearrange the equation of the line to make y the subject.

Gradient ....

y-intercept .... **[___ / 3 marks]**

d) $y - x = 10$

Gradient ....

y-intercept .... **[___ / 3 marks]**

e) $8x + 4y = 3$

Gradient ....

y-intercept .... **[___ / 3 marks]**

2. Write the equation of the line parallel to $y = 4x - 8$ that passes through the point (0, 5).

.... **[___ / 1 mark]**

3. Work out the equation of the line that passes through the two points.

a) (0, −1) and (2, 3)

.... **[___ / 3 marks]**

b) (−3, 5) and (1, 1)

.... **[___ / 3 marks]**

4. A line, L, has equation $y = 4 - 3x$. Sajid says that the line $3x + y = 0$ is parallel to L. Is Sajid correct? Explain your reasoning.

.... **[___ / 2 marks]**

Perpendicular lines

1. Match the equations of lines on the left with equations of perpendicular lines on the right.

$y = \frac{1}{2}x + 2$

$2y = 3x - 4$

$2x = 6 - 3y$

$y = x - 2$

$x + 2y - 1 = 0$

$y = -2x + 1$

$y + x = \frac{1}{2}$

$y - 2x = 0$

[I got ___ / 3 marks]

2. Ivan says that the lines $y = 2x + 1$ and $y = \frac{1}{2}x - 1$ are perpendicular. Is Ivan correct? Explain your reasoning.

> **Hint**
> How do gradients of perpendicular lines relate to each other?

[___ / 1 mark]

3. Work out the equation of the line that is perpendicular to the line $3x - 6y + 1 = 0$ and passes through the point $(4, -2)$.

[___ / 4 marks]

Linear inequalities

 1. n is an integer and $-1 \leq n < 5$. List the possible values of n

.... **[I got ___ / 1 mark]**

 2. n is an integer and $-6 < 2n \leq 8$. List the possible values of n

.... **[___ / 2 marks]**

 3. Solve these inequalities and display the solutions on number lines.

   a) $3x + 5 > 2$

> **Hint**
> Remember to write the inequality
> symbol in your final answers.

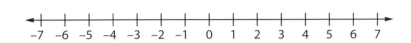

.... **[___ / 3 marks]**

   b) $20 - 5x \geq 0$

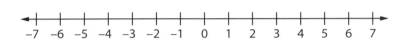

.... **[___ / 3 marks]**

 4. a) Find the set of values of x for which $1 < 3x + 4 \leq 22$

.... **[___ / 3 marks]**

   b) Show the solution to part **a** on the number line.

.... **[___ / 1 mark]**

5. Find the set of values of x that satisfies both of these inequalities.

   $4x + 1 \geq 3$

   $5 - x > 3$

.... **[___ / 3 marks]**

Regions on graphs

1. Write the inequality that describes each of these shaded regions.

a)

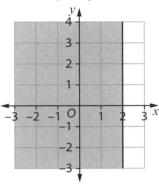

.... [I got ___ / 1 mark]

b)

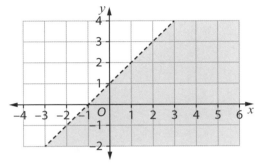

.... [___ / 1 mark]

2. On the graph, find the region that satisfies these inequalities.

$$y < 2x \qquad y \geq -2 \qquad x + y \geq 1$$

Label your region R

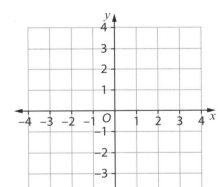

> **Hint**
> Draw some straight lines first to find the boundaries of the region.

[___ / 3 marks]

3. a) Write the three inequalities that define the shaded region.

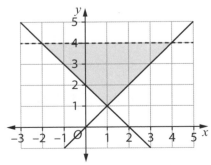

.... [___ / 3 marks]

b) Write the points in the region with integer coordinates.

.... [___ / 1 mark]

21

Linear simultaneous equations

1. Solve each pair of simultaneous equations.

a) $2x + 5y = 11$
$3x - 2y = -12$

.... **[I got ___ / 3 marks]**

b) $2x - 7y = 12$
$5x - y = -3$

.... **[___ / 3 marks]**

c) $3x + 8y = 12$
$2x + 12y = 13$

.... **[___ / 3 marks]**

d) $6x - 4y = 9$
$5x + 3y = -2$

.... **[___ / 3 marks]**

2. Two families go to the cinema. The first family buys one adult ticket and three child tickets and pays £39. The second family buys two adult tickets and four child tickets and pays £62

a) Form a pair of simultaneous equations to describe this situation.

> **Hint**
> If you have two bits of information about two unknowns, write two simultaneous equations.

.... **[___ / 2 marks]**

b) Solve your equations to find the cost of an adult ticket and the cost of a child ticket.

.... **[___ / 3 marks]**

3. The mass of 20 apples and 30 satsumas is 4050 g. The mass of 12 apples and 15 satsumas is 2205 g. Find the mass of one apple and the mass of one satsuma.

.... **[___ / 4 marks]**

Expanding brackets

1. Expand

   a) $y(3 - 5y)$

   .... **[I got ___ / 1 mark]**

   b) $(2x - y)3xy$

   .... **[___ / 2 marks]**

2. Expand and simplify if possible

   a) $(x + 2)(y + 1)$

   .... **[___ / 2 marks]**

   b) $(2a - 5)(2 + a)$

   .... **[___ / 2 marks]**

   c) $(a + b)^2$

   .... **[___ / 2 marks]**

   d) $(2m + 3n)(3m - 2n)$

   .... **[___ / 2 marks]**

   e) $(4x + 1)^2$

   .... **[___ / 2 marks]**

3. Find an expression for the area of the triangle. Give your answer in expanded form.

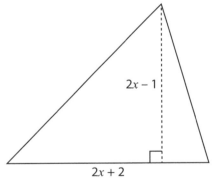

> **Hint**
> Here, algebra is combined with geometry. Remember the formula:
> Area of a triangle = $\frac{1}{2}$ × base × height

   .... **[___ / 3 marks]**

4. Expand and simplify $(x - 1)(2 - x)(x + 4)$.

   .... **[___ / 4 marks]**

5. A cube has side length $(x + 1)$ cm. Find an expression for the volume of the cube in the form
   $ax^3 + bx^2 + cx + d$

   ....cm^3 **[___ / 3 marks]**

Factorising 1

 1. Factorise

    a) $6a - 15b$

    .... **[I got __ / 1 mark]**

    b) $x^2 + x$

    .... **[__ / 1 mark]**

 2. Factorise fully

    a) $16x + 12xy$

> **Hint**
> When you're told to factorise 'fully', make sure you take the highest common factor out of the brackets.

    .... **[__ / 2 marks]**

    b) $x^2y + y^2x$

    .... **[__ / 2 marks]**

    c) $8p - 4p^2q + 6pq$

    .... **[__ / 2 marks]**

 3. Fill in the missing length on the diagram. The area is given as $x^2 + 3x$ and the height as x

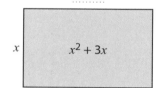

    .... **[__ / 1 mark]**

4. Factorise

    a) $p^2 - 9p - 36$

    .... **[__ / 2 marks]**

    b) $x^2 + 9p - 10$

    .... **[__ / 2 marks]**

    c) $y^2 - 14y + 49$

    .... **[__ / 2 marks]**

    d) $x^2 + 8x + 16$

    .... **[__ / 2 marks]**

 5. A rectangle has area $x^2 + 6x - 27$. Find expressions for the lengths of the two sides of the rectangle.

$$x^2 + 6x - 27$$

    .... **[__ / 2 marks]**

Factorising 2

 1. Factorise

    a) $x^2 - 49$

.... **[I got ___ / 1 mark]**

    b) $y^2 - 81$

.... **[___ / 1 mark]**

    c) $4b^2 - 1$

.... **[___ / 1 mark]**

    d) $p^2 - 9q^2$

.... **[___ / 1 mark]**

 2. The area of a parallelogram is $x^2 - 121$. Write expressions for the base and height of the parallelogram in terms of x

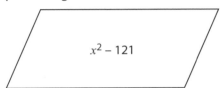

$x^2 - 121$

> **Hint**
> The area of a parallelogram is base × height.

.... **[___ / 2 marks]**

 3. Factorise

    a) $6x^2 + 5x - 4$

.... **[___ / 2 marks]**

    b) $12x^2 + 20x + 3$

.... **[___ / 2 marks]**

 4. Pavel says that $2x^2 + 7x + 6$ factorises to $(2x + 6)(x + 1)$, since the sum of 6 and 1 is 7 and the product of 6 and 1 is 6. Pavel is wrong. Explain why.

.... **[___ / 1 mark]**

 5. A square has area $9x^2 + 30x + 25$. Find the perimeter of the square in terms of x

.... **[___ / 3 marks]**

Solving quadratic equations

1. Solve

   a) $x^2 - 7x - 8 = 0$

.... **[I got ___ / 3 marks]**

   b) $x^2 + 5x = 0$

.... **[___ / 3 marks]**

   c) $x^2 - 1 = 0$

.... **[___ / 3 marks]**

2. Solve

   a) $x^2 - 12x = -35$

> **Hint**
> Before solving, make sure one side of the equation is 0

.... **[___ / 4 marks]**

   b) $x^2 + 3x = 10$

.... **[___ / 4 marks]**

   c) $x^2 = 144$

.... **[___ / 2 marks]**

3. Solve

   a) $6x^2 + 13x - 5 = 0$

.... **[___ / 3 marks]**

   b) $7x^2 - 19x - 6 = 0$

.... **[___ / 3 marks]**

4. Here is a rectangle. The area of the rectangle is 5 cm².

   a) Show that $2x^2 - 5x - 3 = 0$

```
          _____
         |                  |
         |      5 cm²        | (x – 2) cm
         |_____|
              (2x – 1) cm
```

.... **[___ / 3 marks]**

   b) Find the length of the shortest side of the rectangle.

....cm   **[___ / 3 marks]**

The quadratic formula

Grade 7

1. Solve these equations. Give your answers to 3 significant figures where appropriate.

   a) $3x^2 - 7x - 10 = 0$

   .... **[I got ___ / 3 marks]**

   b) $5x^2 + 4x - 20 = 0$

   .... **[___ / 3 marks]**

   c) $25 + 10x - 2x^2 = 0$

   .... **[___ / 3 marks]**

Grade 8

2. Solve these equations. Give your answers in the form $a \pm b\sqrt{c}$, where a, b and c are integers.

   Hint
   When you've substituted into the formula, remember to simplify your surds.

   a) $x^2 - 10x + 7 = 0$

   .... **[___ / 3 marks]**

   b) $x^2 + 2x - 11 = 0$

   .... **[___ / 3 marks]**

   c) $2x^2 + 22 = 16x$

   .... **[___ / 3 marks]**

Grade 8

3. Here is a trapezium. The lengths of the parallel sides are $(x + 2)$ cm and $(x + 4)$ cm. The height is $(x - 1)$ cm. The area of the trapezium is 10 cm².

   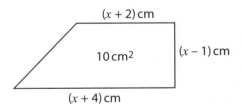

   a) Show that $x^2 + 2x - 13 = 0$

   .... **[___ / 3 marks]**

   b) Find the height of the trapezium to 2 decimal places.

   ....cm **[___ / 3 marks]**

27

Completing the square

1. Write these expressions in the form $(x + p)^2 + q$

    a) $x^2 + 6x + 5$

 [I got ___ / 2 marks]

    b) $x^2 - 4x + 10$

[___ / 2 marks]

    c) $x^2 - 10x$

[___ / 2 marks]

    d) $x^2 + x + 1$

[___ / 2 marks]

2. a) Complete the square for the expression $x^2 - 2x - 11$

[___ / 2 marks]

    b) Hence, solve the equation $x^2 - 2x - 11 = 0$
       Give your answer in the form $a \pm b\sqrt{3}$, where a and b are integers.

 [___ / 2 marks]

3. Write these expressions in the form $a(x + p)^2 + q$

    a) $2x^2 + 8x + 7$

 [___ / 3 marks]

    b) $12 + 10x - x^2$

[___ / 3 marks]

Algebraic fractions 1

1. Simplify

a) $\dfrac{4x^2 - 12x}{2x}$

.... **[I got ___ / 2 marks]**

b) $\dfrac{x^2 - x - 2}{x^2 - 6x + 8}$

.... **[___ / 3 marks]**

c) $\dfrac{4x^2 - 1}{2x^2 + x}$

.... **[___ / 3 marks]**

2. a) Simplify $\dfrac{3x - 4}{6x^2 + 7x - 20}$

.... **[___ / 3 marks]**

b) Hence, solve the equation $\dfrac{3x - 4}{6x^2 + 7x - 20} = 1$

> **Hint**
> Replace the fraction in part **b** with its simplified form from part **a**.

.... **[___ / 2 marks]**

3. Solve the equation $\dfrac{1}{x - 3} = \dfrac{x}{x + 5}$

.... **[___ / 3 marks]**

29

Algebraic fractions 2

 1. Simplify $\dfrac{2x - 8}{3x - 15} \times \dfrac{x - 5}{x - 3}$

.... **[I got ___ / 3 marks]**

 2. Simplify $\dfrac{x}{x^2 + 2x - 35} \div \dfrac{6x^3}{3x + 21}$

.... **[___ / 4 marks]**

 3. Work out a simplified expression for the width of this rectangle.

The height is given by $\dfrac{1}{x}$ and the area is equal to $\dfrac{x^2}{x^2(x + 1)}$

Hint
Simplify any fractions you use before you do any operations on them.

$$\text{Area} = \dfrac{x^2}{x^2(x + 1)} \qquad \dfrac{1}{x}$$

.... **[___ / 4 marks]**

 4. Given that $x^2 : (x - 1) = 4 : 1$, find the value of x

.... **[___ / 4 marks]**

Algebraic fractions 3

 1. Write each of these as a single fraction in its simplest form.

a) $\dfrac{2}{x} + \dfrac{3}{2x}$

.... [I got ___ / 2 marks]

b) $\dfrac{1}{p} - \dfrac{1}{q}$

.... [___ / 2 marks]

c) $\dfrac{4}{x+1} + \dfrac{3}{x+2}$

.... [___ / 3 marks]

d) $\dfrac{x}{x-2} - \dfrac{x-2}{x+3}$

.... [___ / 3 marks]

 2. Find the exact solutions of the equation $\dfrac{3}{2x-1} + \dfrac{2}{2x+1} = 1$

> **Hint**
> Make the left side into a
> single fraction first.

.... [___ / 5 marks]

3. An equilateral triangle and an isosceles triangle have side lengths as shown in the diagram. Find the difference between the perimeters of the two triangles.

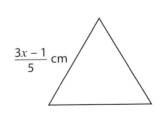

.... cm   [___ / 4 marks]

Rearranging formulae

 1. Make x the subject of the formulae.

    a) $2x^2 - 3 = y$

    .... **[I got ___ / 2 marks]**

    b) $a\sqrt{x} + b = c$

    .... **[___ / 2 marks]**

 2. The power, P watts, in a circuit is given by the formula

$$P = I^2 R$$

    where I is the current in amps and R is the resistance in ohms.
    Rearrange the formula to make I the subject.

    .... **[___ / 2 marks]**

 3. Fleur is rearranging a formula to make x the subject. Her steps are shown. Explain where Fleur has gone wrong.

$$y = a^2 x - b$$
$$y + b = a^2 x$$
$$\sqrt{y + b} = ax$$
$$\frac{\sqrt{y + b}}{a} = x$$

....

....

.... **[___ / 2 marks]**

 4. Make p the subject of the formulae.

    a) $mp - q = ap$

    .... **[___ / 3 marks]**

    b) $\dfrac{1}{p} + \dfrac{1}{r} = \dfrac{1}{t}$

    .... **[___ / 3 marks]**

Quadratic graphs 1

1. a) Complete the table of values for the graph of $y = x^2 - x - 1$

x	−2	−1	0	1	2	3
y		1				5

[I got ___ / 2 marks]

b) Draw the graph of $y = x^2 - x - 1$

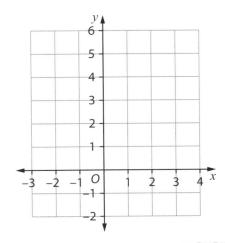

[___ / 2 marks]

c) Use your graph to estimate the coordinates of the turning point of the graph.

Hint
The turning point is the maximum or minimum.

.... **[___ / 1 mark]**

2. Here is the graph of $y = 2 - x^2$

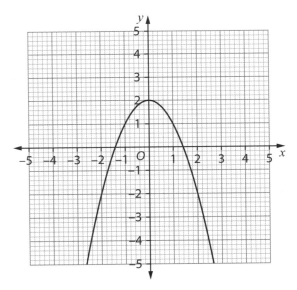

a) Use the graph to estimate the roots of $2 - x^2 = 0$

.... **[___ / 2 marks]**

b) Write the coordinates of the turning point of $y = 2 - x^2$

.... **[___ / 1 mark]**

c) Use your graph to estimate the values of x for which $y = -3$

.... **[___ / 2 marks]**

33

1. Daniel wants to sketch the graph of $y = 16 - x^2$

Hint
This is the difference of two squares.

   a) Where should Daniel's sketch graph cross the x-axis?

.... **[I got ___ / 2 marks]**

   b) Write the coordinates of the turning point of $y = 16 - x^2$

.... **[___ / 1 mark]**

   c) Daniel says the turning point is a maximum point. Is Daniel correct? Explain your reasoning.

.... **[___ / 1 mark]**

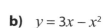

2. Sketch these graphs, showing any points of intersection with the axes.

   a) $y = (x - 2)(x + 3)$

[___ / 3 marks]

   b) $y = 3x - x^2$

[___ / 3 marks]

   c) $y = 2x^2 + 7x + 6$

[___ / 3 marks]

3. Work out the coordinates of the turning points of the graphs of these equations. State whether or not each graph will cross the x-axis and explain how you know.

   a) $y = x^2 - 6x + 3$

.... **[___ / 3 marks]**

   b) $y = 2x^2 + 10x + 20$

.... **[___ / 4 marks]**

Quadratic inequalities

1. Solve each of these inequalities. Represent your solutions on the number lines.

a) $x^2 - 4 \leq -3$

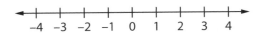

.... **[I got ___ / 3 marks]**

b) $7x^2 \geq 28$

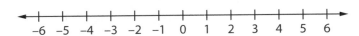

.... **[___ / 3 marks]**

2. Solve each of these inequalities. Write your answers using set notation.

a) $x^2 - 8x + 15 \leq 0$

.... **[___ / 4 marks]**

b) $3x^2 - x - 4 > 0$

.... **[___ / 4 marks]**

c) $x^2 - 30 < -7x$

.... **[___ / 4 marks]**

Non-linear simultaneous equations

 1. Solve algebraically these pairs of simultaneous equations.

    a) $x + y = 3$

          $y = x^2 + 3x - 2$

[I got ___ / 4 marks]

    b) $x^2 + y^2 = 10$

          $y + x = 2$

[___ / 4 marks]

    c) $2x^2 + y^2 = 9$

          $2y + x = 0$

> **Hint**
> Be careful when squaring; look at the coefficients too.

[___ / 4 marks]

 2. a) Use algebra to find the coordinates of any points of intersection between the circle $x^2 + y^2 = 8$ and the line $x - y = 4$

[___ / 5 marks]

    b) Explain how you know, without drawing the graphs, that the line $y = x - 4$ is tangent to the circle $x^2 + y^2 = 8$

[___ / 2 marks]

Solutions from graphs

 1. Use a graphical method to find the solutions to the simultaneous equations

$$y = (x - 2)^2$$
$$y = x$$

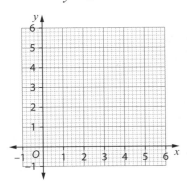

$x =$ .... and $y =$ ....

$x =$ .... and $y =$ .... **[I got ___ / 4 marks]**

 2. The graph of $y = x^2 - 3x - 18$ is shown.

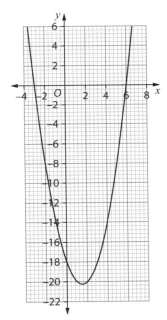

a) Use a graphical method to find the solutions to the simultaneous equations

$$y = x^2 - 3x - 18$$
$$y = 2x - 12$$

$x =$ .... and $y =$ ....

$x =$ .... and $y =$ .... **[___ / 3 marks]**

b) Use the graph to estimate the solutions to the equation $x^2 - 3x - 14 = 0$

.... **[___ / 3 marks]**

Cubic and reciprocal graphs

Grade 6

1. a) Complete the table of values for $y = 2x^3 + 1$

x	−2	−1	0	1	2
y	−15				17

[I got ___ / 2 marks]

b) Draw the graph of $y = 2x^3 + 1$

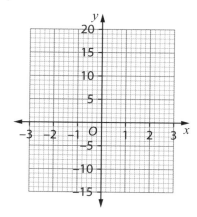

[___ / 2 marks]

c) Use your graph to estimate the root of $2x^3 + 1 = 0$

> **Hint**
> Roots are intersections with the x-axis.

.... [___ / 1 mark]

Grade 6

2. a) Complete the table of values for $y = -\dfrac{2}{x}$

x	−3	−2	−1	0	1	2	3
y	$\dfrac{2}{3}$	1		undefined		−1	

[___ / 2 marks]

b) Draw the graph of $y = -\dfrac{2}{x}$

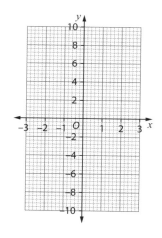

[___ / 2 marks]

c) Use your graph to estimate the solutions to the simultaneous equations $y = -\dfrac{2}{x}$ and $y = -x$

$x =$ .... and $y =$ ....

$x =$ .... and $y =$ .... [___ / 3 marks]

Exponential graphs

1. Write the correct equation from this list underneath each of the graphs.

$$y = 3^x \qquad y = x^3 \qquad y = \frac{3}{x} \qquad y = \left(\frac{1}{3}\right)^x$$

 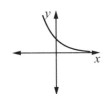

....

[I got ___ / 2 marks]

2. Sketch the graph of $y = 0.5^x$ for $-2 \leq x \leq 3$

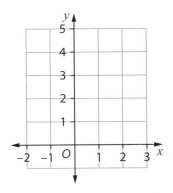

[___ / 2 marks]

3. The price, £P, of a house is given by the equation $P = 200\,000 \times 1.2^t$, where t is the number of years since the house was bought.

a) What price was the house bought for?   £.. **[___ / 1 mark]**

b) Work out the price of the house after 3 years.

£.. **[___ / 2 marks]**

c) Sketch the graph of P against t

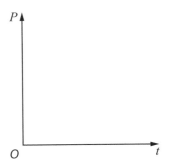

> **Hint**
> Think about the shape of the graph and where it crosses the P-axis.

[___ / 2 marks]

4. The sketch shows the graph of $y = ab^x$ where $a > 0$ and $b > 0$. The graph passes through the points $(1, 10)$ and $(-1, 0.4)$. Find the values of a and b

> **Hint**
> Start by forming two equations.

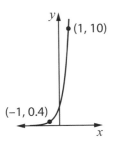

$a = $ ....

$b = $ .... **[___ / 3 marks]**

39

Equation of a circle

 1. The circle $x^2 + y^2 = 1$ has centre at (0, 0) and radius 1. Angela says the circle must pass through the point (1, 1). Show that Angela is wrong.

[I got ___ / 2 marks]

 2. The graph shows a circle, centre (0, 0).

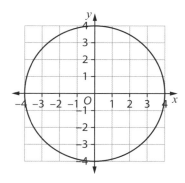

    a) Write the equation of the circle. .... [___ / 1 mark]

    b) Show that the point $(2\sqrt{2}, 2\sqrt{2})$ lies on the circle.

[___ / 2 marks]

    c) Write the equation of the tangent to the circle that passes through the point (0, −4).

.... [___ / 1 mark]

 3. The graph shows the circle with equation $x^2 + y^2 = 10$. It passes through the points A, B, C and D, which lie on the axes. Prove that $ABCD$ is a square.

> **Hint**
> Always draw a sketch if you're not given one.

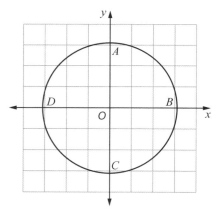

[___ / 4 marks]

 4. The circle, C, has equation $x^2 + y^2 = 5$. Find the equation of the tangent to C at the point (1, 2).

.... [___ / 5 marks]

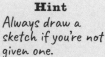

Trigonometric graphs

Grade 8 **1. a)** Sketch the graph of $y = \cos x$ for $-360° \leq x \leq 360°$

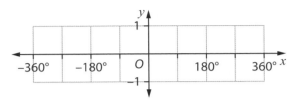

[I got ___ / 2 marks]

b) Write the coordinates of the first minimum point on the graph where $x > 0$

.... [___ / 1 mark]

Grade 8 **2. a)** Sketch the graph of $y = \sin x$ for $0° \leq x \leq 450°$

[___ / 2 marks]

b) The value of $\sin 45°$ is $\dfrac{1}{\sqrt{2}}$. Write all the other angles, $\theta°$,

for which $\sin\theta = \dfrac{1}{\sqrt{2}}$ in the interval $0° \leq \theta \leq 450°$

> **Hint**
> Mark the point you're given on the graph and look for other points with the same y-value.

.... [___ / 2 marks]

Grade 8 **3. a)** Sketch the graph of $y = \tan x$ for $-180° \leq x \leq 360°$

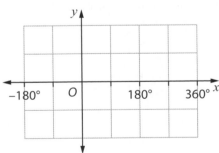

[___ / 2 marks]

b) Write the value of $\tan 30°$

.... [___ / 1 mark]

c) Use the graph to work out the value of

    i) $\tan 210°$ .... [___ / 1 mark]

    ii) $\tan(-30°)$ .... [___ / 1 mark]

Graph transformations 1

1. The graph of $y = f(x)$ is shown on each grid. Sketch these graphs.

a) $y = f(x) - 2$

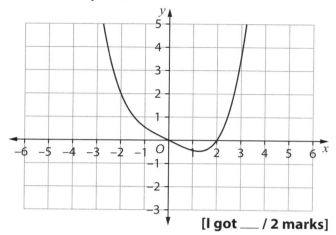

[I got ___ / 2 marks]

b) $y = f(x + 2)$

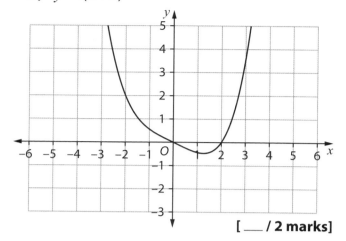

[___ / 2 marks]

c) $y = f(x - 2)$

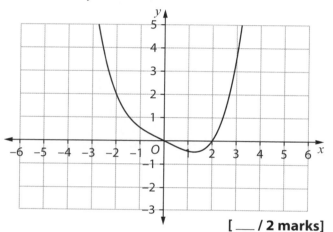

[___ / 2 marks]

d) $y = 1 + f(x)$

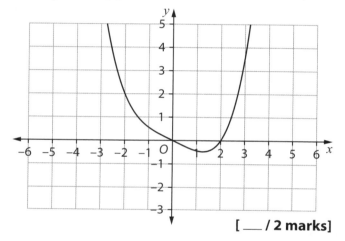

[___ / 2 marks]

2. Sketch the graph of $y = \sin(x + 90)°$ for $0° \leq x \leq 360°$

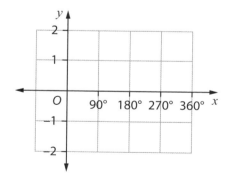

[___ / 2 marks]

3. The graph with equation $y = x^2 - 4x$ is shown.

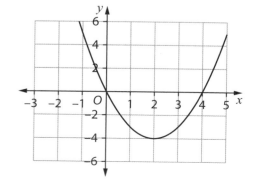

a) Give the coordinates of the minimum point of the graph with equation $y = x^2 - 4x + 1$

.... [___ / 1 mark]

b) On the same axes, sketch the graph with equation
$y = (x + 1)^2 - 4(x + 1)$. [___ / 2 marks]

42

Graph transformations 2

1. The graph of $y = f(x)$ is shown.

Sketch these graphs on the same set of axes, labelling each one.

a) $y = -f(x)$ **[I got ___ / 2 marks]**

b) $y = f(-x)$ **[___ / 2 marks]**

c) $y = 1 - f(x)$ **[___ / 2 marks]**

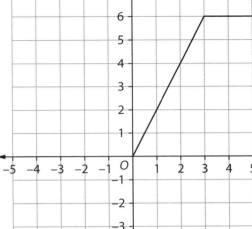

2. Sketch the graph of $y = -\cos x$ for $-180° \leq x \leq 180°$

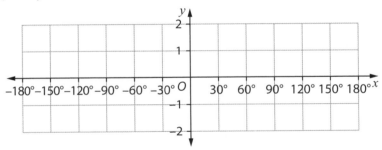

[___ / 2 marks]

3. The graph of $y = f(x)$ is shown, where $f(x) = x^3 - x^2 - x$

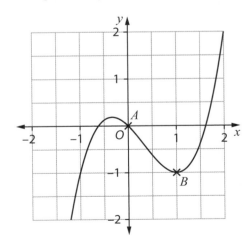

a) The graph is transformed to the graph of $y = -f(x)$.

    i) Give the coordinates of point A under this transformation.

         .... **[___ / 1 mark]**

    ii) Give the coordinates of point B under this transformation.

         .... **[___ / 1 mark]**

b) On the same axes, sketch the graph with equation $y = f(-x)$.

         [___ / 2 marks]

c) The curve is reflected in the x-axis then translated up two units. Write the equation of the transformed graph.

.... **[___ / 2 marks]**

Simple kinematic graphs

Grade 6

1. Here is a speed–time graph showing Krystyna's speeds for a race.

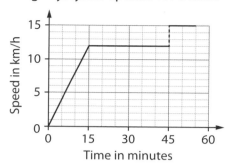

a) After how many minutes does Krystyna finish the race?

.... minutes   **[I got ___ / 1 mark]**

b) Write the time when Krystyna's speed is 8 km/h.

.... minutes   **[___ / 1 mark]**

c) Describe Krystyna's journey/speed during the race.

....

....   **[___ / 3 marks]**

d) Work out the total length of the race.

.... km   **[___ / 3 marks]**

Grade 6

2. Kai goes on a bike ride from home one day. Here is a travel graph showing part of Kai's bike ride.

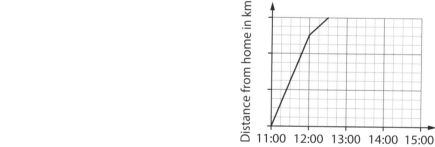

a) For the first hour, Kai cycles at a speed of 25 km/h. How far does he travel in the first hour and a half of his ride?

.... km   **[___ / 2 marks]**

b) At 12:30, Kai stops for lunch for 45 minutes before cycling back home at 20 km/h. Complete the travel graph.

[___ / 2 marks]

Estimating areas

Grade 8

1. The velocity–time graph shows the velocity, v m/s, of a particle t seconds after it is released.

   a) Using two strips of equal width, estimate the area under the graph.

   .... **[I got ___ / 3 marks]**

   b) Using four strips of equal width, estimate the area under the graph.

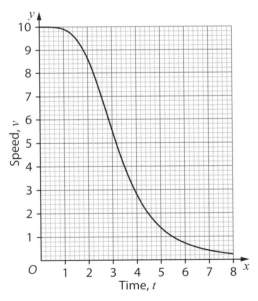

   .... **[___ / 3 marks]**

   c) Explain why your answer to part **a** is smaller than your answer to part **b**.

   > **Hint**
   > What has changed from
   > part **a** to part **b**?

   .... **[___ / 1 mark]**

   d) Explain what the area under the graph tells you about the particle.

   .... **[___ / 1 mark]**

Grade 8

2. The speed–time graph shows the speed, v m/s, of a ball as it rolls along a road for t seconds.

   a) Work out an estimate of the total distance the ball travels in the first three seconds. Use three strips of equal width.

   ....m **[___ / 3 marks]**

   b) i) Work out an estimate of the total distance the ball travels in the second three seconds. Use three strips of equal width.

   ....m **[___ / 3 marks]**

   ii) State whether your answer is an overestimate or an underestimate and give a reason.

   .... **[___ / 1 mark]**

Rates of change

1. David mows his lawn every few weeks. The graph shows the height of his lawn over a period of 12 weeks one summer.

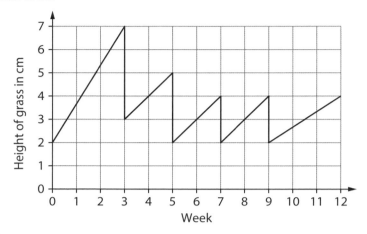

> **Hint**
> The steeper the graph, the faster the rate of change.

a) In which weeks does David cut the lawn?

.... **[I got ___ / 1 mark]**

b) Between which weeks does the grass grow at the slowest rate?

.... **[___ / 1 mark]**

c) What was the rate of growth of the grass, in cm/week, between weeks 5 and 7?

.... cm/week **[___ / 1 mark]**

2. Here are the cross-sections of three swimming pools.

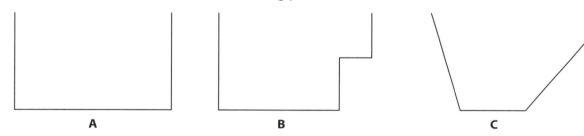

Each pool is filled with water from a hose. Match each pool to the correct graph showing the depth of water in the pool over time.

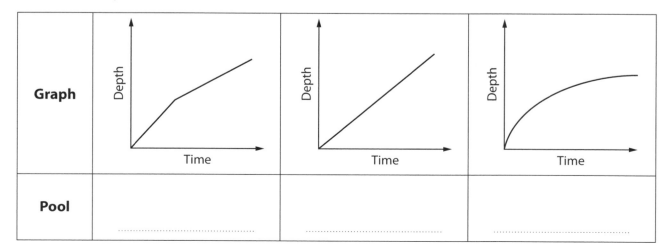

[___ / 2 marks]

Gradients of curves

Grade 8

1. A ball is released from the top of a tower. Here is the distance–time graph for its fall to the ground.

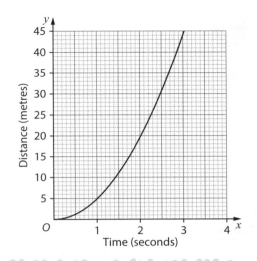

a) Calculate the average speed of the ball in the first two seconds.

.... m/s   **[I got ___ / 2 marks]**

b) Estimate the speed of the ball when it has been travelling for 1 second.

Hint
Average speed needs a chord; speed at a point needs a tangent.

.... m/s   **[___ / 3 marks]**

Grade 8

2. Janusz goes on a train journey. The speed–time graph shows the speed of the train throughout the journey.

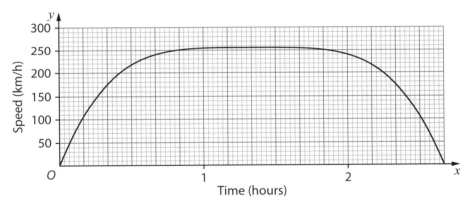

a) Calculate the train's average acceleration during the first 30 minutes of the journey.

.... km/h²   **[___ / 2 marks]**

b) Explain what is happening to the train's speed after 1.5 hours of travel.

.... **[___ / 1 mark]**

c) Calculate the train's deceleration at 2 hours.

.... km/h²   **[___ / 3 marks]**

Types of sequence

1. Complete the table for each sequence. The first row has been done for you.

	Position-to-term rule (nth term)	First four terms	Term-to-term rule	Seventh term	Hundredth term	Type of sequence
e.g.	$2n-1$	1, 3, 5, 7	Add 2	13	199	Arithmetic
a)	$5n+2$					
b)	5×2^n					
c)	$n^2 - 2n$					
d)		1, 1, 2, 3				

[I got ___ / 18 marks]

2. The nth term of a sequence is $8n + 3$

    a) Which term in the sequence is 51?

        [___ / 2 marks]

    b) Show that 64 is not a number in the sequence.

        [___ / 2 marks]

    c) Find the first number in the sequence to exceed 100

> **Hint**
> Write and solve an inequality.

        [___ / 3 marks]

3. The nth term of a sequence is $n^2 - 30$

    a) Find the 4th number in the sequence.

        [___ / 2 marks]

    b) Is the number 114 in this sequence? Explain your answer.

        [___ / 2 marks]

4. A Fibonacci sequence starts $m, n, m + n, \ldots$

    a) Write an algebraic expression for

        i) the fourth term in the sequence

        [___ / 1 mark]

        ii) the seventh term in the sequence.

        [___ / 2 marks]

    b) If the first term in the sequence is 3 and the difference between the first and third terms is 5, find the value of the eighth term in the sequence.

        [___ / 3 marks]

Arithmetic sequences

Grade 4

1. Complete the table for each sequence. The first one has been done for you.

	Sequence	Term-to-term rule	Position-to-term rule (*n*th term)	Tenth term
e.g.	2, 6, 10, 14	Add 4	$4n - 2$	$(4 \times 10) - 2 = 38$
a)	17, 23, 29, 35			
b)	−1, 2, 5, 8			
c)	4, 1, −2, −5			
d)	20, 15, 10, 5			
e)	3, 3.5, 4, 4.5			

[I got ___ / 15 marks]

2. An arithmetic sequence has first term 5 and third term 11
What is the *n*th term of the sequence?

> **Hint**
> Work out some terms in the sequence first.

[___ / 2 marks]

3. Calculate the sum of the 50th and 60th terms in the sequence that starts 12, 9, 6, 3, …

[___ / 3 marks]

4. Gloria's salary in her new job is £24 000 in the first year. Every year she gets a pay rise so that her annual salaries form an arithmetic sequence. When her annual salary reaches £27 000 she gets no further pay rises. In her fourth year she is paid £24 900
In what year does she reach her maximum salary?

[___ / 3 marks]

5. Here is a number sequence: $3, \dfrac{5}{2}, \dfrac{7}{3}, \dfrac{9}{4}, \dfrac{11}{5}, \ldots$

> **Hint**
> Look at the numerators and denominators separately.

a) Find the next term in the sequence.

[___ / 1 mark]

b) Find an expression for the *n*th term of the sequence.

[___ / 3 marks]

c) Find the product of the 6th and 9th terms of the sequence.

[___ / 2 marks]

Quadratic sequences

Grade 7 **1.** Write the nth term of these quadratic sequences.

    a)   1, 4, 9, 16, …

    .... **[I got ___ / 1 mark]**

    b)   0, 3, 8, 15, …

    .... **[___ / 1 mark]**

    c)   3, 12, 27, 48, …

    .... **[___ / 1 mark]**

Grade 7 **2.** Find the next two terms in these sequences.

    a)   5, 8, 13, 20, …

    .... **[___ / 2 marks]**

    b)   −2, 5, 14, 25, …

    .... **[___ / 2 marks]**

Grade 8 **3.** A sequence has nth term $n^2 + 2n + 2$

    Work out which term in the sequence has a value of 50

> **Hint**
> Set up and solve an equation.

    .... **[___ / 3 marks]**

Grade 8 **4.** Find the nth term of these sequences.

    a)   10, 12, 16, 22, …

    .... **[___ / 3 marks]**

    b)   −9, 2, 17, 36, …

    .... **[___ / 3 marks]**

Grade 8 **5.** Rachel thinks that every term in the sequence $n^2 + 4n + 6$ is positive. Explain how you know Rachel is correct.

    .... **[___ / 1 mark]**

Iteration 1

1. a) Show that the equation $x^4 - 12x = 0$ has a solution between 2 and 3

[I got ___ / 2 marks]

b) Starting with $x_0 = 2$, use the iteration formula $x_{n+1} = \sqrt[4]{12x_n}$ to find the solution to the equation in part **a** to 3 decimal places.

.... **[___ / 3 marks]**

2. a) Show that the equation $x^3 - 2x + 1 = 0$ has a solution between 0.6 and 0.7

[___ / 2 marks]

b) Starting with $x_0 = 0.6$, use the iteration formula $x_{n+1} = \dfrac{-1}{(x_n)^2 - 2}$ to find x_1, x_2 and x_3 correct to 2 decimal places.

.... **[___ / 2 marks]**

c) Describe what happens to the values of x_n as n gets large.

> **Hint**
> Try more iterations on your calculator and see what happens.

.... **[___ / 1 mark]**

3. a) Show that the equation $x^2 - \sqrt{x} - 1 = 0$ has a solution between 1 and 2

[___ / 2 marks]

b) Starting with $x_0 = 1$, use the iteration formula $x_{n+1} = \dfrac{1 + \sqrt{x_n}}{x_n}$ to find x_1, x_2, x_3 and x_4 correct to 3 significant figures.

.... **[___ / 2 marks]**

c) Explain what happens to the x-values as n increases.

.... **[___ / 1 mark]**

Iteration 2

1. The graph with equation $y = x^3 + 5x^2 - 1$ is shown. Dara wants to find the roots of the graph.

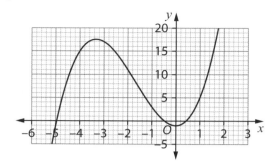

a) Explain why Dara needs to solve the equation $x^3 + 5x^2 - 1 = 0$

.... **[I got ___ / 1 mark]**

b) Show that the equation $x^3 + 5x^2 - 1 = 0$ can be rearranged to $x = \dfrac{1 - 5x^2}{x^2}$

[___ / 2 marks]

c) Starting with $x_0 = -4$, use the iteration formula $x_{n+1} = \dfrac{1 - 5(x_n)^2}{(x_n)^2}$ to find the value of a root of the graph. Give your answer to 2 decimal places.

.... **[___ / 3 marks]**

d) Show that the equation $x^3 + 5x^2 - 1 = 0$ can be rearranged to $x = \sqrt{\dfrac{1 - x^3}{5}}$

[___ / 2 marks]

e) Starting with $x_0 = 0$, use the iteration formula $x_{n+1} = \sqrt{\dfrac{1 - (x_n)^3}{5}}$ to find the value of another root of the graph. Give your answer to 2 decimal places.

.... **[___ / 3 marks]**

f) Starting with $x_0 = -1$, use the iteration formula $x_{n+1} = \dfrac{1 - (x_n)^3}{5x_n}$ to find the value of the final root of the graph. Give your answer to 1 decimal place.

.... **[___ / 3 marks]**

Functions

1. $f(x) = x^2 - 2x$

   a) Find the value of

      i) $f(1)$

      .... **[I got ___ / 2 marks]**

      ii) $f(-5)$

      .... **[___ / 2 marks]**

      iii) $f(0)$

      .... **[___ / 2 marks]**

   b) Find the values of x for which

      i) $f(x) = 15$

      .... **[___ / 3 marks]**

      ii) $f(x) = 4x$

      .... **[___ / 3 marks]**

2. $f(x) = 3x - 1$ and $g(x) = \dfrac{1}{x}$

   a) Find the value of

      i) $gf(1)$

      .... **[___ / 3 marks]**

      ii) $fg\left(\dfrac{1}{2}\right)$

      .... **[___ / 3 marks]**

   b) Write $gf(x)$ in terms of x

      .... **[___ / 1 mark]**

   c) Solve the equation $gf(x) = 2$

      .... **[___ / 3 marks]**

Inverse functions

1. Find the inverse of these functions.

a) $f(x) = \dfrac{x - 1}{2}$

.... **[I got ___ / 3 marks]**

b) $g(x) = x^2 - 4, x \geq 0$

.... **[___ / 3 marks]**

c) $h(x) = \dfrac{x}{2x + 3}, x \neq -\dfrac{3}{2}$

.... **[___ / 4 marks]**

d) $k(x) = \sqrt{x^3 + 5}$

.... **[___ / 3 marks]**

2. The function f is given by $f(x) = x - 5$ and a function g is given by $g(x) = 2^x$

a) Find $gf^{-1}(x)$

.... **[___ / 2 marks]**

b) Solve the equation $gf^{-1}(x) = 8$

.... **[___ / 2 marks]**

$k(x) = x^2$ when $x \geq 0$

c) Find the values of a for which $k^{-1}(a) = f(a)$. Give your answers to 2 decimal places.

.... **[___ / 4 marks]**

Algebraic proof

1. Courtney says that the product of two prime numbers is always odd. Show that Courtney is wrong.

[I got ___ / 1 mark]

2. Prove that $(m + n)^2 + (m - n)^2 \equiv 2(m^2 + n^2)$

[___ / 3 marks]

3. Prove algebraically that these statements are true.

a) The sum of five consecutive integers is divisible by 5

[___ / 3 marks]

b) The sum of six consecutive integers is never divisible by 6

[___ / 3 marks]

c) The sum of the squares of any two even numbers is divisible by 4

> **Hint**
> When you see 'any two' numbers, use different letters for them.

[___ / 3 marks]

d) The sums of the squares of two consecutive odd numbers is even.

[___ / 3 marks]

e) The difference between the squares of two consecutive odd numbers is divisible by 8

[___ / 3 marks]

4. The first four terms of an arithmetic sequence are –3, 0, 3, 6. A new sequence is made by squaring each of the terms in the arithmetic sequence. Prove that every term in the new sequence is divisible by 9

[___ / 4 marks]

Ratio

1. The angles in a parallelogram are in the ratio $1:3:1:x$

   a) Write down the value of x

.... **[I got ___ / 1 mark]**

   b) Work out the sizes of all four angles.

> **Hint**
> What's the sum of the angles in a quadrilateral?

.... **[___ / 2 marks]**

2. The lengths of the sides of a right-angled triangle are in the ratio $5:12:13$

   The shortest side has a length of 2 cm. What is the perimeter of the triangle?

....cm   **[___ / 3 marks]**

3. The ratio of pencils to erasers in a school stockroom is $7:2$

   There are 90 more pencils than erasers.

   How many pencils are there?

.... **[___ / 2 marks]**

4. The points A, B, C and D form a straight line $ABCD$

   The ratio of the length of AB to BC is $6:5$

   The ratio of the length of BC to CD is $10:13$

   The total length of AD is 105 cm.

   Work out the length of BC

> **Hint**
> Consider multiplying one of the ratios by a number.

....cm   **[___ / 3 marks]**

5. Kayleigh is two years younger than Hayley.

   Bailey is twice as old as Kayleigh.

   The sum of their three ages is 38

   Find the ratio of Bailey's age to Hayley's age to Kayleigh's age.

.... **[___ / 4 marks]**

Harder ratio problems

1. Carl and Friedrich are playing a trump card game, using all 44 cards from the pack.

After a few rounds, Carl is holding 20% more cards than Friedrich.

Work out how many cards they each have.

Carl: ....

Friedrich: .... **[I got ___ / 3 marks]**

2. The ratio of blue cars to red cars in a traffic survey is $2:1$. In a follow-up survey, the number of blue cars has increased by 50% and the number of red cars has increased by 25%.

What is the new ratio of blue cars to red cars?

Write your answer in the form $a:b$, where a and b are integers.

.... **[___ / 3 marks]**

3. The ratio of integer x to integer y is $3:2$

When x is increased by 8 and y is halved, the ratio becomes $4:1$

Work out the values of x and y

.... **[___ / 5 marks]**

4. There are some copper coins and silver coins on a table. Each coin is either large or small.

The ratio of copper coins to silver coins is $4:3$

The ratio of small copper coins to large copper coins is $3:7$

The ratio of small silver coins to large silver coins is $1:2$

Work out what fraction of all of the coins are small coins.

.... **[___ / 5 marks]**

5. Given that $(2x-5):6 = 1:(6-x)$, find the possible values of x

> **Hint**
> If $a:b=c:d$, then $\dfrac{a}{b}=\dfrac{c}{d}$

.... **[___ / 4 marks]**

Percentage change

1. Increase £50 000 by 3%.

£.. **[I got ___ / 2 marks]**

2. A puddle of water has a volume of 4 litres.

During a sunny spell, the puddle decreases to a volume of 2.5 litres.

By what percentage has the volume of the puddle decreased?

.... **[___ / 2 marks]**

3. Harvey draws a square with area 16 cm².

He then rubs out the square and draws a new one with area 25 cm².

Work out the percentage increase in the side length of his square.

> **Hint**
> Area of square = length × length

.... **[___ / 3 marks]**

4. The table shows Kenny's weekly test scores in English and Maths.

	Week 1	Week 2	Week 3	Week 4
Maths	50	62	78	90
English	58	58	57	

The total of Kenny's English scores is 15% lower than the total of his Maths scores.

Work out the missing English score in the table.

.... **[___ / 4 marks]**

5. The length of a six-year-old iguana is 22 inches.

As a hatchling, the iguana's length was 6 inches.

By what percentage has the length of the iguana increased? Give your answer to 3 significant figures.

.... **[___ / 2 marks]**

6. A blockbuster movie initially plays for 3 hours and 15 minutes.

However, after some editing, the playing time is 3 hours.

Calculate the percentage decrease in the playing time of the movie.

> **Hint**
> Convert the times into minutes first.

.... **[___ / 3 marks]**

Using multipliers

Grade 4

1. A number is multiplied by 1.4

Write the percentage the number increases by.

.... **[I got ___ / 1 mark]**

Grade 4

2. An egg's mass decreases by 11% when you remove its shell.

After removing its shell, an egg weighs 44.5 grams.

Calculate the mass of the egg before removing its shell.

.... g **[___ / 3 marks]**

Grade 5

3. In a cricket match, the bowler releases the ball at a speed of 90 miles per hour.

The next ball bowled is 7% slower.

Use a multiplier method to determine the speed of the slower ball.

.... mph **[___ / 2 marks]**

Grade 5

4. Gemma chooses a number and increases it by 20%.

She then writes down the answer and decreases it by 20%.

Ben says that Gemma's final answer is wrong because it isn't the same as the original number.

Is he right? Explain your answer.

....

.... **[___ / 3 marks]**

Grade 5

5. A number is increased by 50%, before being decreased by 25%.

Work out the percentage by which the original number has increased.

.... **[___ / 3 marks]**

Grade 7

6. The numerator of a fraction is increased by 48% whilst its denominator is decreased by $87\frac{1}{2}$%. The resulting fraction is $\frac{37}{42}$

Work out the value of the original fraction in its simplest form.

> **Hint**
> Consider the numerator and denominator separately.

.... **[___ / 3 marks]**

59

Growth and depreciation

1. Two banks have an interest rate of 6% per annum. Bank A gives compound interest and Bank B gives simple interest.

    a) In January 2015, Jemma invests £2450 in Bank A and Paul invests £2450 in Bank B. How much more money will Jemma have than Paul in January 2022?

> **Hint**
> Compound interest is when the interest also earns interest.

    £... **[I got ___ / 4 marks]**

    b) Phoebe invests money in Bank A. She needs at least £5000 in her account by January 2025. Work out how much, in whole pounds, Phoebe needs to invest in January 2015 to reach this figure.

    £... **[___ / 3 marks]**

2. A population of mayflies is decreasing at a rate of 3.5% per year.

On January 1st 2020, the population of mayflies is 3 000 000

In which year will the population first drop below 1 500 000?

.... **[___ / 3 marks]**

3. The value of an oil painting is increasing at a rate of x% per year.

Initially, the painting is worth £4000. After five years, it is worth £4300

Work out the value of x to 1 decimal place.

.... **[___ / 3 marks]**

4. James bought a flat and the value of the flat fell by 3% in the first year. During the next two years, the value went up by 7% per year. At the end of the third year, his flat was worth £285 000

    a) Calculate the percentage change in the value of the flat to 3 sf.

> **Hint**
> Write down a multiplier for each year and then multiply.

.... **[___ / 3 marks]**

    b) Work out how much James paid for his flat.

    £... **[___ / 2 marks]**

Compound measures

Grade 4

1. Water is poured into an empty tank at a rate of 20 cm³/s.

After how long will the tank contain 2400 cm³ of water?

.... **[I got ___ / 2 marks]**

Grade 5

2. The density of copper is 8.94 g/cm³.

Calculate the mass of a piece of copper with a volume of 0.6 cm³.

.... **[___ / 2 marks]**

Grade 5

3. A force of 36 N is applied to an area of 0.45 m².

Calculate the pressure, stating the units with your answer.

.... **[___ / 2 marks]**

Grade 5

4. 5 m³ of wrought iron has a mass of 38 700 000 g.

Calculate the density of the wrought iron in kg/m³.

> **Hint**
> Look at the units first!

.... **[___ / 3 marks]**

Grade 6

5. a) A garden snail travels 5.64 m at a speed of 0.047 km/h.

Work out how long it takes. Give your answer in minutes and seconds.

.... **[___ / 4 marks]**

b) A slug travels 0.78 metres per minute.

Determine whether the garden snail or the slug is faster. Justify your answer.

> **Hint**
> Think about units.

.... **[___ / 3 marks]**

Grade 6

6. Florence is driving on the motorway at a constant speed of 67 mph. Her satnav tells her it is 6.7 miles to the next exit. Florence thinks it will take her 10 minutes. Is she correct? Show your working.

> **Hint**
> Be careful converting between hours and minutes.

.... **[___ / 3 marks]**

Direct & inverse proportion 1

Grade 4

1. 100 kilograms (kg) is approximately equal to 220 pounds (lb).

    a) Draw a conversion graph with kilograms from 0 to 200

[I got ___ / 2 marks]

    b) Use the graph to estimate what 300 lb is in kg.

.... kg   **[___ / 2 marks]**

Grade 5

2. 'Dogs Love Bach' sells dog food in 3 kg bags. They are offering three bags for £12.99

'Woof & Ready' sells the same dog food in 2 kg bags. They are offering four bags for £11.00

Which dog food seller is offering better value? Show your working.

....   **[___ / 3 marks]**

Grade 5

3. A 12 acre plot of land in France costs 58 800 euros.

A 15 acre plot of land in Argentina costs 4 520 000 Argentine pesos.

1 euro = 64.19 Argentine pesos.

Work out which plot of land costs less per acre.

....   **[___ / 3 marks]**

Grade 5

4. A team of 12 builders can complete the building of a house in six days.

    a) How many days would it take 18 builders?

....   **[___ / 2 marks]**

    b) Write how many builders would be needed to complete the house in three days.

....   **[___ / 2 marks]**

    c) Sketch a graph to show the relationship between the number of builders and the time taken to build a house.

[___ / 2 marks]

Direct & inverse proportion 2

 1. T is inversely proportional to W

$W = 4$ when $T = 5$

Find the value of T when $W = 8$

.... **[I got ___ / 2 marks]**

 2. p is directly proportional to q

When $q = 4$, $p = 50$

a) Find a formula for p in terms of q

.... **[___ / 2 marks]**

b) Find the value of q when $p = 40$

.... **[___ / 2 marks]**

 3. y is proportional to the cube of x

$y = 54$ when $x = t$

Show that $y = 432$ when $x = 2t$

.... **[___ / 3 marks]**

 4. f is inversely proportional to g

g is directly proportional to h^2

Given that $g = 3$ and $h = 0.5$, when $f = 6$, find a formula for f in terms of h

> **Hint**
> You may wish to use constants of proportionality to relate the variables here.

.... **[___ / 4 marks]**

 5. The velocity, V, of a small marble is proportional to the square root of its kinetic energy, E

If the velocity is increased by 20%, by what percentage will the kinetic energy increase?

.... **[___ / 3 marks]**

Measures

1. An adult ostrich has a maximum speed of 70 kilometres per hour (km/h).

    a) Given that 1 mile is approximately equal to 1.6 km, work out the approximate maximum speed of the ostrich in miles per hour. Give your answer to the nearest integer.

        .... mph   **[I got ___ / 2 marks]**

    b) Work out the ostrich's speed in metres per second (m/s) to 1 decimal place.

        .... m/s   **[___ / 3 marks]**

2. 1 stone (st) ≈ 6.35 kilograms (kg) and 1 kg ≈ 2.2 pounds (lb).

In the United Kingdom, the average mass of an adult is 75.8 kg.

In the United States, the average mass is 180.62 lb.

In Australia, the average mass is 12.25 st.

In which of these countries is the average mass the highest? Show your full working.

> **Hint**
> Convert all masses to the same units.

        ....   **[___ / 3 marks]**

3. Convert

    a) 5 cm² to mm²

        .... mm²   **[___ / 2 marks]**

    b) 2500 mm³ to cm³

        .... cm³   **[___ / 2 marks]**

    c) 0.03 km³ to m³.

        .... m³   **[___ / 2 marks]**

4. A rectangular fish tank, with dimensions as shown in the diagram, is half-filled with water. How many litres of water does the tank contain?

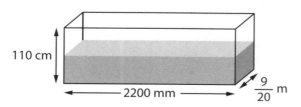

        .... litres   **[___ / 4 marks]**

Angle rules

1. Work out the size of angle x in the diagram. Give a reason for each stage of your working.

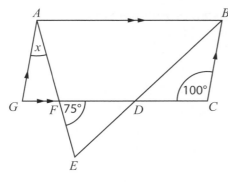

Hint
Use the names of different types of angles in parallel lines.

Diagram not drawn to scale

....° **[I got ___ / 3 marks]**

2. Work out the values of c and d. You must show all of your working.

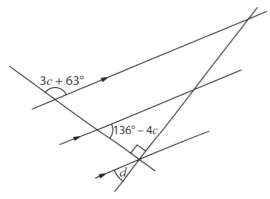

Diagram not drawn to scale

$c = $ ....° $d = $ ....° **[___ / 4 marks]**

3. A circular pie is cut into four pieces, as shown below. AC is the diameter of the pie.

Work out the size of the angle for the largest slice of pie. Give a reason for each stage of your working.

Hint
Remind yourself how to solve simultaneous equations.

Diagram not drawn to scale

....° **[___ / 4 marks]**

Triangles & quadrilaterals

Grade 3

1. The quadrilateral $ABCD$ is a rhombus.

Work out the value of angle x, giving full reasons for each step of your working.

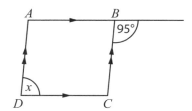

Diagram not drawn to scale

....° **[I got ___ / 3 marks]**

Grade 4

2. In the diagram, angle BFA is 44°. Work out the size of angle FDE

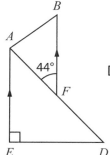

Diagram not drawn to scale

....° **[___ / 3 marks]**

Grade 5

3. PQR and STU are both equilateral triangles of the same size.

T is the midpoint of PR. Q is the midpoint of SU

Work out the size of angle t. Give reasons for each step of your working.

> **Hint**
> What is the size of each angle in an equilateral triangle?

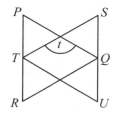

....° **[___ / 4 marks]**

Grade 6

4. Work out the values of x and y for the kite shown.

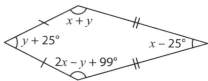

$x =$ ....° $\quad y =$ ....° **[___ / 4 marks]**

Polygons

Grade 4

1. Part of a regular polygon is shown, along with its exterior angle.

Write the name of the shape. Give a reason for your answer.

Diagram not drawn to scale

.... **[I got ___ / 2 marks]**

Grade 4

2. An irregular hexagon contains interior angles with sizes 41°, 59°, 83°, 90° and 147°. Calculate the size of its remaining interior angle.

.... ° **[___ / 3 marks]**

Grade 4

3. The sum of the interior angles of a polygon is 1620°.

Work out how many sides the polygon has.

.... **[___ / 2 marks]**

Grade 5

4. The diagram shows a square, two equilateral triangles and two regular octagons.

Work out the size of angle x

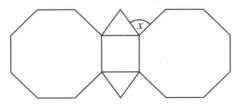

Diagram not drawn to scale

> **Hint**
> Consider the rule for the sum of angles around a point.

.... ° **[___ / 4 marks]**

Grade 5

5. Jemima says she has drawn a regular polygon with an interior angle of 80°.

Sophia says that it is impossible.

Who is correct? Justify your answer.

....

.... **[___ / 3 marks]**

67

Circle theorems 1

Grade 7

1. Write the size of angle x in each of these circles, giving a reason for your answer.

a)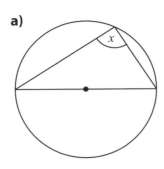

b)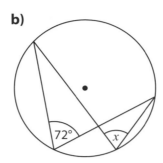

c)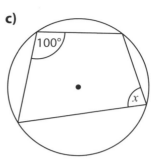

.... °

.... °

.... °

....

....

....

[I got ___ / 6 marks]

Grade 8

2. Work out the size of angle z. You must give a reason for each stage of your working.

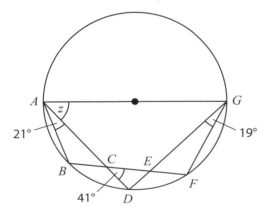

> **Hint**
> State the names of any circle theorems used and show all calculations clearly.

.... ° **[___ / 5 marks]**

Grade 8

3. a) Write the size of angle y in the diagram, stating the circle theorem used.

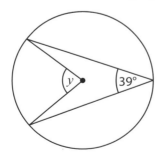

.... °

.... **[___ / 2 marks]**

b) Prove that angles in the same segment of a circle are equal.

You may use, without proof, the circle theorem you used in part **a**.

[___ / 4 marks]

Circle theorems 2

1. Write the value of x in each of these diagrams, giving a reason for your answer.

a)

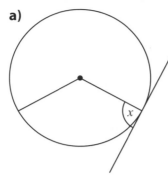

b)

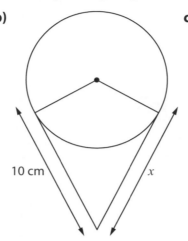

10 cm

x

c)

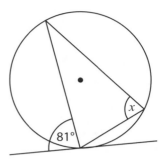

81°

x

....° ....° ....°

....

[I got ___ / 6 marks]

2. Work out the size of angle p. You must give a reason for each stage of your working.

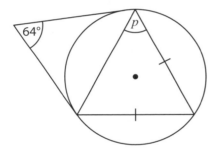

64°

p

> **Hint**
> State the names of any circle theorems used and show all calculations clearly.

....° **[___ / 4 marks]**

3. Prove that two tangents to a circle, which meet at a point outside of the circle, are equal in length.

You may use, without proof, the fact that the angle between the tangent and radius of a circle is a right angle.

[___ / 4 marks]

Transformations

Grade 4

1. Describe the transformations fully.

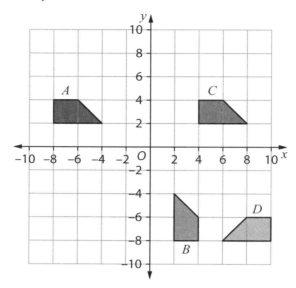

Hint
If unsure, use a piece of tracing paper to help you.

a) A to C .... **[I got __ / 2 marks]**

b) B to A .... **[__ / 2 marks]**

c) D to B .... **[__ / 3 marks]**

Grade 5

2. a) Use the diagram shown for this question.

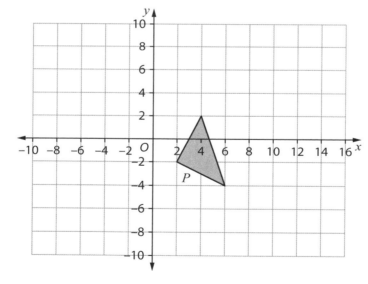

Hint
For part b, start by drawing triangle T

i) Reflect triangle P in the line $y = 0$. Label the image Q **[__ / 2 marks]**

ii) Rotate triangle P 90° anticlockwise about (−2, −2). Label the image R **[__ / 2 marks]**

iii) Translate triangle P by the vector $\begin{pmatrix} -8 \\ 4 \end{pmatrix}$. Label the image S **[__ / 1 mark]**

b) Another triangle, T, has vertices with coordinates (10, 8), (12, 2) and (14, 6).

Describe the single transformation that maps triangle T onto triangle P

.... **[__ / 3 marks]**

Enlargement

1. a) Enlarge shape A with scale factor $\frac{1}{2}$ about the centre of enlargement (0, 0). Label your image B

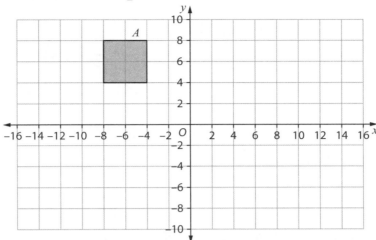

[I got ___ / 2 marks]

b) On the same grid, enlarge shape A with scale factor –1 about the point (0, 0).

Label your image C **[___ / 2 marks]**

c) Write **two** other single transformations that map shape A onto shape C

....

.... **[___ / 3 marks]**

2. Rotate shape P 90° clockwise about the point (–6, 3) and then enlarge it with scale factor –2 about the point (–2, 0). Label your final image Q

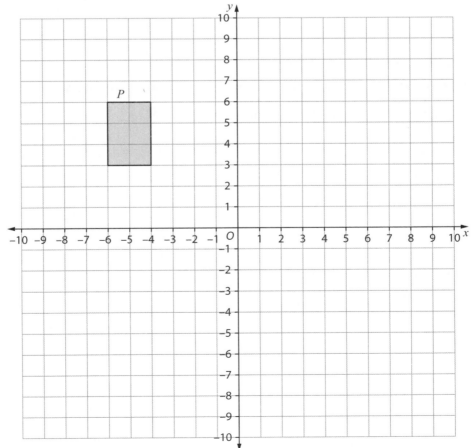

[___ / 4 marks]

Congruent shapes

1. The two triangles *ABC* and *FED* are congruent.

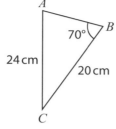

Diagrams not to scale

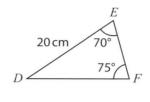

a) Write the length of *DF* .... **[I got ___ / 1 mark]**

b) Write the size of angle *CAB* .... **[___ / 1 mark]**

2. Given that *AB* = *DE*, prove that triangles *CBA* and *CDE* are congruent.

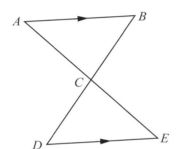

> **Hint**
> Remember angle rules for parallel lines.

[___ / 3 marks]

3. *ABCD* is a parallelogram. *EFGH* is a rhombus.

J, E, F and C lie on a straight line. B, F, G and K also lie on a straight line.

Prove that triangles *ABG* and *CDE* are congruent.

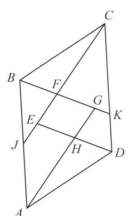

[___ / 4 marks]

Similar shapes

1. Show that these two triangles are similar.

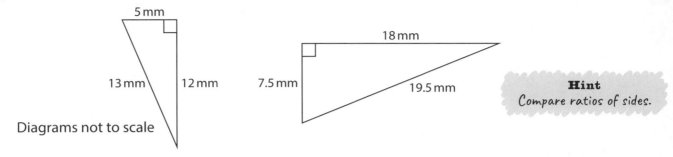

5 mm

13 mm   12 mm   7.5 mm

18 mm

19.5 mm

Diagrams not to scale

Hint
Compare ratios of sides.

[I got ___ / 2 marks]

2. In the diagram, *EB* is parallel to *DC*. *ABE* and *ACD* are similar triangles. *AC* = 11.5 cm, *AB* = 9.2 cm and *AE* = 8.4 cm. Work out the length of *ED*

Diagram not to scale

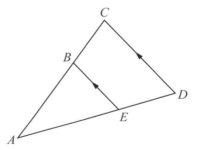

....cm   **[___ / 2 marks]**

3. Two similar metal bars, A and B, are made from exactly the same type of metal.

Bar A has length 10 cm and mass 1.5 kg.

Work out the mass of bar B if its length is 22 cm.

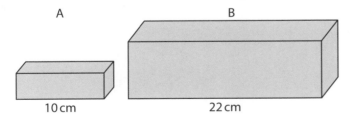

A   B

10 cm   22 cm

....kg   **[___ / 3 marks]**

4. Two solids are similar. The larger solid has a surface area of 360 cm² and a volume of 675 cm³. The smaller solid has a volume of 25 cm³. Work out the surface area of the smaller solid.

Hint
Find the volume scale factor first. Use this to find the area scale factor.

....cm²   **[___ / 3 marks]**

Area and perimeter

1. In the Dutch village of Kaatsheuvel stands a sculpture called 'Arbelos'.

The sculpture is made using three semicircles and is arranged as shown in the diagram.

Work out the perimeter of the sculpture, giving your answer to 3 significant figures.

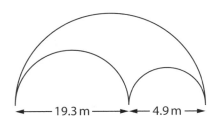

> **Hint**
> You will need to know the diameters of all three semicircles.

....m   **[I got ___ / 3 marks]**

2. This compound shape is made using a semicircle on top of an isosceles trapezium.

Work out the area of the compound shape to 1 decimal place.

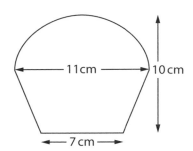

....cm²   **[___ / 4 marks]**

3. A trapezium and a triangle have the same area.

The trapezium has parallel sides of length 9.4 cm and x cm, and a height of 12.8 cm.

The triangle has a base of length 12.8 cm and a height of 17.9 cm.

Work out the length x

> **Hint**
> Sketch the shapes first.

....cm   **[___ / 3 marks]**

4. The diagram below has been created using two identical quarter circles.

Find the exact area of the shaded region.

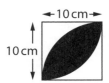

> **Hint**
> You'll need to find the area of the quarter circles and the area of the square.

....cm²   **[___ / 3 marks]**

Plans and elevations

1. The solid object is made from six identical cubes.

Hint
Plans can be drawn in any orientation, as long as it's from above.

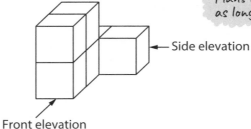

← Side elevation

↗ Front elevation

On the grids below, draw the named elevations and the plan.

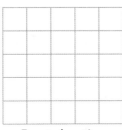 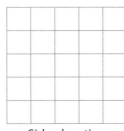 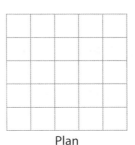

Front elevation   Side elevation   Plan

[I got ___ / 3 marks]

2. Here are the front and side elevations of a solid shape.

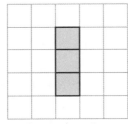 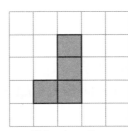 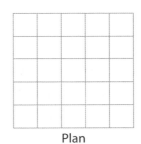

Front elevation   Side elevation   Plan

a) On the grid, draw the plan of the solid shape.   **[___ / 1 mark]**

b) In the space below, draw a 3D sketch of the solid shape.

[___ / 2 marks]

c) Write the number of

   i) vertices   ....   **[___ / 1 mark]**

   ii) edges   ....   **[___ / 1 mark]**

   iii) faces the solid has.   ....   **[___ / 1 mark]**

Prisms and cylinders

1. An unopened cylindrical can of baked beans has a height of 11 cm and a radius of 4 cm. Work out

   a) the volume of the can in terms of π

....cm³   **[I got ___ / 2 marks]**

   b) the surface area of the can to 3 significant figures.

> **Hint**
> A closed cylinder has three surfaces.

....cm²   **[___ / 4 marks]**

2. The triangular prisms shown have the same volume. Work out the height h. State your units.

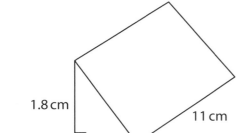

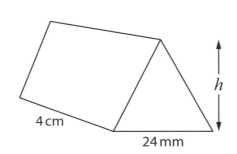

....   **[___ / 4 marks]**

3. The volume of a solid wooden cube is $2\sqrt{2}\, \text{m}^3$.

A cylindrical hole, of radius 0.25 m, is drilled through the length of the cube and its centre.

Work out the total surface area of the six external faces of the resulting solid. Give your answer in the form $a + b\pi$

> **Hint**
> Start by finding the length of the cube.

....m²   **[___ / 3 marks]**

4. Karen fills two cylindrical jugs of different sizes with water.

The ratio of the volume of the larger jug to the volume of the smaller jug is 2 : 1

The total volume of the two jugs is 2400π cm³.

The larger jug has a radius of 12 cm.

> **Hint**
> Start by finding the volume of the larger jug.

   a) Calculate the height of the larger jug to 3 sf.

....cm   **[___ / 4 marks]**

   b) Calculate the radius of the smaller jug to 3 sf if the radius is equal to the height.

....cm   **[___ / 3 marks]**

Spheres and pyramids

$$\text{Volume of a sphere} = \frac{4}{3}\pi r^3 \qquad \text{Surface area of a sphere} = 4\pi r^2$$

 1. The Great Pyramid of Giza has a square base of length 230 m and a height of 147 m.

Work out the volume of the pyramid to 2 significant figures.

Hint Find the area of the base first.

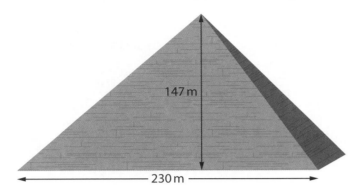

147 m

230 m

....m³ **[I got ___ / 3 marks]**

 2. A sphere has surface area of 400π cm². Work out the radius of the sphere.

Hint Form and solve an equation for r

....cm **[___ / 2 marks]**

 3. A triangular-based pyramid consists of four equilateral triangles of side length 8 cm.

Work out the exact surface area of the pyramid. State your units.

.... **[___ / 4 marks]**

 4. A thin hemispherical bowl has a radius of 25 cm.

How much water could be poured into the bowl before it overflows?

Give your answer to 3 significant figures.

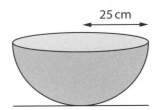

25 cm

....cm³ **[___ / 3 marks]**

77

Cones and frustums

1. A solid cone has height 24 cm and radius 10 cm.

Work out, giving your answers in terms of π,

a) the volume of the cone

> **Hint**
> Volume of a cone = $\frac{1}{3}\pi r^2 h$
> Curved surface area of a cone = $\pi r l$

....cm³   **[I got ___ / 2 marks]**

b) the surface area of the cone.

....cm²   **[___ / 4 marks]**

2. A cork bottle-stopper is in the form of a frustum of a cone.

The dimensions of the stopper are as shown in the diagram.

Work out, in terms of π, the volume of cork required to make the stopper.

> **Hint**
> Remember the cut-off cone is similar to the large cone.

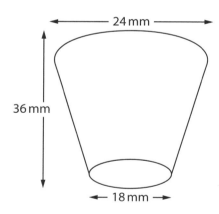

....mm³   **[___ / 5 marks]**

3. Teresa models an ice cream cone out of plastic.

The bottom cone part is a solid cone with radius 6 cm and height 15 cm.

The top ice cream part is a solid hemisphere.

The base of the hemisphere is the same size as the base of the cone.

Calculate, in terms of π, the volume of plastic Teresa uses to make the model.

> **Hint**
> Drawing a diagram might help.

....cm³   **[___ / 3 marks]**

Constructing triangles

1. a) Only one of these triangles can be constructed. Which one?

A: A triangle with sides 7 cm, 8 cm and 16 cm   B: A triangle with sides 3 cm, 4 cm and 6 cm

C: A triangle with sides 9 cm, 12 cm and 22 cm   D: A triangle with sides 15 cm, 30 cm and 60 cm

.... **[I got ___ / 1 mark]**

b) Using a ruler and a pair of compasses, construct the triangle you have chosen in part **a**.

[___ / 3 marks]

2. Accurately draw triangle ABC where AB = 6.4 cm, AC = 4.8 cm and angle BAC = 120°.

> **Hint**
> Draw a small sketch first.

[___ / 3 marks]

3. Construct triangle DEF where $DE = 66$ mm, $EF = \frac{2}{3} DE$ and $FD = \frac{3}{4} EF$

[___ / 3 marks]

Perpendiculars and bisectors

1. a) Using a ruler and a pair of compasses, construct the perpendicular bisector of the line segment *AB*. You must show your construction lines.

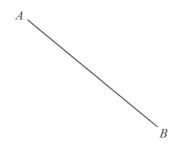

[I got ___ / 2 marks]

b) Using a ruler and a pair of compasses, construct the bisector of angle *CDE*. You must show your construction lines.

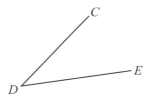

[___ / 2 marks]

2. Using a ruler and a pair of compasses, construct the line perpendicular to the line segment *FH* that passes through *G*. You must show your construction lines.

> **Hint**
> Start by drawing arcs either side of *G*

[___ / 3 marks]

3. Using a ruler and a pair of compasses, construct an angle of 45°.
You must show your construction lines.

[___ / 3 marks]

Loci

1. Shade the area that is further from A than from B but is less than 3 cm away from B

Show all construction lines.

A ——————————————— B

[I got ___ / 4 marks]

2. A triangular plot of land is shown.

Milly farms the area of land that is closer to CD than to CE and is also less than 500 m from C

Shade the area of land that Milly farms. Show all construction lines.

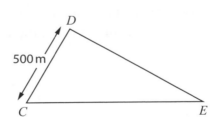

> **Hint**
> You will need to draw a bisector and a circle.

[___ / 4 marks]

3. Bollards are to be placed exactly 2.5 m from a T-shaped go-kart track (shown). Using a scale of 1 : 125, draw the locus that accurately represents the positioning of the bollards if they are to be placed all the way around the track.

[___ / 3 marks]

Pythagoras' theorem

Grade 4

1. Only one of these triangles is right-angled. Which one?

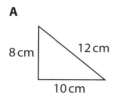 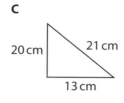 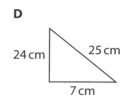

| A | B | C | D |

A: 8 cm, 12 cm, 10 cm

B: 16 cm, 19 cm, 14 cm

C: 20 cm, 21 cm, 13 cm

D: 24 cm, 25 cm, 7 cm

.... **[I got ___ / 2 marks]**

Grade 5

2. Point A has coordinates $(-1, 3)$. Point B has coordinates $(2, 8)$.

Work out the length of the line segment AB to 3 significant figures.

> **Hint**
> A sketch is useful for this type of question.

.... **[___ / 4 marks]**

Grade 5

3. The diagram shows the dimensions of a prize-winning biscuit in a baking competition. The biscuit is in the shape of an isosceles triangle. Work out the height of the biscuit to 1 decimal place.

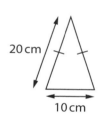

20 cm

10 cm

.... cm **[___ / 3 marks]**

Grade 6

4. The diagram shows three identical steps. Work out the height h of each step to 1 decimal place.

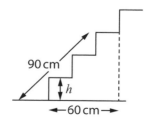

90 cm

h

60 cm

> **Hint**
> Work out the height of a right-angled triangle.

.... cm **[___ / 4 marks]**

Trigonometry 1

Grade 5

1. Work out the length of the side labelled x in each of these triangles. Give your answers to 1 decimal place.

a)

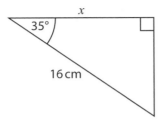

b)

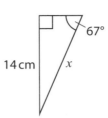

.... cm

.... cm

[I got ___ / 4 marks]

Grade 5

2. Work out the height of this trapezium to 3 significant figures.

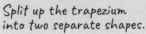

Hint
Split up the trapezium into two separate shapes.

.... cm   **[___ / 3 marks]**

Grade 5

3. From where Taylor is lying on the ground, the angle of elevation of a helicopter is 26°.

The helicopter is flying at a vertical height of 1000 m above the ground.

How far is the helicopter from Taylor? Give your answer to 2 significant figures.

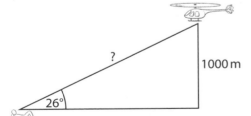

.... m   **[___ / 2 marks]**

Grade 6

4. Work out the length of side b in the diagram below.

Give your answer to 1 decimal place.

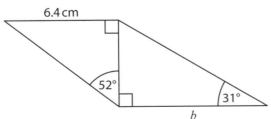

.... cm   **[___ / 3 marks]**

83

Trigonometry 2

1. Work out the size of the angle x in each of these triangles.

Write your answers to 1 decimal place.

a)

x
7 cm
4 cm

b)

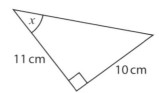

x
11 cm
10 cm

c)

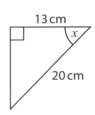

13 cm
x
20 cm

.... ° .... ° .... °

[I got ___ / 6 marks]

2. Triangle PQR is an isosceles triangle. Work out angle PQR to 1 decimal place.

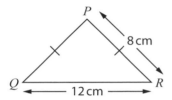

P
8 cm
Q
12 cm
R

Hint
Split the isosceles triangle into two right-angled triangles.

.... ° **[___ / 3 marks]**

3. ABC is a triangle. $AC = 7$ cm, $BC = 16$ cm and angle $BAC = 90°$.

Sketch the triangle and work out angle BCA

.... ° **[___ / 3 marks]**

4. A hang glider is flying at an altitude of 1.2 km when it starts its descent towards the ground.

Work out the angle of depression if the hang glider is 3 km from its landing zone.

Give your answer to 3 significant figures.

.... ° **[___ / 3 marks]**

Bearings

 1. A speedboat (S) is positioned due east of a dinghy (D). The bearing of a hovercraft (H) from the dinghy (D) is 080°. The bearing of the same hovercraft from the speedboat is 280°.
On the diagram, draw the position of the hovercraft. Label it H

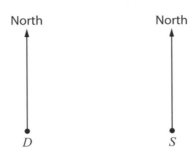

North

North

D

S

[I got ___ / 3 marks]

 2. Point B is 8 km due north of point A

Point C is 11 km due east of point A

Work out the bearing of B from C to the nearest degree.

> **Hint**
> Draw a sketch.

....° **[___ / 4 marks]**

 3. A buoy is 30 metres away from a look-out post on a bearing of 045°.

A swimmer is 40 metres from the same look-out post on a bearing of 315°.

Work out the distance of the swimmer from the buoy.

....m **[___ / 4 marks]**

85

Exact values of sin, cos, tan

1. Work out the length of the side labelled x in each of these triangles.

a)

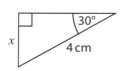

b)

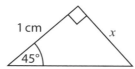

c)

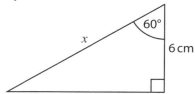

.... cm   .... cm   .... cm

[I got ___ / 9 marks]

2. Arthur has completed a table of exact trigonometric ratios, but some of the values are incorrect.

	0°	30°	45°	60°	90°
$\sin\theta$	0	$\frac{1}{2}$	$\frac{1}{\sqrt{2}}$	$\frac{\sqrt{3}}{2}$	0
$\cos\theta$	1	$\frac{\sqrt{3}}{2}$	$\frac{\sqrt{3}}{2}$	$\frac{1}{2}$	0
$\tan\theta$	0	$\sqrt{3}$	1	$\frac{\sqrt{3}}{2}$	undefined

a) Identify the incorrect values and circle them in the table.   **[___ / 4 marks]**

b) For each value that you have circled, clearly write the correct values below.

.... **[___ / 4 marks]**

3. Work out the exact value of x in each triangle shown. Rationalise the denominators if applicable.

a)

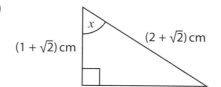

b)

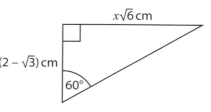

.... °   ....cm

[___ / 6 marks]

Pythagoras' theorem in 3D

 1. The longest diagonal of the cuboid shown is 13 cm.

The length of the cuboid is 12 cm and its width is 3 cm.

Work out the height, h, of the cuboid.

 Hint
Use Pythagoras to write an
equation for the diagonal.

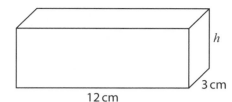

....cm **[I got ___ / 3 marks]**

 2. The 3D shape below is made using 1 cm cubes. Vertices P and Q are labelled.

Work out the length of the line PQ

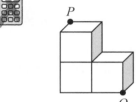

....cm **[___ / 2 marks]**

 3. $ABCDE$ is a square-based pyramid with vertex E directly above the centre of the base of the pyramid.

The square base has side length $\sqrt{2}$ cm and AE is $\sqrt{3}$ cm.

Calculate the height of the pyramid.

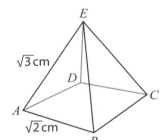

....cm **[___ / 3 marks]**

 4. A cylindrical container is three-quarters full of water. The diameter of the container is 11 cm. A solid triangular prism is added to the container and is completely submerged, with the water level rising to the very top of the container without overflowing. The cross-section of the prism is an equilateral triangle of side length 4 cm. The diagonal of each rectangular side of the prism is 14 cm.

Work out the height of the container to 3 significant figures.

....cm **[___ / 5 marks]**

Trigonometry in 3D

1. *VWXY* is a tetrahedron with faces that are all identical equilateral triangles of side length 3 m.

The vertex *Y* is directly above the centre of the base of the tetrahedron.

Work out the angle between the side *XY* and the base of the tetrahedron to the nearest degree.

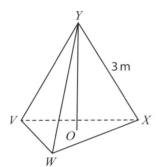

> **Hint**
> Let the midpoint of *WX* be *M*, and then consider the right-angled triangle *MOX*

....° **[I got ___ / 4 marks]**

2. Graham is standing near his office block and measures the angle of elevation to the top of the building to be 72°. He moves 45 m further away from the block and measures the angle of elevation to be 36°.

How tall is his office block? Give your answer to 3 significant figures.

> **Hint**
> Find two expressions for the height and solve simultaneously.

....m **[___ / 4 marks]**

3. The hypotenuse of a right-angled triangle is $\frac{2\sqrt{5}}{3}$ cm and its height is $\frac{\sqrt{15}}{3}$ cm.

Show that the angle of elevation is 60°.

[___ / 4 marks]

sine and cosine rules

1. Work out the length x in each triangle shown. Give your answers to 1 decimal place.

a)

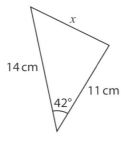

b)

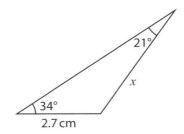

....cm

....cm

[I got ___ / 6 marks]

2. Work out the angle x in each triangle shown. Give your answers to 1 decimal place.

a)

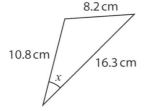

b)

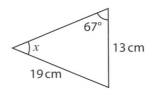

....°

....°

[___ / 6 marks]

3. A triangle has vertices A, B and C

$AB = 10$ cm, $BC = 6$ cm and angle CAB is 25°.

Given that angle ACB is obtuse, work out angle ACB to 1 decimal place.

Hint
Draw a sketch.

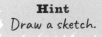

....° **[___ / 4 marks]**

4. Work out the length of side BC in the diagram. Give your answer to 1 decimal place.

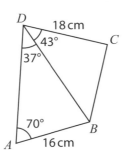

....cm **[___ / 5 marks]**

89

Area of a triangle

1. Work out the area of each triangle shown. Give your answers to 2 decimal places.

a)

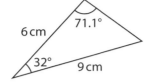

6 cm 71.1° 32° 9 cm

b)

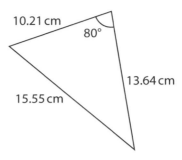

10.21 cm 80° 13.64 cm 15.55 cm

....cm²

....cm²

[I got ___ / 4 marks]

2. A triangular lawn has sides of length 13 m, 11 m and 4 m.

Work out the area of the lawn to 3 significant figures.

....m²   **[___ / 4 marks]**

3. *ABC* is a right-angled triangle with hypotenuse *AB* = 25 m.

Angle *ABC* is 32° and side *AC* is also one side of the triangle *ACD*. The other two sides of triangle *ACD* measure 36 m and 26 m.

Work out the area of shape *ABCD* to 1 decimal place.

> **Hint**
> Start by drawing a sketch.

....m²   **[___ / 5 marks]**

Sectors, arcs & segments

1. Giving your answers to 1 decimal place and clearly stating your units, work out

a) the area of the sector

.... **[I got ___ / 3 marks]**

b) the arc length.

.... **[___ / 3 marks]**

2. A pizza has a radius of 12 cm. Jason takes a slice of the pizza. The remaining pizza has a perimeter of 90 cm.

To the nearest degree, work out the angle, θ, of Jason's slice of pizza.

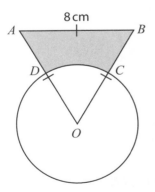

> **Hint**
> The perimeter of a sector is the sum of the arc length and twice the radius.

.... ° **[___ / 5 marks]**

3. The diagram shows the intersection of a circle, centre O, and an equilateral triangle, OAB

$AB = 8$ cm. C and D are the midpoints of OA and OB respectively.

a) Work out the exact area of the shaded region $ABCD$

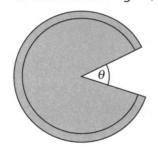

.... cm² **[___ / 4 marks]**

b) A chord is drawn on the circle from C to D. Work out, to 1 decimal place, the area of the minor segment formed.

.... cm² **[___ / 3 marks]**

Vectors 1

1. *PQRSTU* is a regular hexagon. $\overrightarrow{OP} = 2\mathbf{a}$ and $\overrightarrow{OQ} = 3\mathbf{b}$

Write these vectors in terms of **a** and **b**

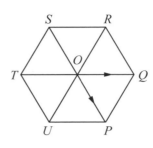

a) $\overrightarrow{OT}$ .... **[I got ___ / 1 mark]**

b) $\overrightarrow{PQ}$ .... **[___ / 1 mark]**

c) $\overrightarrow{OU}$ .... **[___ / 1 mark]**

d) $\overrightarrow{UQ}$ .... **[___ / 1 mark]**

 2. If $\mathbf{p} = \begin{pmatrix} 4 \\ 3 \end{pmatrix}$ and $\mathbf{q} = \begin{pmatrix} 2 \\ -5 \end{pmatrix}$, draw a **triangle** of vectors on the grid below representing **p**, **q** and **p** + **q**

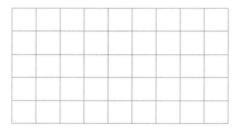

> **Hint**
> Remember to draw an arrow on each vector to indicate its direction.

[___ / 4 marks]

 3. In the grid shown, $\overrightarrow{OA} = \begin{pmatrix} 0 \\ 2 \end{pmatrix}$, $\overrightarrow{OB} = \begin{pmatrix} 2 \\ 4 \end{pmatrix}$ and $\overrightarrow{OD} = \begin{pmatrix} 1 \\ 1 \end{pmatrix}$.

Given that *ABCD* is a rectangle, write the column vector that represents $\overrightarrow{OC}$

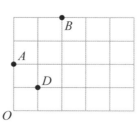

.... **[___ / 2 marks]**

Vectors 2

1. In the diagram, $\overrightarrow{OA} = $ **a** and $\overrightarrow{OB} = $ **b**

M is the midpoint of $\overrightarrow{OA}$ and N lies on $\overrightarrow{AB}$ such that $AN:NB = 4:1$

Find $\overrightarrow{MN}$ in terms of **a** and **b**

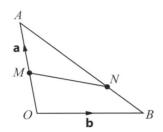

2. In the diagram, $\overrightarrow{OP} = $ **p** and $\overrightarrow{OQ} = $ **q**

PQR is a straight line such that $PQ:QR = 2:3$

Show that $\overrightarrow{OR}$ is parallel to 5**q** $- 3$**p**

> **Hint**
> Parallel vectors are a constant multiple of each other.

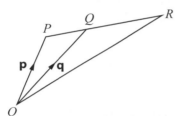

[___ / 5 marks]

3. In the diagram, $\overrightarrow{OX} = $ **x**, $\overrightarrow{OY} = $ **y** and $\overrightarrow{OZ} = k$**y** for some value k

M is the midpoint of $\overrightarrow{OX}$ and N lies on $\overrightarrow{XY}$ such that $XN:NY = 5:2$

Find the value of k such that MNZ is a straight line.

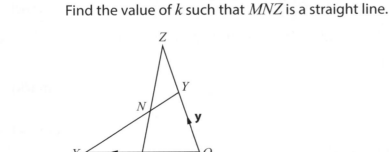

Sampling

1. Sam wants to predict the football results for upcoming matches. He uses a list of results for matches that took place five years ago.

a) What type of data is Sam using?

.... **[I got ___ / 2 marks]**

b) Explain why the data might not be reliable.

.... **[___ / 1 mark]**

2. a) Write one advantage of using secondary data rather than primary.

.... **[___ / 1 mark]**

b) Write one disadvantage of using secondary data rather than primary.

.... **[___ / 1 mark]**

3. 180 sixth form students want to celebrate their end-of-course exam results.

A sample of 40 students is taken to decide how they should celebrate.

Their preferences are shown in the table.

Type of celebration	Frequency
Cinema trip	11
Party	10
Meal out	11
Day at funfair	8

a) Work out how many of the 180 students you think would like a day at the funfair.

.... **[___ / 2 marks]**

b) State one assumption that you have made in your answer to part **a**.

.... **[___ / 1 mark]**

4. a) Write what is meant by a random sample.

.... **[___ / 1 mark]**

Harriet wants to do a questionnaire about the favourite foods of students in her school.

She selects five of her best friends to take part.

b) Identify **i)** the population .... **[___ / 1 mark]**

ii) the sample. .... **[___ / 1 mark]**

c) Give a reason why her sample might be biased.

.... **[___ / 1 mark]**

d) Write two ways that her sample can be improved.

.... **[___ / 2 marks]**

Capture–recapture method

Grade 8

1. A team of researchers wishes to know the approximate number of gulls at a seaside resort.
   They tag 50 gulls and then return to the resort two days later.
   Of the 234 gulls that they manage to capture, 18 of them are tagged.

   Hint
   Use the proportion in the sample to estimate the proportion in the whole population.

   a) Estimate the number of gulls at the seaside resort.

   .... **[I got ___ / 3 marks]**

   b) State one assumption that you have made.

   .... **[___ / 1 mark]**

Grade 8

2. An entomologist wants to estimate the number of grasshoppers in a particular field.
   She captures 12 grasshoppers and tags them before releasing them again.
   The following day, she captures 40 grasshoppers and finds that 3 of them are tagged.

   a) Estimate the number of grasshoppers that are in the field.

   .... **[___ / 3 marks]**

   b) State one reason why the estimate might not be reliable.

   .... **[___ / 1 mark]**

Grade 8

3. Chesney has collected a large jar of one penny coins and he wants to estimate their total value. He empties the jar and places a small sticker on 15 of the coins, before putting them all back in the jar.
   He then selects some of the coins at random.
   Out of 136 coins that Chesney selects from the jar, he finds that 4 of them have a sticker on them.
   Estimate how much money Chesney has in the jar.

   .... **[___ / 3 marks]**

Grade 8

4. A team of marine biologists estimates that a particular body of water contains 1000 dolphins.
   To arrive at this estimate, they tagged some dolphins.
   Out of 440 dolphins that they subsequently captured, 22 were tagged.
   Given that the marine biologists used the capture–recapture method, work out how many dolphins were originally tagged.

   .... **[___ / 3 marks]**

Averages and spread

1. Ginger rolled a dice 20 times. Her results are shown below.

5	3	4	6	3	1	3	3	5	3
6	6	2	3	1	1	1	5	4	2

a) Complete the frequency table to show Ginger's results.

Score on dice	Tally	Frequency
1		
2		
3		
4		
5		
6		

[I got ___ / 2 marks]

b) Write   **i)**   the mode .... [___ / 1 mark]

       ii)   the range .... [___ / 1 mark]

       iii)   the median. .... [___ / 1 mark]

2. The mean of 10 numbers is 63. The mean of 4 of the numbers is 51

Work out the mean of the remaining 6 numbers.

> **Hint**
> *Work out the sum of all the numbers.*

.... [___ / 3 marks]

3. The tables show the number of goals scored by Fermat United and Gauss Town in their last 20 matches.

Fermat United

Number of goals, g	Frequency, f
0	0
1	12
2	8
3	0

Gauss Town

Number of goals, g	Frequency, f	
0	5	
1	6	
2	5	
3	4	

a) Work out the mean number of goals scored by Gauss Town.

.... [___ / 3 marks]

The mean number of goals scored by Fermat United is 1.4

b) i) What is the range of goals scored by Fermat United?

.... [___ / 1 mark]

   ii) On average, which team scored more goals per match? Explain your answer.

.... [___ / 2 marks]

   iii) Which team is more consistent? Explain your answer.

.... [___ / 2 marks]

Grouped data

1. 100 worms are measured.

The table shows their measurements in cm.

Length (x cm)	Frequency, f	Midpoint	$f \times$ midpoint
$0 < x \le 8$	50	4	200
$8 < x \le 16$	30	12	
$16 < x \le 24$	20		400
Total	100		

a) Complete the missing values in the table. **[I got ___ / 2 marks]**

b) Write the modal class.

.... **[___ / 1 mark]**

c) Work out an estimate for the mean length.

.... cm **[___ / 2 marks]**

2. 71 people take part in a 5 km race.

The table shows their finishing times in minutes.

a) Write the class interval that contains the median.

Time (t minutes)	Frequency
$20 < t \le 25$	10
$25 < t \le 30$	17
$30 < t \le 35$	24
$35 < t \le 40$	11
$40 < t \le 45$	9

.... **[___ / 2 marks]**

b) Work out an estimate for the mean finishing time.

Give your answer to the nearest minute.

> **Hint**
> Insert extra columns in the table, as in Question 1

.... minutes **[___ / 3 marks]**

c) Explain why your answer to part **b** is only an estimate.

.... **[___ / 1 mark]**

3. Jamie says, 'I can't estimate the mean score because I don't know the value of y.'

Score (x)	Frequency
$0 < t \le 4$	$3y$
$4 < t \le 8$	$7y$

Jamie is wrong. Work out an estimate of the mean score.

.... **[___ / 3 marks]**

Interquartile range

Grade 6

1. Work out the interquartile range of the numbers in this list.

10   14   16   17   18   21   22   25   25   30   32

Hint
Remember to use
$\frac{1}{4}(n+1)$ and $\frac{3}{4}(n+1)$.

[I got ___ / 3 marks]

Grade 6

2. A stem-and-leaf diagram is shown below.   Key: 1 | 1 means 11

```
1 | 1  2  6  9  9
2 | 0  1  1  1  2  3
3 | 2  4  9
4 | 5  6  7  7  7
```

Work out

a) the mean to 1 decimal place

[___ / 2 marks]

b) the median

[___ / 2 marks]

c) the interquartile range.

[___ / 2 marks]

Grade 6

3. The interquartile range of the numbers on these cards is 3
What is the value of the missing number?

| 3 | | 5 | 6 | 7 | 8 | 9 |

[___ / 2 marks]

Grade 7

4. The back-to-back stem-and-leaf diagram shows the percentage scores obtained by a group of students in a maths test and a physics test.

```
      Physics           Maths
   6  4  1  0  0 | 5 | 2  2  3  6  8
         8  6 | 6 | 1  4  7  7  7  8
5  4  2  2  2  1  1 | 7 | 8  9  9  9
```

Key: 0 | 5 | 2
means 50 for
Physics and
52 for Maths

Hint
Think about what the medians
and interquartile ranges tell you
about the results in the tests.

Use the median and interquartile range to compare the results in the maths and physics tests.

[___ / 5 marks]

Simple charts

1. Linda planted 400 flower bulbs.

She planted a mix of daffodil, tulip and hyacinth bulbs.

The incomplete table and pie chart show some information about these bulbs.

Type of bulb	Number planted
Daffodil	180
Tulip	....
Hyacinth	....
Total	400

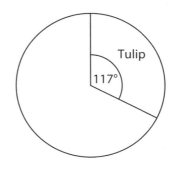

Complete the table and pie chart.

[I got ___ / 3 marks]

2. The frequency polygon shows the masses of some puppies.

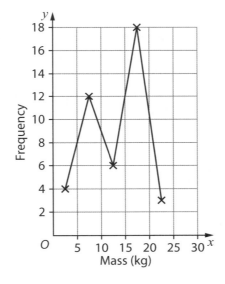

a) Use the frequency polygon to complete the grouped frequency table.

Mass (m kg)	Frequency
$0 < m \leq$	
$< m \leq 10$	12
$< m \leq$	6
$< m \leq 20$	
	3

[___ / 2 marks]

b) Estimate the mean mass of a puppy to the nearest kg.

....kg   [___ / 4 marks]

Scatter graphs

1. The table shows the number of absences of some students along with their final examination scores.

Number of absences	0	2	5	10	17	20	25	30	35	40
Examination score	90	85	76	75	75	50	35	80	40	20

a) Draw a scatter diagram to show this data.

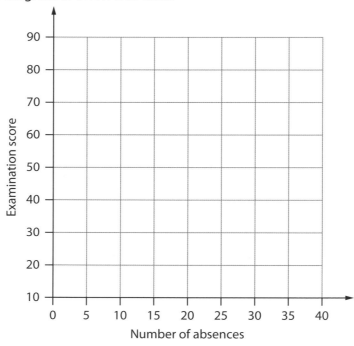

Number of absences

[I got ___ / 2 marks]

b) One of the points is an outlier. Circle the outlier on your graph and give a possible reason for the outlier.

Hint
An outlier does not follow the general trend of the data.

....

[___ / 2 marks]

c) What type of correlation does the graph show?

....

[___ / 1 mark]

2. Cooper claims that the first scatter graph shows a relationship but the second one does not.

 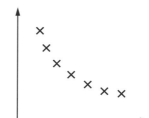

Is Cooper right? Explain your answer.

....

[___ / 1 mark]

Lines of best fit

1. A scatter graph shows that there is positive correlation between the number of sandcastles made at a beach and the number of electric fans sold in a shop.

Trevor says that the increase in the number of sandcastles causes an increase in the number of sales of electric fans. Explain why Trevor is wrong.

.... **[I got ___ / 1 mark]**

2. The scatter graph shows the relationship between the uphill gradient of some hills and the speed of some cyclists.

Speed (km/h) vs Gradient (%) scatter graph

> **Hint**
> An outlier is a point that doesn't follow the trend of most of the data.

a) Give a reason why you might ignore an outlier when drawing a line of best fit.

.... **[___ / 1 mark]**

b) What type of correlation does the graph show?

.... **[___ / 1 mark]**

c) Ignoring the outlier, draw a line of best fit on the scatter graph. **[___ / 1 mark]**

d) Use the line of best fit to estimate the uphill gradient of a hill if a cyclist is travelling at 15 km/h.

.... **[___ / 1 mark]**

e) By how many km/h would you expect the speed of a cyclist to decrease for every 1% increase in the gradient of a hill?

....km/h **[___ / 2 marks]**

f) Marta uses the line of best fit to estimate that a cyclist travelling up a hill with 40% gradient should be travelling at a speed of 5 km/h.

Comment on Marta's assumption.

.... **[___ / 1 mark]**

Time series

Grade 4

1. Describe the general trend in this time series graph.

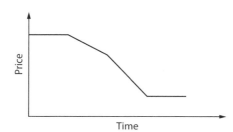

.... **[I got ___ / 1 mark]**

Grade 4

2. The table shows the monthly profits made by a shop over a period of seven months.

Month	Jan	Feb	Mar	Apr	May	Jun	July
Profit (£)	3000	3500	4200	4500	4000	5000	6000

a) Construct a time series graph for this data.

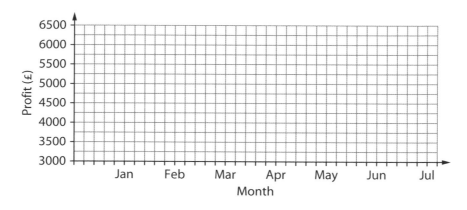

[___ / 2 marks]

b) Describe the general trend of the data. .... [___ / 1 mark]

c) What might be misleading about this graph?

.... [___ / 1 mark]

Grade 4

3. The time series graph shows the attendance figures at a football ground over an eight-week period.

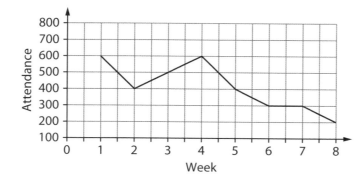

a) Describe the general trend of the data. .... [___ / 1 mark]

b) In which two weeks was attendance at its highest?

.... [___ / 1 mark]

c) Use the general trend to predict the attendance in Week 9

.... [___ / 1 mark]

Box plots

1. The lengths of 25 aardvarks, in metres, are shown below.

| 1.3 | 1.6 | 1.8 | 1.9 | 1.1 | 1.4 | 1.5 | 1.0 | 0.8 | 0.8 | 1.5 | 1.7 |
| 1.7 | 1.9 | 1.4 | 1.1 | 0.8 | 2.0 | 1.7 | 2.0 | 1.3 | 1.4 | 1.8 | 0.9 | 1.1 |

Draw a box plot to represent this information.

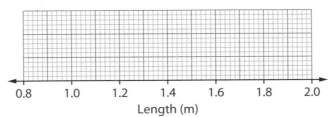

Hint
Remember to start with an ordered list.

[I got ___ / 4 marks]

2. The table shows some information about the time taken in minutes for a year 10 class to complete their maths homework.

Minimum	Interquartile range	Maximum	Lower quartile	Median
22	8	48	32	34

a) Draw a box plot to represent this information.

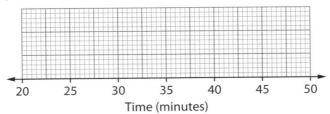

[___ / 2 marks]

The box plot shows the distribution of times for a year 11 class to complete their homework.

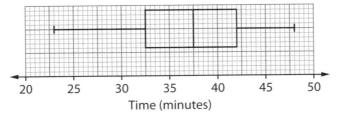

b) Compare the distribution of the year 11 times to the year 10 times.

....

....

[___ / 3 marks]

103

Cumulative frequency

1. The frequency table shows the times taken for 200 students to get ready for school.

Time (*t* minutes)	Frequency
$0 < t \le 5$	30
$5 < t \le 10$	74
$10 < t \le 15$	56
$15 < t \le 20$	22
$20 < t \le 25$	18

a) On the grid, draw a cumulative frequency graph to represent this information.

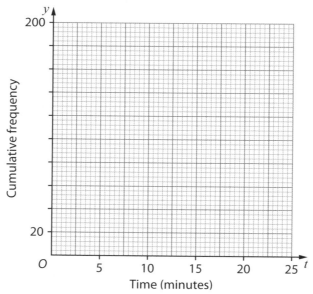

Hint
Adding a column for cumulative frequency to a frequency table helps with plotting these graphs.

[I got ___ / 2 marks]

b) Find the median time.

....minutes   **[___ / 1 mark]**

2. The cumulative frequency graph shows the width, in mm, of 44 assorted plasters.

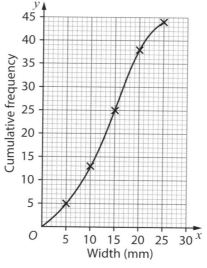

a) Find an estimate for the interquartile range.

....mm   **[___ / 2 marks]**

b) Estimate how many plasters have a width greater than 20 mm.

....   **[___ / 2 marks]**

Histograms

1. The frequency table shows the speeds, in km/h, of some cars on a motorway.

   a) Complete the missing information in the table and in the histogram.

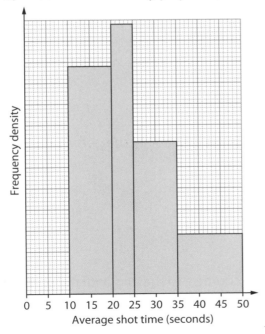

Speed (s km/h)	Frequency
$65 < s \leq 70$	
$70 < s \leq 80$	44
$80 < s \leq 85$	
$85 < s \leq 100$	18

> **Hint**
> Frequency density = $\dfrac{frequency}{class\ width}$

[I got ___ / 4 marks]

   b) Estimate the mean speed of the cars.

....km/h   **[___ / 3 marks]**

   c) Work out the class interval that contains the median.

....km/h   **[___ / 2 marks]**

2. The histogram shows the average shot time, in seconds, of some billiards players.

27 players took less than 20 seconds to play a shot.

   a) Estimate how many players took more than 30 seconds.

....   **[___ / 3 marks]**

   b) Explain why your answer to part **a** is only an estimate.

....   **[___ / 1 mark]**

Theoretical probability

Grade 4

1. The probability of winning a particular game is x

The probability of losing the game is $x + \frac{1}{2}$

The game cannot be drawn. Work out the value of x

Hint
The probabilities must add up to 1. Use your algebra skills.

.... **[I got ___ / 2 marks]**

Grade 4

2. A bag contains white, yellow, pink and orange counters.

The table shows the probabilities of selecting each colour of counter from the bag.

Colour	White	Yellow	Pink	Orange
Probability	0.3	0.15	0.26	

a) Work out the probability of selecting an orange counter.

.... **[___ / 2 marks]**

b) What is the probability of **not** selecting a white or orange counter?

.... **[___ / 2 marks]**

c) There are 200 counters in the bag. Work out how many are yellow.

.... **[___ / 2 marks]**

Grade 5

3. A bag contains 4 red, 6 yellow and 5 blue counters.

a) Grace takes a counter randomly from the bag. What is the probability she gets a purple counter?

.... **[___ / 1 mark]**

b) Grace replaces her counter. She then adds more red counters to the bag until the probability of getting red is $\frac{1}{2}$. How many red counters does she add?

.... **[___ / 2 marks]**

Outcomes and possibility spaces

1. Two fair 6-sided dice are thrown. This possibility space shows all of the possible outcomes.

> **Hint**
> There are 36 possible outcomes.

Write the probability that the dice show

    a) a 4 on both dice   **[I got ___ / 1 mark]**

    b) a 4 on just one of the dice   **[___ / 1 mark]**

    c) one even number and one odd number.   **[___ / 1 mark]**

2. Rick writes a 2-digit odd number.

    a) Work out how many different numbers Rick could write.

                                                       [___ / 2 marks]

    b) What is the probability that he writes a number whose digits are both the same?

                                                       [___ / 2 marks]

3. There are 7 yellow balls and 6 red balls on a pool table.

Two of the balls are potted consecutively (and not replaced). In how many ways can this be done if

    a) any colour ball can be potted in any order

                                                       [___ / 2 marks]

    b) one ball is red and the other is yellow?

                                                       [___ / 3 marks]

4. Three cards are drawn from a standard deck of 52 playing cards and not replaced.

In how many ways can the three cards be selected if the first and third card are both hearts?

Note that there are 13 hearts in a standard deck.

                                                       [___ / 4 marks]

Probability experiments

1. The frequency tree shows the outcomes of 40 people who took a driving test.

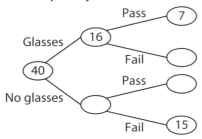

a) Complete the frequency tree. **[I got ___ / 2 marks]**

b) Write the probability that a person chosen at random wears glasses and passes the test.

.... **[___ / 1 mark]**

2. Zebedee plays six games of chess. He wins $\frac{1}{3}$ of them and loses the rest. He plays eight games of draughts. He loses 25% of them and wins the rest.

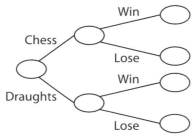

a) Complete the frequency tree. **[___ / 2 marks]**

b) A game is chosen at random. Write the probability that the game is chess and he loses.

.... **[___ / 1 mark]**

3. When dropped onto a hard surface, a plastic cup will land the right way up, on its side, or upside down.

a) Sheena is doing an experiment to find out which is the more likely outcome. She drops a plastic cup 50 times and records the results. Complete the table.

	Right way up	On its side	Upside down
Frequency	8		
Relative frequency		0.44	

[___ / 2 marks]

b) She then drops the plastic cup a further 100 times and it lands upside down 36 times.

Based on this, was the probability of the cup landing upside down higher in the first or second experiment? Show your working.

.... **[___ / 2 marks]**

Expected results

Grade 4

1. The probability of a report being submitted on time is 0.85

   a) Out of 60 reports, how many would you expect to be submitted on time?

   .... **[I got ___ / 2 marks]**

   b) Out of 170 reports, 160 are submitted on time.
   Is this more or fewer than what you would have expected? Explain your answer.

   .... **[___ / 2 marks]**

Grade 4

2. An unbiased 8-sided dice has the numbers 1, 2, 2, 3, 3, 4, 4 and 4 on its faces.

   a) If the dice is thrown once, what is the probability that it will land on 4?

   .... **[___ / 1 mark]**

   b) If the dice is thrown 40 times, how many times would you expect it to land on 3?

   .... **[___ / 2 marks]**

   c) The dice is thrown repeatedly and lands on the number 4 a total of 36 times.
   Estimate how many times the dice was thrown.

   .... **[___ / 2 marks]**

Grade 4

3. The sides of a biased 5-sided spinner are numbered 1, 2, 3, 4 and 5

   The table shows the probabilities of landing on each number.

Number	1	2	3	4	5
Probability	0.2	0.4	0.16	0.13	

   If the spinner is spun 2500 times, how many times would you expect it to land on 5?

   .... **[___ / 3 marks]**

Grade 6

4. A manufacturer of light bulbs claims that 92% of light bulbs they produce last for longer than 25 000 hours. The light bulbs are sold in packs of two. A shop buys 500 packs.

   Work out an estimate for the number of packs of light bulbs that will have exactly one light bulb that lasts longer than 25 000 hours.

   .... **[___ / 3 marks]**

Tree diagrams

Grade 6

1. Jess and Bryan both collect football stickers.

Jess has 12 spare stickers that she is happy to give away.

5 of the stickers show pictures of players who are defenders. The rest show midfielders.

She tells Bryan that he can randomly choose any 2 of her stickers to keep.

Hint
Draw a tree diagram!

a) What is the probability that Bryan chooses 2 midfielders?

.... **[I got ___ / 2 marks]**

b) Work out the probability that Bryan's 2 stickers feature players who play in different types of positions.

.... **[___ / 3 marks]**

Grade 7

2. Nkem plays a game of darts with her friend. They then play a game of backgammon.

The tree diagram below shows Nkem's probabilities of winning and losing each game.

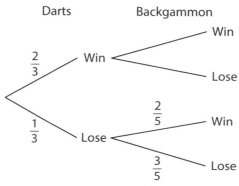

The probability that Nkem wins both games is $\frac{1}{2}$.

a) Complete the two missing probabilities on the tree diagram. **[___ / 3 marks]**

b) Work out the probability that Nkem's friend wins at most one of the two games.

.... **[___ / 3 marks]**

Grade 7

3. Two people are chosen at random from a group of 4 French speakers and 7 English speakers.

Using a tree diagram, show that the probability of selecting one French speaker and one English speaker is just over 50%.

[___ / 4 marks]

Conditional probability 1

1. The two-way table shows some information about the number of items of food and drink purchased at a fast-food stand.

Drink / Food	Milkshake	Lemonade	Water	None	Total
Burger	33	24	16	25	98
Hotdog	28	18	8	22	76
None	12	4	10	0	26
Total	73	46	34	47	200

One of the purchasers is chosen at random. Work out the probability that

a) they purchased a hotdog and water

.... **[I got ___ / 1 mark]**

b) they bought lemonade given that they didn't buy a burger.

Hint
Remember to restrict the possibility space.

.... **[___ / 2 marks]**

2. The two-way table shows some information about the languages studied by some students at a school.

Language	Year 9	Year 10	Total
French	35	52	87
German	34	17	51
Other	7	5	12
Total	76	74	150

One of the pupils is chosen at random. Work out the probability that

a) it is a year 9 student who studies French

.... **[___ / 1 mark]**

b) it is a year 10 student given that they study German.

.... **[___ / 2 marks]**

3. A coin and a dice are repeatedly thrown together. Some of the results are shown in the two-way table.

Dice / Coin	Even number	Odd number
Heads		23
Tails	24	

Hint
Think about what the fraction numerators and denominators represent.

The probability of getting tails, given that an odd number is rolled on the dice, is $\frac{26}{49}$

The probability of rolling an odd number on the dice, given that you get heads on the coin, is $\frac{23}{50}$

Complete the two missing values in the table.

[___ / 2 marks]

Conditional probability 2

1. The tree diagram shows the probabilities of a hockey player scoring a penalty on two consecutive attempts.

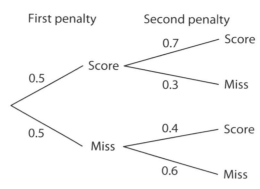

First penalty   Second penalty

a) Work out the probability that the hockey player scores with the 2nd penalty.

.... **[I got ___ / 2 marks]**

b) Work out the probability that the hockey player scores with the 1st penalty given that they miss the 2nd penalty.

Hint

$$P(A \text{ given } B) = \frac{P(A \text{ and } B)}{P(B)}$$

.... **[___ / 3 marks]**

2. Two events are scheduled to take place. The probability that events A and B both take place is 0.375. The probability that event A takes place, given that event B takes place, is 0.45

Work out the probability that event B does not take place.

.... **[___ / 4 marks]**

3. A bag contains only red and blue balls. The ratio of red balls to blue balls is 4 : 5

Two balls are taken at random from the bag without replacement.

The probability that the first ball is red and the second ball is blue is $\frac{40}{159}$

Work out how many red balls are in the bag at the start.

.... **[___ / 4 marks]**

Set notation

1. 60 people were asked if they read fiction or non-fiction books.
20 said they read only non-fiction. Five said they don't read either. 28 people said they read fiction only. Complete the Venn diagram.

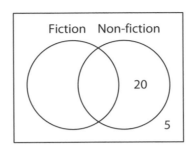

[I got ___ / 2 marks]

2. There are 79 students in a college. 44 study art. 12 study both art and music. 11 don't study either. Complete the Venn diagram.

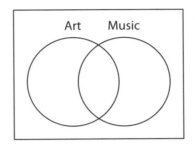

> **Hint**
> *Fill in the intersection first.*

[___ / 4 marks]

3. In the Venn diagram, $A \cap B = \{7, 9\}$

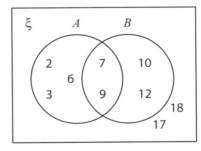

Write the numbers that are in the set

a) $A \cup B$ .... **[___ / 1 mark]**

b) A' .... **[___ / 1 mark]**

4. $\xi = \{1, 2, 4, 8, 16, 25, 27, 64\}$, $A = \{$square numbers$\}$, $B = \{$cube numbers$\}$

a) Draw a Venn diagram for this information.

[___ / 4 marks]

b) Write the numbers that are in the set $A \cap B$

.... **[___ / 1 mark]**

Probability from Venn diagrams

Grade 5

1. $\xi = \{1, 2, 3, 5, 6, 9, 10, 11, 17, 21, 25\}$, $P = \{$prime numbers$\}$, $G = \{$numbers greater than 10$\}$

 a) Draw a Venn diagram for this information.

 [I got ___ / 4 marks]

 b) One of the numbers in the diagram is chosen at random. Find the probability that the number is in

 i) set $P \cap G$ .... [___ / 1 mark]

 ii) set G' .... [___ / 1 mark]

 iii) set P only. .... [___ / 1 mark]

Grade 7

2. The Venn diagram shows the number of customers who purchased apples, pears and bananas at a grocer's shop.

Apples

24

6   13

12

11   14

8

Pears   Bananas

 a) Write the probability that a randomly chosen customer does not buy apples.

 .... [___ / 2 marks]

 b) Given that a randomly chosen customer bought bananas, what is the probability that they also bought apples?

> **Hint**
> 'Given' means that the
> possibility space is restricted.

 .... [___ / 2 marks]

Grade 8

3. 200 people are asked which of the continents Europe, North America and Africa they have visited during the last three years.

48 people had visited Africa. 5 people had visited each of Europe, North America and Africa.

Of the 58 people who had visited North America, 34 had not visited Europe or Africa.

16 people had visited both Europe and North America, whilst 19 people had visited both Europe and Africa. 22 people had visited none of the three continents.

 a) Work out the probability that a randomly chosen person visited Europe.

 .... [___ / 4 marks]

 b) Given that a randomly chosen person visited North America, work out the probability that they also visited Africa.

 .... [___ / 2 marks]

Paper 1 (Non-Calculator)

Higher Tier

(Time: 1 hour 30 minutes)

- Answer **all** questions.
- You must **show all your working**.
- Diagrams are **NOT** accurately drawn, unless indicated.
- **Calculators may not be used**.

[I got ___ / 80 marks]

---

1. Yootha eats $\frac{2}{5}$ of a pizza. Zoe eats $\frac{1}{8}$ of the remaining pizza.

Work out the fraction of the pizza that has been eaten altogether.

.... **[I got ___ / 3 marks]**

2. Each of the cards below contains a number.

The mode of the numbers is –3

The mean of the numbers is 7

a) Fill in the correct numbers on each of the blank cards.

[___ / 2 marks]

b) Write the range and the median of the numbers.

Range = ... Median = ... **[___ / 2 marks]**

c) Which of the averages is most suitable for these numbers? Explain your reasoning.

....

.... **[___ / 2 marks]**

3. A small bag of sweets costs 75 pence.

   A large bag of sweets costs 90 pence.

   The large bag contains 35% more sweets than the small bag.

   Which bag of sweets is better value?

   Justify your answer with full working.

   .... [___ / 3 marks]

4. Each of these equations matches to one of the graphs.

   $$y = \frac{1}{x} \qquad y = x^2 \qquad y = x^3 \qquad y = x$$

   Write the correct equation below each graph.

   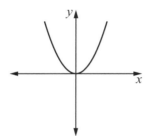 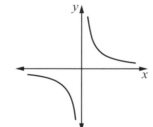 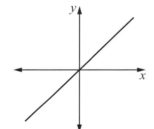 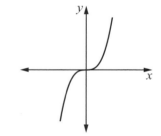

   ....

   [___ / 2 marks]

5. A piece of wood is cut into two pieces, A and B.

   The ratio of the length of A to the length of B is 2:7, and B is 90 cm longer than A.

   Work out the length of the piece of wood before it was cut.

   ....cm   [___ / 3 marks]

Further practice & support: Q3 p.58; Q4 p.38; Q5 p.57

6. In the space below, make an accurate drawing of an equilateral triangle using only a ruler and a pair of compasses.

   Show all of your construction lines.

   [___ / 2 marks]

7. Simplify $(2 \times 10^{-4}) \times (3 \times 10^3)^2$

   Give your answer in standard form.

   [___ / 3 marks]

8. a) Write 168 as a product of its prime factors.

   [___ / 2 marks]

   b) When a number, n, is cubed, the answer is the same as the answer to 168×441

   Given that $441 = 3^2 \times 7^2$, work out the value of n

   [___ / 2 marks]

Further practice & support: Q6 p.79; Q7 p.14; Q8 p.11

9. A researcher wants to estimate the number of catfish in a particular lake. She catches a sample of 12 catfish and tags them. A few days later, she returns and catches 20 catfish at random, 6 of which are tagged. Estimate the number of catfish in the lake.

[___ / 3 marks]

10. Work out $3\frac{2}{3} \times 2\frac{1}{4} \div 2\frac{1}{2}$. Give your answer as a mixed number in its simplest form.

[___ / 3 marks]

11. The first four terms of a Fibonacci-type sequence are shown below.

$$3x - 13 \qquad y \qquad x + 5 \qquad 3y - 6$$

Each term is the sum of the previous two terms. Find the values of x and y

$x =$ ....

$y =$ .... [___ / 5 marks]

12. Steven says that there are no integers a, b and c such that the ratio

$$(\sin 45°)^2 : (\cos 30°)^2 : (\tan 60°)^2$$

can be written in the form $a : b : c$. Is Steven right? Show your working.

[___ / 3 marks]

Further practice & support: Q9 p.95; Q10 p.6; Q11 p.22; Q12 p.86

13. Sam says that the graph of $y = x^2 - 10x + 7$ has exactly one turning point.

a) Without finding the turning point, explain why Sam is correct.

.... [___ / 1 mark]

b) Find the coordinates of the turning point of $y = x^2 - 10x + 7$

.... [___ / 2 marks]

14. $PQRS$ is a rhombus.

a) Prove that the diagonals, PR and QS, divide the rhombus into four congruent triangles.
You may assume that the diagonals bisect each other.

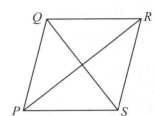

[___ / 3 marks]

b) Use your answer to part **a** to show that the diagonals of a rhombus are perpendicular.

[___ / 2 marks]

15. Write $\dfrac{1 + \sqrt{2}}{3\sqrt{5}}$ in the form $\dfrac{\sqrt{a} + \sqrt{b}}{c}$, where a, b and c are integers.

.... [___ / 2 marks]

Further practice & support: Q13 p.28; Q14 p.72; Q15 p.9

16. Line l_1 intersects the coordinate axes at points A and B as shown. B has coordinates $(0, 5)$.

Line l_2 passes through the points $(a, 7)$ and $(7, 16)$ and is perpendicular to line l_1

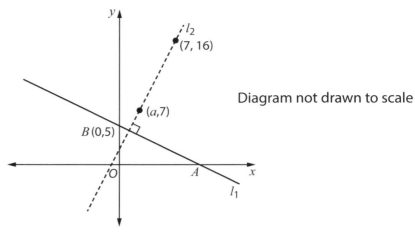

Diagram not drawn to scale

The area of triangle OAB is 25 square units.

Work out the value of a

.... **[___ / 4 marks]**

17. Solve $4^2 \times 8^2 = \dfrac{1}{2^x}$

.... **[___ / 3 marks]**

Further practice & support: Q16 p.19; Q17 p.10

18. The histogram shows the times taken by some students to solve a puzzle.

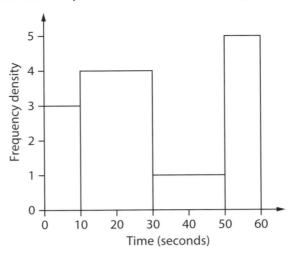

a) Work out how many students took less than 10 seconds to solve the problem.

.... [__ / 2 marks]

b) i) Work out an estimate for the median time taken.

.... seconds   [__ / 4 marks]

ii) Explain why your answer to part **b** can only be an estimate.

.... [__ / 1 mark]

19. a) Becky says that the inverse of a function f(x) is $\frac{1}{f(x)}$

Explain Becky's misunderstanding.

.... [__ / 1 mark]

b) Find the inverse function of f(x), where $f(x) = \frac{1-x}{2x+4}$, $x \neq -2$

.... [__ / 3 marks]

20. At time $t = 0$, Riley passes point A, running at a constant speed of 8 km/h.

At the same instant, Jordan, running in the opposite direction, passes point B at a constant speed of 2.5 m/s. The distance between A and B is 8500 m.

8 km/h

Riley

2.5 m/s

Jordan

A ◄─────────── 8500 m ───────────► B

a) Which of the runners is travelling faster? Show your working.

.... [___ / 2 marks]

b) Work out the time in minutes when the runners pass each other.

....minutes [___ / 3 marks]

c) Work out how far the runners will be from A when they pass each other.

.... [___ / 2 marks]

21. a) Prove that $(a^b + 1)(a^b - 1) = (a^{2b} - 1)$

[___ / 2 marks]

b) a and b are integers greater than 1. Show that $a^{2b} - 1$ can never be a prime number.

[___ / 3 marks]

End of paper

Further practice & support: Q20 p.61; Q21 p.23

Paper 2 (Calculator) 🖩

Higher Tier

(Time: 1 hour 30 minutes)

- Answer **all** questions.
- You must **show all your working**.
- Diagrams are **NOT** accurately drawn, unless indicated.
- **Calculators may be used**.

[I got ___ / 80 marks]

---

1. a) A number x is rounded to 2 decimal places. The result is 0.87

Write down the error interval for x

.... $\leq x <$ .... [I got ___ / 2 marks]

b) A number y is truncated to a whole number. The result is 7

Write down the error interval for y

.... $\leq y <$ .... [___ / 2 marks]

2. In a sale, a sign states that everything is 23% off the original price.

The sale price of a coat is £48.77

The coat label shows the original price was £59.99

Is the sign correct? Explain your reasoning.

.... [___ / 3 marks]

3. In a test, class 3A has a median score of 45 and a range of 20

For the same test, class 3B has a median score of 39 and a range of 8

Compare the data for the two classes, explaining your answers in context.

....

.... [___ / 2 marks]

4. The diameter of Earth is 12 742 000 m.

The diameter of Jupiter is $1.429\,84 \times 10^8$ m.

Sebastian claims that the diameter of Jupiter is over 1000 times greater than the diameter of Earth.

Is Sebastian right? Explain your answer.

....

....

.... **[___ / 3 marks]**

5. The distance from Nairobi to Mombasa is 440 km.

A car travels from Nairobi to Mombasa in 4 hours and 20 minutes.

Work out the average speed of the car in km/h to 1 decimal place.

....km/h   **[___ / 3 marks]**

6. Andrew has some jelly beans. 25% of them are white, $\frac{1}{6}$ are red and the rest are green.

Work out the ratio of red jelly beans to green jelly beans in its simplest form.

....   **[___ / 3 marks]**

7. The radius, r, of a cylinder is equal to its height.

The volume of the cylinder is 1000 cm³. Work out the value of r to 1 decimal place.

....cm   **[___ / 3 marks]**

Further practice & support: Q4 p.13; Q5 p.61; Q6 p.57; Q7 p.76

8. The points P, Q, R and S lie along the same straight line.

The distances between the points are such that $PQ:QR = 5:3$ and $QR:RS = 4:7$

   a) Write down the ratio $PQ:QR:RS$

.... **[___ / 2 marks]**

   b) If $PQ = 10\,cm$, work out the distance PS

....cm   **[___ / 2 marks]**

9. The first six terms of a sequence are

      7   11   21   37   59   87

   a) Write the next two terms in the sequence.

.... **[___ / 1 mark]**

   b) Work out the nth term of the sequence.

.... **[___ / 3 marks]**

10. A piece of sterling silver consists of 92.5% silver and 7.5% nickel.

The density of silver is 10.490 g/cm³ and the density of nickel is 9.908 g/cm³.

Work out, to 2 decimal places, the density of the sterling silver.

....g/cm³   **[___ / 3 marks]**

Further practice & support: Q8 p.57; Q9 p.50; Q10 p.61

11. Celine, Dean and Eileen share some marshmallows between them in the ratio $3:2:5$

Eileen gives five of her marshmallows to Dean, one of which he eats.

The ratio of marshmallows is then $4:4:5$

Work out how many marshmallows each person had to begin with.

Celine.................................... Dean.................................... Eileen.................................... [___ / **3 marks**]

12. a) Expand fully $(x-1)(x-2)(x-3)$

.... [___ / **3 marks**]

b) Using part **a**, prove that $n^4 - 6n^3 + 11n^2 - 6n$ is always even for all integer values of $n > 3$

[___ / **2 marks**]

13. $x = 0.70\dot{2}$

Prove algebraically that x can be written as $\frac{26}{37}$

[___ / **3 marks**]

14. Chad is trying to solve a quadratic inequality but he has gone wrong. Here is his working:

Line 1 $\qquad\qquad 12x^2 + x - 6 < 0$

Line 2 $\qquad\qquad (4x + 3)(3x - 2) < 0$

Line 3 $\qquad\qquad 4x + 3 < 0$ and $3x - 2 < 0$

Line 4 $\qquad\qquad x < -\frac{3}{4}, x < \frac{2}{3}$

a) On which line has Chad started to go wrong? Explain your answer.

.... [___ / **2 marks**]

b) Solve the inequality $12x^2 + x - 6 < 0$

.... [___ / **2 marks**]

Further practice & support: Q11 p.57; Q12 p.23/24; Q13 p.8; Q14 p.35

15. A six-character access code is needed for an online bank account. The first character must be a letter (A to Z). The remaining characters must be single digit numbers (0 to 9). A number may be used more than once.

Enter access code

_ _ _ _ _ _

    a) Work out how many possible access codes there are.

.... [__ / 2 marks]

    b) The rules for access codes are changed. Under the new rules, both the first and last characters of the code must be letters, with the remaining characters being single digit numbers. Under the new rules, no number or letter may be used more than once in the access code.

       How many six-character access codes are possible now?

.... [__ / 2 marks]

16. The diagram consists of three overlapping trapezia (large, medium, small) with the same centre.

The two parallel sides of the large trapezium measure 80 cm and 120 cm.

The medium trapezium is an enlargement of the large trapezium with scale factor 0.75

The small trapezium is an enlargement of the medium trapezium with scale factor 0.5

The area of the shaded region is 4050 cm².

Work out the height, h, of the large trapezium.

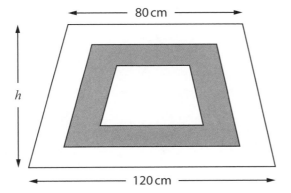

....cm   [__ / 5 marks]

Further practice & support: Q15 p.107; Q16 p.74

17. The point O lies at the centre of plane $ABCD$ in the cuboid $ABCDEFGH$ shown.

$AE = 8\,\text{cm}$, $EH = 15\,\text{cm}$ and $GH = 5\,\text{cm}$.

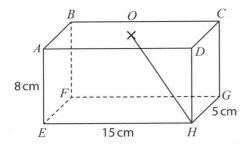

Work out the angle between the line OH and the plane $EFGH$ to 1 decimal place.

....° [___ / 4 marks]

18. Prove that the angle in a semicircle is a right angle.

Do not use circle theorems in your proof.

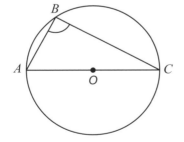

[___ / 4 marks]

Further practice & support: Q17 p.88; Q18 p.66

19. Use the Venn diagram shown for this question.

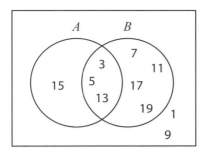

a) i) Write which numbers are in the set $A \cup B$

.... [__ / 1 mark]

ii) Write which numbers are in A'

.... [__ / 1 mark]

b) A number is chosen at random from set B. Find the probability that the number is also in set A

.... [__ / 2 marks]

20. A ship travels 10 km on a bearing of 110° from A to B. It then travels 6 km on a bearing of 230° from B to C, before returning to A directly from C

Work out the bearing on which the ship travels to A from C

....° [__ / 5 marks]

Further practice & support: Q19 p.114; Q20 p.85

21. The graph below shows the velocity, v, of a skateboarder over a short period of time, t

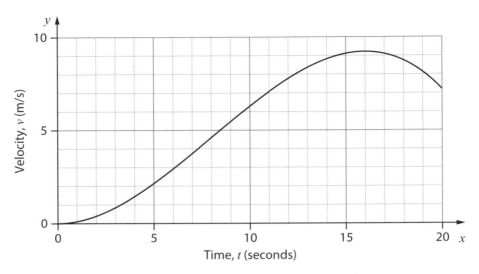

a) Estimate the acceleration when $t = 5$

....m/s^2 [___ / 3 marks]

b) **i)** Using two strips of equal width, estimate the area under the curve between $t = 15$ and $t = 20$
Show all working and give your answer to 2 significant figures.

....   [___ / 3 marks]

ii) State what your answer to part **i** represents.

....   [___ / 1 mark]

End of paper

Further practice & support: Q21 p.44

Paper 3 (Calculator)

Higher Tier

(Time: 1 hour 30 minutes)

- Answer **all** questions.
- You must **show all your working**.
- Diagrams are **NOT** accurately drawn, unless indicated.
- **Calculators may be used**.

[I got ___ / 80 marks]

1. Make a the subject of the formula $s = ut + \frac{1}{2}at^2$

.... [I got ___ / 2 marks]

2. ABC is an isosceles triangle with $AC = BC = 15\,cm$ and $AB = 6\,cm$.

    Work out the size of angle CAB, giving your answer to 1 decimal place.

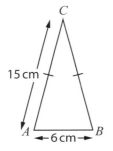

.... ° [___ / 3 marks]

3. The length of a rectangle is twice the width.

    The area of the rectangle is $20\,cm^2$.

    Work out the length of the rectangle.

....cm [___ / 4 marks]

Further practice & support: Q1 p.32; Q2 p.83, Q3 p.74

4. a) Solve the inequality $2x - 5 \leq 7 - x$

[___ / 2 marks]

b) Represent your answer to part **a** on a number line.

[___ / 1 mark]

c) n is an integer such that $-1.5 < 3n \leq 9$

Write down all of the possible values of n

[___ / 2 marks]

5. Prove that the product of two even numbers is always divisible by 4

[___ / 3 marks]

6. Describe fully the single transformation that maps shape A onto shape B

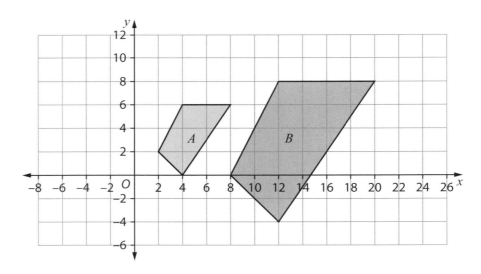

[___ / 3 marks]

Further practice & support: Q4 p.20; Q5 p.55; Q6 p.71

7. A savings account in a bank earns 3% compound interest per year.

An initial amount of money is deposited in the account and, at the end of one year, there is a total of £711.22 in the bank account.

How much money was initially deposited in the account?

£ .... [___ / 2 marks]

8.

Length (x cm)	Frequency
$0 < x \leq 10$	8
$10 < x \leq 20$	3
$20 < x \leq 30$	y
$30 < x \leq 40$	15
$40 < x \leq 50$	3

An estimate of the mean length is 25.5 cm.

Work out the value of y

.... [___ / 4 marks]

9. At a post office, there are some medium parcels and large parcels.

The parcels are to be posted either 1st or 2nd class.

The ratio of medium parcels to large parcels is $3:5$

The ratio of 1st class medium parcels to 2nd class medium parcels is $1:2$

The ratio of 1st class large parcels to 2nd class large parcels is $3:2$

What fraction of the parcels are posted 1st class?

.... [___ / 4 marks]

Further practice & support: Q7 p.60; Q8 p.97; Q9 p.57

10. In the repeating pattern below, *AB*, *CD* and *EF* are equal in length and are parallel.

BC = *DE* and are parallel. *EF* is $\sqrt{2}$ m and the total height and length of the pattern are as shown in the diagram.

Work out the exact total length, in metres, of *ABCDEF*

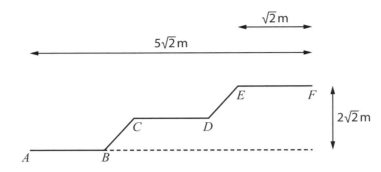

....m   [___ / 4 marks]

11. A regular pentagon of side length *p* cm is drawn inside a circle such that all of its vertices lie on the circumference of the circle.

The radius of the circle is 5 cm.

Work out the length of *p* to 1 decimal place.

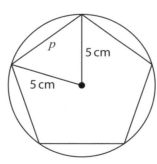

....cm   [___ / 3 marks]

Further practice & support: Q10 p.82; Q11 p.89

12. The box plots show information about the number of goals scored by the 1st team and 2nd team at a football club.

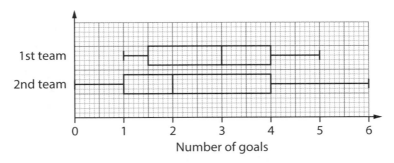

Compare the number of goals scored by the two teams.

....

.... [___ / 2 marks]

13. p is inversely proportional to q^2

q is directly proportional to r

$p = 36$ and $r = \frac{2}{9}$ when $q = \frac{1}{3}$. Find a formula for p in terms of r

.... [___ / 4 marks]

14. The prime factor decomposition of a number N is $2^2 \times 3^2$

The prime factor decomposition of a number M is $5^2 \times 7$

Jools claims that the numbers N and M do not share a common factor.

Is Jools right? Justify your answer.

....

.... [___ / 2 marks]

15. Show that $\dfrac{3}{2x-1} - \dfrac{1}{3-x} = \dfrac{5(2-x)}{(2x-1)(3-x)}$

[___ / 3 marks]

Further practice & support: Q12 p.103; Q13 p.63; Q14 p.11; Q15 p.31

16. The equation $3x^3 + x^2 - 3x - 5 = 0$ has one solution.

a) Show that this solution lies in the interval $1 < x < 1.5$

[__ / 2 marks]

b) Show that $3x^3 + x^2 - 3x - 5 = 0$ can be written as $x = \sqrt[3]{\dfrac{3x - x^2 + 5}{3}}$

[__ / 2 marks]

c) Use the iteration $x_{n+1} = \sqrt[3]{\dfrac{3x_n - x_n^2 + 5}{3}}$ to find the solution to $3x^3 + x^2 - 3x - 5 = 0$ to 4 decimal places. Use a starting value of $x_0 = 1.5$

[__ / 3 marks]

17. The graph of $y = f(x) = \cos x$ is shown for $0 \le x \le 360°$ on the grid below.

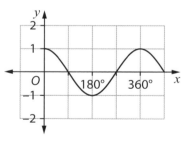

a) The graph has a **period** of 360°. Explain what this means.

[__ / 1 mark]

b) On the grid above, sketch the graph of $y = f(x + 90)$.

[__ / 1 mark]

c) The graph of $y = f(x)$ is reflected in the x-axis and translated up 1 unit. Write the equation of the transformed graph.

$y =$ ....

[__ / 2 marks]

Further practice & support: Q16 p.52; Q17 p.41/43

18. A circle has equation $x^2 + y^2 = 25$

  a) Show that point A with coordinates $(-4, 3)$ lies on this circle.

[___ / 1 mark]

  b) On the grid, make a sketch of the circle, indicating the coordinates of the centre and the coordinates where the circle meets the coordinate axes.

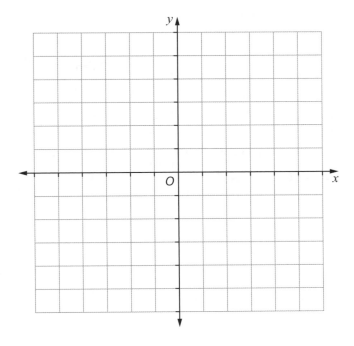

[___ / 2 marks]

  c) A right-angled triangle, ABC, has each of its vertices on the circle.
  The coordinates of A and B are $(-4, 3)$ and $(3, 4)$ respectively.
  Given that vertex C has a negative y-coordinate, find the two possible positions of vertex C. Give a reason for your answer.

[___ / 3 marks]

19. Solve algebraically the pair of simultaneous equations

$$5x + y = 10 \qquad 10xy = -48$$

$x =$ .... $y =$ .... [___ / 5 marks]

20. In a game, players select cards at random, one at a time, from a pack.

The pack contains x cards and, once selected, a card is not replaced in the pack.

Six of the cards are green. The rest are blue.

Two cards are selected from the pack.

a) Complete the probability tree diagram shown.

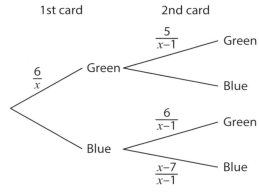

1st card　　　　　2nd card

$\dfrac{6}{x}$ — Green

$\dfrac{5}{x-1}$ — Green

Blue

$\dfrac{6}{x-1}$ — Green

Blue

$\dfrac{x-7}{x-1}$ — Blue

[___ / 2 marks]

b) The probability that neither of the cards is blue is $\dfrac{1}{42}$

How many cards (x) are there in the pack?

[___ / 4 marks]

21. $OABC$ is a trapezium. $\overrightarrow{OA} = \mathbf{a}$, $\overrightarrow{OB} = \mathbf{b}$ and $\overrightarrow{OC} = 3\overrightarrow{AB}$

N is a point on AB such that $AN:NB = 2:3$

P is a point on OB and NC such that $NP:PC = 1:k$, where k is a rational number.

Work out the value of k

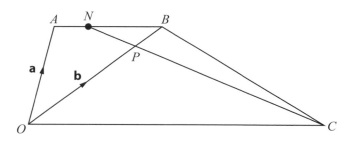

$k =$ .... [___ / 4 marks]

End of paper

Further practice & support: Q20 p.110; Q21 p.93

Guided answers

Page 1, Calculations

1. a
$$\begin{array}{r} {}^{1}\,{}^{14}\,{}^{1} \\ 2\!\!\!/5.043 \\ -\,17.820 \\ \hline 7.223 \end{array}$$

1 mark *for lining up the digits correctly in columns;*
1 mark *for correct answer.*

b
$$\begin{array}{r} 74 \\ \times\;26 \\ \hline 4\overset{2}{4}4 \\ +1480 \\ \hline 1924 \\ {}_{1} \end{array}$$

Since $74 \times 26 = 1924$,
$7.4 \times 0.26 = 1924 \div 10 \div 100 = 1.924$
1 mark *for multiplying 74×26 to get 1924;* ***1 mark*** *for correct answer.*

c $17.12 \div 0.8 = 171.2 \div 8$
$$\begin{array}{r} 2\;1.\,4 \\ 8\,\overline{)17^1 1.^3 2} \end{array}$$
$171.2 \div 8 = 21.4$
1 mark *for dividing 171.2 by 8;* ***1 mark*** *for correct answer.*

2. a $(12 - 4 \times 2)^3 = (12 - 8)^3 = 4^3 = 64$
1 mark *for correct answer.*

b $\dfrac{4 \times 5^2}{4 \times 5 \div 2} = \dfrac{4 \times 25}{10} = \dfrac{100}{10} = 10$
1 mark *for correct answer.*

c $5\sqrt{50 - 1} + 6 \times 3 = 5 \times \sqrt{49} + 6 \times 3 = 5 \times 7 + 6 \times 3$
$\qquad\qquad\qquad = 35 + 18 = 53$
1 mark *for correct answer.*

d $5 + (-3.2) \times 4 = 5 + (-12.8) = -7.8$
1 mark *for correct answer.*

e $(1 - 0.1) \times 4 - (-10) = 0.9 \times 4 - (-10) = 3.6 - (-10)$
$\qquad\qquad\qquad\qquad = 13.6$
1 mark *for 3.6;* ***1 mark*** *for correct answer.*

f $\dfrac{(-0.2) \times (-6)}{-1 + 0.7} = \dfrac{1.2}{-0.3} = -4$
1 mark *for either 1.2 in the numerator or −0.3 in the denominator;* ***1 mark*** *for correct answer.*

3. Supermarket A: £4.65 ÷ 6 = £0.775 per burger
Supermarket B: £6.59 ÷ 8 = £0.82375 per burger
0.775 < 0.82375
Therefore, Supermarket A is better value.
1 mark *for 0.775;* ***1 mark*** *for 0.82375;* ***1 mark*** *for correct conclusion with full justification. Total 3 marks.*

4. Area of fence = $1.4 \times 10.5 = 14.7\,\text{m}^2$
Cost = $14.7 \times 0.6 = £8.82$
1 mark *for multiplying lengths;* ***1 mark*** *for multiplying by cost per square metre;* ***1 mark*** *for correct answer. Total 3 marks.*

Page 2, Rounding & truncation

1. a 20 190 **b** 20 200
c 20 000 **d** 20 000
1 mark *for each correct answer.*

2. a 0.007 **b** 0.0068 **c** 0.006 80
1 mark *for each correct answer.*

3. a 21.568 361…
b i 22 **ii** 21.5
1 mark *for each correct answer.*

3. a 0.018 8813…
b i 0.01 **ii** 0.019
1 mark *for each correct answer.*

4. 32 ÷ 3.66 = 8.743…
He can only buy whole bags, so round up to the next integer: 9 bags.
Total cost = 9 × 4.99 = £44.91
$\qquad\qquad$ = £45 to the nearest pound
1 mark *for correct division;* ***1 mark*** *for rounding up and multiplying by £4.99;* ***1 mark*** *for correct answer. Total 3 marks.*

5. Shirley has rounded 0.065 29 to 2 dp instead of 2 sf. The correct answer is 0.065
1 mark *for a correct explanation.*

Page 3, Estimation

1. $\dfrac{317 + 48.6}{9.683} \approx \dfrac{300 + 50}{10} \approx \dfrac{350}{10} \approx 35$
1 mark *for rounding to 1 sf;* ***1 mark*** *for correct answer.*

2. $\dfrac{2.67 \times 1.36}{0.11 + 0.42} \approx \dfrac{3 \times 1}{0.1 + 0.4} \approx \dfrac{3}{0.5} \approx 6$
1 mark *for rounding to 1 sf;* ***1 mark*** *for correct answer.*

3. Number of fish at start of January ≈ 1000
Increase ≈ 20 fish per day
Five months ≈ 5 × 30 ≈ 150 days
Number of fish after five months ≈ 150 × 20 + 1000 ≈ 4000
1 mark *for rounding rate of increase to 1 sf;* ***1 mark*** *for correct calculation for the number of fish after five months;* ***1 mark*** *for correct answer. Total 3 marks.*

4. Number of portions sold ≈ 100
Sale price per portion ≈ £9.00
Cost per portion ≈ £3.00
Profit per portion ≈ £9.00 – £3.00 ≈ £6.00
Total profit ≈ £6.00 × 100 ≈ £600
1 mark *for rounding portions, sale price and cost to 1 sf;* ***1 mark*** *for a profit calculation;* ***1 mark*** *for correct answer. Total 3 marks.*
Note that there are alternative methods.

5. Distance driven ≈ 400 km
Average speed ≈ 80 km/h
Time driving ≈ $\dfrac{400}{80}$ ≈ 5 hours
Time for whole journey ≈ 5 hours 30 minutes (including the break)
Time of arrival is roughly 2 pm (8.30 am + $5\frac{1}{2}$ hours).
1 mark *for rounding distance and speed to 1 sf;* ***1 mark*** *for finding the time taken;* ***1 mark*** *for correct answer. Total 3 marks.*

6. a $\sqrt{36} < \sqrt{47} < \sqrt{49}$, so $6 < \sqrt{47} < 7$
$\sqrt{47} = 6.9$ to 1 dp
1 mark *for an answer of 6.8 or 6.9*
b $\sqrt{196} < \sqrt{200} < \sqrt{225}$, so $14 < \sqrt{200} < 15$
$\sqrt{200} = 14.1$ to 1 dp
1 mark *for an answer of 14.1 or 14.2*

Page 4, Error intervals & bounds

1. a $105 \le p < 115$ **b** $107.5 \le p < 112.5$
1 mark for each correct minimum; 1 mark for each correct maximum.

2. a $4.665 \le x < 4.675$ **b** $4500 \le x < 5500$
1 mark for each correct minimum; 1 mark for each correct maximum.

3. a $9 \le y < 10$ **b** $2.5 \le y < 2.6$
1 mark for each correct minimum; 1 mark for each correct maximum.

4. Sienna can see a truncation to 1 dp so the error interval is $1.8 \le x < 1.9$
1 mark for correct minimum and maximum; 1 mark for correct interval notation.

5. Lower bound for the length is 14.5 cm, so lower bound for the area is $14.5^2 = 210.25 \, \text{cm}^2$.
Upper bound for the length is 15.5 cm, so upper bound for the area is $15.5^2 = 240.25 \, \text{cm}^2$.
Error interval for the area, $x \, \text{cm}^2$, is $210.25 \le x < 240.25$
1 mark for 14.5^2; 1 mark for 15.5^2; 1 mark for correct error interval. Total 3 marks.

6. Error interval for the speed, s km/h, is $109.5 \le s < 110.5$
Error interval for the distance, d km, is $44.5 \le d < 45.5$
Lower bound for the time taken is $\frac{44.5}{110.5} = 0.4027\ldots$ hours
Upper bound for the time taken is $\frac{45.5}{109.5} = 0.4155\ldots$ hours
Both of these answers round to 0.4 hours to 1 dp, so this is an appropriate degree of accuracy.
1 mark for upper and lower bounds for speed; 1 mark for upper and lower bounds for distance; 1 mark for lower bound for time; 1 mark for upper bound for time; 1 mark for correct answer. Total 5 marks.

Page 5, Adding & subtracting fractions

1. a $\frac{2}{9} + \frac{5}{6} = \frac{4}{18} + \frac{15}{18} = \frac{19}{18}$ or $1\frac{1}{18}$
1 mark for finding a common denominator; 1 mark for correct answer.

b $3\frac{1}{6} - 2\frac{3}{4} = \frac{19}{6} - \frac{11}{4} = \frac{38}{12} - \frac{33}{12} = \frac{5}{12}$
1 mark for converting mixed numbers to improper fractions; 1 mark for finding a common denominator; 1 mark for correct answer. Total 3 marks.

2. $\frac{1}{8} + \frac{2}{3} = \frac{3 + 16}{24} = \frac{19}{24}$
$1 - \frac{19}{24} = \frac{24}{24} - \frac{19}{24} = \frac{5}{24}$
1 mark for finding a common denominator of 24; 1 mark for adding to get $\frac{19}{24}$; 1 mark for correct answer. Total 3 marks.

3. $2\frac{4}{5} - \frac{7}{8} + 1\frac{1}{20} = \frac{14}{5} - \frac{7}{8} + \frac{21}{20} = \frac{112}{40} - \frac{35}{40} + \frac{42}{40} = \frac{119}{40}$ m or $2\frac{39}{40}$ m
1 mark for converting mixed numbers to improper fractions; 1 mark for finding a common denominator; 1 mark for correct answer. Total 3 marks.

4. $\frac{3}{4} - \frac{1}{3} = \frac{9 - 4}{12} = \frac{5}{12}$
1 mark for finding a common denominator; 1 mark for correct answer.

5. Perimeter $= 3\frac{1}{2} + 5\frac{2}{5} + 2\frac{1}{5} = 3 + 5 + 2 + \frac{1}{2} + \frac{2}{5} + \frac{1}{5}$
$= 10 + \frac{5}{10} + \frac{4}{10} + \frac{2}{10}$
$= 10 + \frac{11}{10}$
$= 10 + 1\frac{1}{10} = 11\frac{1}{10}$ cm

1 mark for summing the lengths; 1 mark for finding common denominator; 1 mark for correct answer or equivalent. Total 3 marks.

Page 6, Multiplying & dividing fractions

1. $16 \div \frac{2}{3} = \frac{16}{1} \times \frac{3}{2} = \frac{\overset{8}{\cancel{16}} \times 3}{1 \times \underset{1}{\cancel{2}}} = \frac{8 \times 3}{1 \times 1} = \frac{24}{1} = 24$ days
1 mark for writing a division and turning it into a correct multiplication; 1 mark for correct answer.

2. a $1\frac{1}{2} \times 3\frac{5}{6} = \frac{3}{2} \times \frac{23}{6} = \frac{\overset{1}{\cancel{3}} \times 23}{2 \times \underset{2}{\cancel{6}}} = \frac{1 \times 23}{2 \times 2} = \frac{23}{4} = 5\frac{3}{4}$
1 mark for converting to improper fractions; 1 mark for multiplying; 1 mark for correct answer. Accept correct improper fraction or mixed number. Total 3 marks.

b $4\frac{4}{9} \div 2\frac{2}{3} = \frac{40}{9} \div \frac{8}{3} = \frac{40}{9} \times \frac{3}{8} = \frac{\overset{5}{\cancel{40}} \times \overset{1}{\cancel{3}}}{\underset{3}{\cancel{9}} \times \underset{1}{\cancel{8}}} = \frac{5 \times 1}{3 \times 1} = \frac{5}{3} = 1\frac{2}{3}$
1 mark for converting to improper fractions; 1 mark for writing a correct multiplication; 1 mark for correct, simplified answer (improper fraction or mixed number). Total 3 marks.

3. $\frac{1}{4}$ of $\frac{3}{10} = \frac{1}{4} \times \frac{3}{10} = \frac{3}{40}$
1 mark for multiplying; 1 mark for correct answer.

4. Area of triangle $= \frac{1}{2} \times 1\frac{1}{5} \times \frac{6}{5} = \frac{1}{2} \times \frac{6}{5} \times \frac{6}{5} = \frac{18}{25} \, \text{cm}^2$
This is the area of the rectangle.
Length of rectangle $= \frac{18}{25} \div \frac{2}{5} = \frac{18}{25} \times \frac{5}{2} = \frac{\overset{9}{\cancel{18}} \times \overset{1}{\cancel{5}}}{\underset{5}{\cancel{25}} \times \underset{1}{\cancel{2}}}$
$= \frac{9 \times 1}{5 \times 1} = \frac{9}{5} \, \text{cm}$ or $1\frac{4}{5} \, \text{cm}$
1 mark for writing a correct multiplication; 1 mark for writing a division and turning into a correct multiplication; 1 mark for correct, simplified answer (improper fraction or mixed number). Total 3 marks.

5. $3\frac{3}{4} \div \frac{5}{6} = \frac{15}{4} \div \frac{5}{6} = \frac{15}{4} \times \frac{6}{5} = \frac{90}{20} = \frac{9}{2}$ or $4\frac{1}{2}$ or 4.5
Vasiliki can get 4 smaller pieces.
$\frac{1}{2} \times \frac{5}{6} = \frac{5}{12}$ m will be left over.
1 mark for converting to improper fraction and writing a correct multiplication; 1 mark for correct answer to the multiplication and identifying correct number of smaller pieces; 1 mark for correct fraction left over. Total 3 marks.

Page 7, Fractions, decimals & percentages

1. Lin's class: $\frac{6}{25} = \frac{24}{100} = 24\%$
Jay's class: $\frac{8}{32} = \frac{1}{4} = \frac{25}{100} = 25\%$
Lin is not correct. Jay's class has a (slightly) higher proportion of students who read fantasy books.
1 mark for finding either 24% or 25% or for giving both fractions a common denominator; 1 mark for a complete, correct explanation.

2. Since $0.01 = \frac{1}{100}$, multiplying by 0.01 is the same as multiplying by $\frac{1}{100}$, which makes the answer 100 times smaller, so it is equivalent to dividing by 100. Sally is correct.
1 mark for a correct explanation.

3. $\frac{11}{28} = \frac{11}{2 \times 2 \times 7}$
If a fraction produces a terminating decimal, the prime factors in the denominator can only be 2s or 5s. This fraction has a prime factor of 7 in the denominator, so it will produce a recurring decimal.
1 mark for the prime factor decomposition of 28; 1 mark for a correct explanation.

4. $\frac{7}{10} = 70\%$; $70\% + 15\% = 85\%$; $100\% - 85\% = 15\%$

15% of the runs were half marathons.

Since 15% of 20 is 3, Jonathan ran 3 half marathons.

1 mark for adding $\frac{7}{10}$ and 15% (either as percentages or fractions) and subtracting from 100% (or 1); 1 mark for attempting to find 15% of 20; 1 mark for correct answer. Total 3 marks.

Note that there are alternative methods.

5. Area used for housing and services $= \frac{5.5}{22} = \frac{1}{4}$

Fraction of this area used for services $= 1 - \frac{5}{8} = \frac{3}{8}$

Total area used for services $= \frac{3}{8} \times \frac{1}{4} = \frac{3}{32} = 9.375\%$

1 mark for $\frac{3}{8}$; 1 mark for multiplying by $\frac{1}{4}$; 1 mark for correct answer as a percentage. Total 3 marks.

Page 8, Recurring decimals

1. a $18\overline{)1.^{1}0^{10}0^{10}0^{10}0^{10}0}$ gives 0.05555 $\frac{1}{18} = 0.0\dot{5}$

b $33\overline{)20.^{20}0^{2}0^{20}0^{2}0}$ gives 0.6060 $\frac{20}{33} = 0.\dot{6}\dot{0}$

c $7\overline{)3.^{3}0^{2}0^{6}0^{4}0^{5}0^{1}0^{3}0}$ gives 0.4285714 $\frac{3}{7} = 0.\dot{4}2857\dot{1}$

For each part, 1 mark for division; 1 mark for correct answer.

2. Let $x = 0.\dot{5}$

Then $10x = 5.\dot{5}$

Subtracting x from $10x$, you have $9x = 5$, so $x = \frac{5}{9}$

1 mark for finding x and $10x$ and subtracting; 1 mark for correct answer.

3. Let $x = 0.\dot{8}\dot{4}$

Then $100x = 84.\dot{8}\dot{4}$

Subtracting x from $100x$, you have $99x = 84$, so $x = \frac{84}{99} = \frac{28}{33}$

1 mark for finding x and $100x$ and subtracting; 1 mark for $\frac{84}{99}$; 1 mark for correct answer. Total 3 marks.

4. Let $x = 0.0\dot{5}\dot{6}$

Then $10x = 0.\dot{5}\dot{6}$

Also $1000x = 56.\dot{5}\dot{6}$

Subtracting $10x$ from $1000x$, you have $990x = 56$, so $x = \frac{56}{990} = \frac{28}{495}$

1 mark for finding $10x$ and $1000x$ and subtracting; 1 mark for $\frac{56}{990}$; 1 mark for correct answer. Total 3 marks.

Page 9, Surds

1. a $\sqrt{18} - \sqrt{8} = 3\sqrt{2} - 2\sqrt{2} = \sqrt{2}$ $(a = 1)$

1 mark for simplifying both surds; 1 mark for correct answer.

b $\sqrt{200} + \sqrt{72} - \sqrt{98} = 10\sqrt{2} + 6\sqrt{2} - 7\sqrt{2} = 9\sqrt{2}$ $(a = 9)$

1 mark for simplifying the three surds; 1 mark for correct answer.

c $3\sqrt{2} + 7\sqrt{32} = 3\sqrt{2} + 7 \times 4\sqrt{2} = 3\sqrt{2} + 28\sqrt{2} = 31\sqrt{2}$ $(a = 31)$

1 mark for simplifying $7\sqrt{32}$; 1 mark for correct answer.

d $\frac{14}{\sqrt{2}} = \frac{14\sqrt{2}}{2} = 7\sqrt{2}$ $(a = 7)$

1 mark for rationalising the denominator (multiplying numerator and denominator by $\sqrt{2}$); 1 mark for correct answer.

2. a $(1 + \sqrt{3})^2 = (1 + \sqrt{3})(1 + \sqrt{3}) = 1 + \sqrt{3} + \sqrt{3} + 3 = 4 + 2\sqrt{3}$ $(a = 4, b = 2)$

1 mark for expanding the brackets; 1 mark for simplifying expression to correct answer.

b $\frac{8}{2 - \sqrt{3}} = \frac{8(2 + \sqrt{3})}{(2 - \sqrt{3})(2 + \sqrt{3})} = \frac{16 + 8\sqrt{3}}{4 - 3} = \frac{16 + 8\sqrt{3}}{1} = 16 + 8\sqrt{3}$ $(a = 16, b = 8)$

1 mark for rationalising the denominator (multiplying numerator and denominator by $2 + \sqrt{3}$); 1 mark for 1 in the denominator; 1 mark for correct answer. Total 3 marks.

c $\frac{\sqrt{3} - 1}{\sqrt{3} + 1} = \frac{(\sqrt{3} - 1)(\sqrt{3} - 1)}{(\sqrt{3} + 1)(\sqrt{3} - 1)} = \frac{3 - 2\sqrt{3} + 1}{3 - 1} = \frac{4 - 2\sqrt{3}}{2} = 2 - \sqrt{3}$ $(a = 2, b = -1)$

1 mark for rationalising the denominator (multiplying numerator and denominator by $\sqrt{3} - 1$); 1 mark for 2 in the denominator; 1 mark for correct answer. Total 3 marks.

3. $(\sqrt{11} - \sqrt{8})(\sqrt{11} + \sqrt{8}) = 11 + \sqrt{11}\sqrt{8} - \sqrt{11}\sqrt{8} - 8$
$= 11 - 8 = 3$ as required

1 mark for attempt to expand brackets; 1 mark for cancelling middle terms; 1 mark for fully correct working. Total 3 marks.

Page 10, Index notation

1. Peter has multiplied the bases. Since the bases are different, this cannot be simplified as a simple power of 10

1 mark for a correct explanation.

2. $\frac{(2^7 \times 2^4)^{-1}}{2} = \frac{(2^{7+4})^{-1}}{2} = \frac{(2^{11})^{-1}}{2} = \frac{2^{11 \times (-1)}}{2} = 2^{-11-1} = 2^{-12}$

1 mark for 2^{11} in the brackets; 1 mark for correct answer.

3. a $(3^{\frac{1}{4}})^4 = 3^{\frac{1}{4} \times \frac{1}{4}} = 3^{\frac{1}{16}}$

1 mark for correct answer.

b $\sqrt[3]{5^2} = 5^{\frac{2}{3}}$

1 mark for a fractional index with 3 in the denominator; 1 mark for correct answer.

4. a $\left(\frac{2}{5}\right)^3 = \frac{2^3}{5^3} = \frac{8}{125}$

1 mark for correct answer.

b $25^{\frac{1}{2}} = \sqrt{25} = 5$

1 mark for correct answer.

c $8^{\frac{2}{3}} = (\sqrt[3]{8})^2 = 2^2 = 4$

1 mark for 2; 1 mark for correct answer.

d $\left(\frac{16}{9}\right)^{-\frac{3}{2}} = \left(\frac{9}{16}\right)^{\frac{3}{2}} = \left(\frac{\sqrt{9}}{\sqrt{16}}\right)^3 = \left(\frac{3}{4}\right)^3 = \frac{27}{64}$

1 mark for $\frac{9}{16}$; 1 mark for $\frac{3}{4}$; 1 mark for correct answer. Total 3 marks.

5. $3 \times \sqrt{27} = 3 \times (27)^{\frac{1}{2}} = 3 \times (3^3)^{\frac{1}{2}} = 3^1 \times 3^{\frac{3}{2}} = 3^{1 + \frac{3}{2}} = 3^{\frac{5}{2}}$

$n = \frac{5}{2}$ or $2\frac{1}{2}$ or 2.5

1 mark for attempting to rewrite 27 with base 3, 1 mark for $3^{\frac{3}{2}}$; 1 mark for correct answer. Total 3 marks.

6. $64 = 2^6$

$2^x \times 2^y = 2^6 \Rightarrow x + y = 6$ (1)

$4 = 2^2$

$2^x \div 2^y = 2^2 \Rightarrow x - y = 2$ (2)

(1) + (2): $2x = 8 \Rightarrow x = 4$

Substitute into (1): $4 + y = 6 \Rightarrow y = 2$

1 mark for attempting to rewrite 64 and 2 with base 2; 1 mark for either equation correct; 1 mark for attempting to solve simultaneously; 1 mark for correct values for x and y. Total 4 marks.

Page 11, Prime factor decomposition

You might use a factor tree in your working with the same start and end as shown here but with different middle branches.

1.
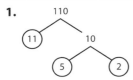

$110 = 2 \times 5 \times 11$
***1 mark** for finding or listing the prime factors; **1 mark** for correct answer.*

2. a
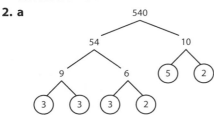

$540 = 2^2 \times 3^3 \times 5$
***1 mark** for finding or listing the prime factors; **1 mark** for correct answer.*

    b Since $15 = 3 \times 5$ and both 3 and 5 are prime factors of 540, then 540 must be divisible by 15
***1 mark** for a correct explanation.*

3. a
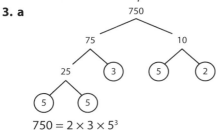

$750 = 2 \times 3 \times 5^3$
***1 mark** for finding or listing the prime factors; **1 mark** for correct answer.*

    b Since $4 = 2 \times 2$, but 750 only contains the factor of 2 once, 750 is not divisible by 4
***1 mark** for a correct explanation.*

4. a $2 \times 3^2 \times 7 \times 13$ is even since 2 is a prime factor.
***1 mark** for correct answer.*

    b To double a number, you multiply by 2, so the prime factor decomposition of a number twice as big will have another factor of 2. This is $2^2 \times 3^2 \times 7 \times 13$
***1 mark** for correct answer.*

5. The prime factors of each number are:
$4 = 2 \times 2; 5 = 5; 6 = 2 \times 3$
Any number divisible by 4, 5 and 6 must have at least two 2s, one 5 and a 3, so the smallest such number is $2^2 \times 3 \times 5$
***1 mark** for listing the prime factors of 4 and 6; **1 mark** for correct answer.*

Page 12, Finding HCF and LCM

1. a $160 = 2^5 \times 5$
***1 mark** for finding or listing the prime factors; **1 mark** for correct answer.*

    b $280 = 2^3 \times 5 \times 7$
A Venn diagram to show the prime factors looks like this:

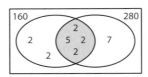

$HCF(160, 280) = 2^3 \times 5 = 40$
***1 mark** for multiplying the common factors; **1 mark** for correct answer.*

    c From the Venn diagram,
$LCM(160, 280) = 2 \times 2 \times 2 \times 2 \times 2 \times 5 \times 7 = 1120$
***1 mark** for multiplying all appropriate factors; **1 mark** for correct answer.*

2.
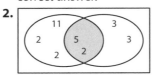

    a $HCF = 2 \times 5 = 10$
    b $LCM = 2 \times 2 \times 11 \times 2 \times 5 \times 3 \times 3 = 3960$
***1 mark** for correct Venn diagram or alternative method; **1 mark** for HCF; **1 mark** for LCM. Total 3 marks.*

3. $225 = 3^2 \times 5^2$
$324 = 2^2 \times 3^4$
A Venn diagram would look like this:

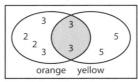
orange   yellow

The HCF of the two numbers is 9, so Fran can sort her books into piles of a maximum of 9 if they are to be the same size.
***1 mark** for the prime factors of 225; **1 mark** for the prime factors of 324; **1 mark** for correct answer. Total 3 marks.*

4. a You know that $4 = 2^2$ must divide into A, but $2 \times 3 \times 7$ only has one 2
Therefore, $x = 2$
    b $A = 2 \times 2 \times 3 \times 7 = 84$
***1 mark** for each correct answer.*

Page 13, Standard form

1. a $1.56 \times 10^8 = 156\,000\,000$ **b** $8.02 \times 10^{-3} = 0.008\,02$
***1 mark** for each correct answer.*

2. a $48\,000\,000\,000 = 4.8 \times 10^{10}$ **b** $0.000\,0703 = 7.03 \times 10^{-5}$
    c $95 \times 10^6 = 9.5 \times 10^7$ **d** $0.68 \times 10^{-4} = 6.8 \times 10^{-5}$
***1 mark** for each correct answer.*

3. $150\,000\,000$ km $= 1.5 \times 10^8$ km
***1 mark** for each correct answer.*

4. Putting all the numbers in either standard or ordinary form:
$2.1 \times 10^4 = 21\,000; 2.3 \times 10^5 = 230\,000;$
$0.21 \times 10^4 = 2.1 \times 10^3 = 2100; 2200 = 2.2 \times 10^3$
The order, starting with the biggest, is $2.3 \times 10^5, 2.1 \times 10^4$, 2200, 0.21×10^4
***1 mark** for converting at least two of the numbers correctly to an alternative form; **1 mark** for any three in the correct order; **1 mark** for all in the correct order. Total 3 marks.*

5. Virus: $0.000\,000\,05 = 5 \times 10^{-8}$ m
Bacteria cell: $4 \times 10^{-7} = 0.000\,0004$ m
The virus is smaller.
***1 mark** for getting both numbers in the same form; **1 mark** for correct conclusion.*

6. Put all the populations in the same form.
If you put them all in standard form, you have:
Angola: 3.18×10^7; Uzbekistan: 3.29×10^7;
Malaysia: 3.19×10^7; Mongolia: 3.2×10^6
Uzbekistan has the biggest population.
1 mark *for putting all numbers in the same form;*
1 mark *for correct answer.*

Page 14, Calculating with standard form

1. a $(5 \times 10^4) + (6 \times 10^5) = 50\,000 + 600\,000$
$= 650\,000 = 6.5 \times 10^5$
1 mark *for converting to ordinary numbers or the same power of 10;* ***1 mark*** *for correct answer.*
b $(9 \times 10^{-3}) - (3 \times 10^{-4}) = 0.009 - 0.0003$
$= 0.0087 = 8.7 \times 10^{-3}$
1 mark *for converting to ordinary numbers or the same power of 10;* ***1 mark*** *for correct answer.*
c $(2.1 \times 10^8) \times (3 \times 10^{-5}) = 6.3 \times 10^{8 + (-5)} = 6.3 \times 10^3$
1 mark *for 10^3;* ***1 mark*** *for correct answer.*
d $(8.2 \times 10^3) \div (4.1 \times 10^7) = 2 \times 10^{3 - 7} = 2 \times 10^{-4}$
1 mark *for 10^{-4};* ***1 mark*** *for correct answer.*

2. Using time $= \frac{\text{distance}}{\text{speed}}$,
time $= \frac{3000}{4 \times 10^3} = \frac{3 \times 10^3}{4 \times 10^3} = \frac{3}{4}$ hour = 45 minutes
1 mark *for dividing distance by speed;* ***1 mark*** *for $\frac{3}{4}$ hour;*
1 mark *for correct answer in minutes. Total 3 marks.*

3. Area $= (1.2 \times 10^2) \times (7 \times 10^3) = 8.4 \times 10^{2+3} = 8.4 \times 10^5 \, \text{km}^2$
1 mark *for multiplying;* ***1 mark*** *for 10^5;* ***1 mark*** *for correct answer. Total 3 marks.*

4. a Circumference $\approx 4 \times 10^9 \times 0.2 = 0.8 \times 10^9 = 8 \times 10^8 \, \text{cm}$
1 mark *for rounding 4.0075;* ***1 mark*** *for multiplication;*
1 mark *for correct answer in standard form. Total 3 marks.*
b It is an underestimate because 4.0075 is rounded down.
1 mark *for correct answer with explanation.*

Page 15, Simplifying expressions

1. a $3p - 5q + 3p^2 + 2q + 2q^2 - 9p^2 = 3p - 3q - 6p^2 + 2q^2$
1 mark *for $-3q$ and $-6p^2$;* ***1 mark*** *for correct answer.*
b $5x^3 - 2xy - 6 + 6x^3 - 2 - 7xy + 8 = 11x^3 - 9xy$
1 mark *for $11x^3$ or $9xy$;* ***1 mark*** *for correct answer.*

2. a Perimeter $= 3x + 3x + 7y + 7y = 6x + 14y$
1 mark *for an unsimplified expression;* ***1 mark*** *for correct answer.*
b Area $= 3x \times 1.5x = 4.5x^2$
1 mark *for an unsimplified expression;* ***1 mark*** *for correct answer.*

3. a $(2a)^3 = 8a^3$
1 mark *for 8;* ***1 mark*** *for a^3*
b $(5a^2b^3)^2 = 25a^4b^6$
1 mark *for 25;* ***1 mark*** *for $a^4 b^6$*
c $\frac{6x^2y^{-3}}{18yx^{-1}} = \frac{1}{3}x^3y^{-4}$ or $\frac{x^3}{3y^4}$
1 mark *for $\frac{1}{3}$;* ***1 mark*** *for $x^3 y^{-4}$ or $\frac{x^3}{y^4}$*
d $\sqrt{x^4 y^6} = (x^4 y^6)^{\frac{1}{2}} = x^2 y^3$
1 mark *for x^2;* ***1 mark*** *for y^3*

4. a $\frac{3^{-2} \times 3^8}{3^7} = \frac{3^6}{3^7} = 3^{-1}$
$3^{-1} = 3^x$, so $x = -1$
1 mark *for 3^6 in the numerator;* ***1 mark*** *for 3^{-1};* ***1 mark*** *for identifying that $x = -1$. Total 3 marks.*

b $2^5 \times 4^2 = 8^x$
$2^5 \times (2^2)^2 = (2^3)^x$
$2^5 \times 2^4 = 2^{3x}$
$2^9 = 2^{3x}$
$3x = 9$, so $x = 3$
1 mark *for writing 4 as 2^2 or 8 as 2^3;* ***1 mark*** *for 2^9 on the left-hand side;* ***1 mark*** *for correct answer. Total 3 marks.*

Page 16, Solving linear equations

1 a $\frac{5-x}{2} = 12$; $5 - x = 24$; $5 = 24 + x$; $x = -19$
1 mark *for $5 - x = 24$;* ***1 mark*** *for correct answer.*
b $\frac{2}{y} = 5$; $2 = 5y$; $y = \frac{2}{5}$
1 mark *for $2 = 5y$;* ***1 mark*** *for correct answer.*
c $3 + p = 4p - 6$; $3 + 6 = 4p - p$; $9 = 3p$; $p = 3$
1 mark *for $9 = 3p$;* ***1 mark*** *for correct answer.*
d $3(3 - 2p) = 4 - 11p$
$9 - 6p = 4 - 11p$
$-6p + 11p = 4 - 9$
$5p = -5$
$p = \frac{-5}{5} = -1$
1 mark *for $5p = -5$;* ***1 mark*** *for correct answer.*

2. Sarah: n, Ewan: $n - 5$, Cameron: $2n$
Total: $n + (n - 5) + 2n = 35$
$4n - 5 = 35$
$4n = 40$
$n = 10$, so Sarah plays 10 holes.
1 mark *for $n - 5$ and $2n$;* ***1 mark*** *for adding and writing equal to 35;* ***1 mark*** *for correct answer. Total 3 marks.*

3. $2x + 3 = 3x - 4$; $3 + 4 = 3x - 2x$; $7 = x$
Rosalind's number is 7
1 mark *for a correct equation;* ***1 mark*** *for a correct rearrangement;* ***1 mark*** *for correct answer. Total 3 marks.*

4. a $2x - 1 = x + 3$; $2x - x = 3 + 1$; $x = 4$
1 mark *for a correct equation;* ***1 mark*** *for a correct rearrangement;* ***1 mark*** *for correct answer. Total 3 marks.*
b If $x = 4$, the shorter side is $x + 3 = 4 + 3 = 7 \, \text{cm}$
(or $2x - 1 = 2 \times 4 - 1 = 7 \, \text{cm}$).
The perimeter is $7 + 7 + y + y = 14 + 2y$
Since $14 + 2y = 34$, $2y = 20$, $y = 10$
This means the area of the rectangle is $10 \times 7 = 70 \, \text{cm}^2$.
1 mark *for finding the length of the shorter side (7 cm);*
1 mark *for setting up an equation to find y;* ***1 mark*** *for $y = 10$;* ***1 mark*** *for correct answer. Total 4 marks.*

Page 17, Linear graphs

1. Work out where graph crosses the axes: (0, 5) and (5, 0).
Find one other point on the line e.g. (1, 4).

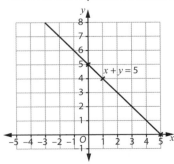

1 mark *for a correct table of values with at least three correct points (or shown in graph);* ***1 mark*** *for the points plotted correctly;* ***1 mark*** *for a correct graph (straight line drawn through the correct points). Total 3 marks.*

2. Work out where graph crosses the axes: (0, 3) and (1.5, 0).
Find one other point on the line e.g. (1, 1).

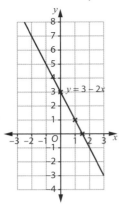

1 mark for a correct table of values with at least three correct points (or shown in graph); 1 mark for the points plotted correctly; 1 mark for a correct graph (straight line drawn through the correct points). Total 3 marks.

3. a

Gradient $= \frac{1}{1} = 1$
Equation is $y = x$
1 mark for $\frac{1}{1}$ or an equivalent correct calculation; 1 mark for the correct gradient; 1 mark for the correct equation. Total 3 marks.

b

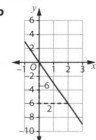

Gradient $= \frac{-6}{2} = -3$
Equation is $y = -3x$
1 mark for $\frac{-6}{2}$ or an equivalent correct calculation; 1 mark for the correct gradient; 1 mark for the correct equation. Total 3 marks.

Page 18, Equations of linear graphs

1. a Gradient = 5, y-intercept = 1
1 mark for gradient; 1 mark for y-intercept.
  b Gradient = −2, y-intercept = 3
1 mark for gradient; 1 mark for y-intercept.
  c $2y = x + 6$ rearranges to $y = \frac{1}{2}x + 3$
Gradient $= \frac{1}{2}$, y-intercept = 3
1 mark for correctly rearranging; 1 mark for gradient; 1 mark for y-intercept. Total 3 marks.
  d $y - x = 10$ rearranges to $y = x + 10$
Gradient = 1, y-intercept = 10
1 mark for correctly rearranging; 1 mark for gradient; 1 mark for y-intercept. Total 3 marks.
  e $8x + 4y = 3$; $4y = 3 - 8x$; $y = \frac{3}{4} - 2x$
Gradient = −2, y-intercept $= \frac{3}{4}$

1 mark for correctly rearranging; 1 mark for gradient; 1 mark for y-intercept. Total 3 marks.

2. A line parallel to $y = 4x - 8$ will also have gradient 4
The line passing through (0, 5) has y-intercept 5, so the equation is $y = 4x + 5$
1 mark for correct answer.

3. a Gradient $= \frac{\text{change in } y}{\text{change in } x} = \frac{3 - (-1)}{2 - 0} = \frac{4}{2} = 2$
Equation is $y = 2x + c$
Since the line goes through (0, −1) the y-intercept is −1
Equation is $y = 2x - 1$
  b Gradient $= \frac{\text{change in } y}{\text{change in } x} = \frac{5 - 1}{-3 - 1} = \frac{4}{-4} = -1$
Equation is $y = -x + c$
Substitute one of the coordinates in for x and y to get e.g. $1 = -1 + c$, giving $c = 2$
Equation is $y = -x + 2$ or $y = 2 - x$
For each part, 1 mark for the gradient; 1 mark for the y-intercept; 1 mark for correct answer. Total 3 marks.

4. $y = 4 - 3x$ has gradient −3
$3x + y = 0$ rearranges to $y = -3x$
This also has gradient −3, so Sajid is correct.
1 mark for rearranging and identifying a gradient of −3; 1 mark for 'Yes' with a correct explanation.

Page 19, Perpendicular lines

1. $y = \frac{1}{2}x + 2$ is perpendicular to $y = -2x + 1$
$2x = 6 - 3y$ rearranges to $y = 2 - \frac{2}{3}x$
$2y = 3x - 4$ rearranges to $y = \frac{3}{2}x - 2$
These are perpendicular.
$x + 2y - 1 = 0$ rearranges to $y = \frac{1}{2} - \frac{1}{2}x$
$y - 2x = 0$ rearranges to $y = 2x$
These are perpendicular.
$y + x = \frac{1}{2}$ rearranges to $y = \frac{1}{2} - x$
This is perpendicular to $y = x - 2$
1 mark for 1 pair correct; 1 mark for 2 pairs correct; 1 mark for all four pairs correct. Total 3 marks.

2. Perpendicular gradients multiply to make −1
Since $2 \times \frac{1}{2} = 1$, not −1, Ivan is not correct.
1 mark for an explanation about the product of the gradients, or for saying that the line perpendicular to $y = 2x + 1$ should have gradient $-\frac{1}{2}$ not $\frac{1}{2}$

3. $3x - 6y + 1 = 0$; $y = \frac{1}{2}x + \frac{1}{6}$
Gradient $= \frac{1}{2}$
Gradient of perpendicular line = −2
Equation of line: $y = -2x + c$
Substitute (4, −2): $-2 = -2(4) + c$; $c = 6$
Equation is $y = -2x + 6$
1 mark for rearranging first equation to find gradient; 1 mark for gradient of perpendicular line; 1 mark for using a correct form of equation of straight line and attempting to find value of constant; 1 mark for correct answer. Total 4 marks.

Page 20, Linear inequalities

1. −1, 0, 1, 2, 3, 4
1 mark for correct answer.
2. $-6 < 2n \le 8$ means that $-3 < n \le 4$
n could be −2, −1, 0, 1, 2, 3, 4
1 mark for dividing by 2; 1 mark for correct answer.

3. a $3x + 5 > 2; 3x > -3; x > -1$

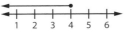

1 mark for $3x > -3$ or $3x = -3$; *1 mark* for $x > -1$; *1 mark* for correct number line. Total 3 marks.

b $20 - 5x \geq 0; 20 \geq 5x; 4 \geq x$

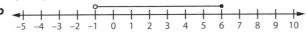

1 mark for $20 \geq 5x$ or $20 = 5x$; *1 mark* for $4 \geq x$ or $x \leq 4$; *1 mark* for correct number line. Total 3 marks.

4. a $1 < 3x + 4 \leq 22; -3 < 3x \leq 18; -1 < x \leq 6$
1 mark for subtracting 4 from both sides; *1 mark* for dividing both sides by 3; *1 mark* for the correct solution with inequality notation. Total 3 marks.

b

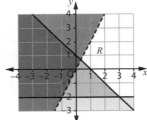

1 mark for correct number line.

5. First inequality: $4x + 1 \geq 3; 4x \geq 2; x \geq \frac{1}{2}$
Second inequality: $5 - x > 3; 5 > 3 + x; 2 > x$ (or $x < 2$)
The set of values that satisfies both inequalities is $\frac{1}{2} \leq x < 2$
1 mark for solving the first inequality; *1 mark* for solving the second inequality; *1 mark* for correct answer. Total 3 marks.

Page 21, Regions on graphs

1. a $x \leq 2$ **b** $y < x + 1$
1 mark for each correct answer.

2.

1 mark for $y = 2x$ dotted; *1 mark* for $y = -2$ and $x + y = 1$ solid; *1 mark* for the correct region. Total 3 marks.

3. a $y \geq x, y < 4, x + y \geq 2$
1 mark for each correct answer.

b The points in the region with integer coordinates are $(1, 1), (0, 2), (1, 2), (2, 2), (-1, 3), (0, 3), (1, 3), (2, 3), (3, 3)$.
1 mark for correct answer (all 9 points).

Page 22, Linear simultaneous equations

1. a $2x + 5y = 11$ (1), $3x - 2y = -12$ (2)
(1) × 2: $4x + 10y = 22$ (3)
(2) × 5: $15x - 10y = -60$ (4)
(3) + (4): $19x = -38; x = -2$
Substitute into (1): $-4 + 5y = 11; 5y = 15; y = 3$
Solution is $x = -2, y = 3$

b $2x - 7y = 12$ (1), $5x - y = -3$ (2)
(2) × 7: $35x - 7y = -21$ (3)
(1) – (3): $-33x = 33; x = -1$
Substitute into (2): $-5 - y = -3; y = -2$
Solution is $x = -1, y = -2$

c $3x + 8y = 12$ (1), $2x + 12y = 13$ (2)
(1) × 2: $6x + 16y = 24$ (3)
(2) × 3: $6x + 36y = 39$ (4)
(3) – (4): $-20y = -15; y = \frac{15}{20} = \frac{3}{4}$ or 0.75

Substitute into (1): $3x + 6 = 12; 3x = 6; x = 2$
Solution is $x = 2, y = 0.75$

d $6x - 4y = 9$ (1), $5x + 3y = -2$ (2)
(1) × 3: $18x - 12y = 27$ (3)
(2) × 4: $20x + 12y = -8$ (4)
(3) + (4): $38x = 19; x = \frac{1}{2}$ or 0.5
Substitute into (1):
$3 - 4y = 9; 4y = -6; y = -\frac{6}{4} = -\frac{3}{2}$ or -1.5
Solution is $x = 0.5, y = -1.5$

*For each part, **1 mark** for correct equation in either x or y; **1 mark** for x solution; **1 mark** for y solution. Total 3 marks.*

2. a Let a be the price of an adult ticket and c the price of a child ticket.
$a + 3c = 39$ (1), $2a + 4c = 62$ (2)
1 mark for the first equation (any letters for your variables score); *1 mark* for the second equation.

b (1) × 2: $2a + 6c = 78$ (3)
(3) – (2): $2c = 16; c = 8$
Substitute into (1): $a + 24 = 39, a = 15$
An adult ticket costs £15 and a child ticket costs £8
1 mark for correct equation in either a or c; *1 mark* for adult ticket is £15; *1 mark* for child ticket is £8. Total 3 marks.

3. Let a be the mass of an apple and s be the mass of a satsuma.
$20a + 30s = 4050$ (1), $12a + 15s = 2205$ (2)
(2) × 2: $24a + 30s = 4410$ (3)
(1) – (3): $-4a = -360; a = 90$
Substitute into (2):
$1080 + 15s = 2205; 15s = 1125; s = 75$
The mass of an apple is 90 g and the mass of a satsuma is 75 g.
1 mark for correct simultaneous equations; *1 mark* for correct equation in either a or s; *1 mark* for apple mass of 90 g; *1 mark* for satsuma mass of 75 g. Total 4 marks.

Page 23, Expanding brackets

1. a $y(3 - 5y) = 3y - 5y^2$
1 mark for correct answer.

b $(2x - y)3xy = 6x^2y - 3xy^2$
1 mark for either $6x^2y$ or $3xy^2$; *1 mark* for correct answer.

2. a $xy + x + 2y + 2$

b $2a^2 - 5a + 4a - 10 = 2a^2 - a - 10$

c $(a + b)(a + b) = a^2 + ab + ba + b^2 = a^2 + 2ab + b^2$

d $6m^2 - 4mn + 9nm - 6n^2 = 6m^2 + 5mn - 6n^2$

e $(4x + 1)(4x + 1) = 16x^2 + 4x + 4x + 1 = 16x^2 + 8x + 1$

*For each part, **1 mark** for a correct expansion without simplifying; **1 mark** for a correct simplified expansion (terms written in any order).*

3. Area $= \frac{1}{2} \times$ base $\times$ height $= \frac{1}{2} \times (2x + 2) \times (2x - 1)$
$\frac{1}{2}$ the base is $x + 1$, so this becomes:
$(x + 1)(2x - 1) = 2x^2 + 2x - x - 1 = 2x^2 + x - 1$
1 mark for writing $\frac{1}{2} \times$ base $\times$ height and putting the expressions $2x + 2$ and $2x - 1$ into this formula; *1 mark* for expanding the brackets correctly (unsimplified); *1 mark* for correct answer. Total 3 marks.

4. $(x - 1)(2 - x)(x + 4)$

$= (2x - x^2 - 2 + x)(x + 4) = (3x - x^2 - 2)(x + 4)$

$= 3x^2 - x^3 - 2x + 12x - 4x^2 - 8 = -x^3 - x^2 + 10x - 8$

1 mark for expanding the first two (or second two) sets of brackets; 1 mark for attempting to multiply this new expression by the third set of brackets; 1 mark for a correct unsimplified expression; 1 mark for a correct simplified expression. Total 4 marks.

5. Volume $= (x + 1)^3 = (x + 1)(x + 1)(x + 1)$

$= (x^2 + 2x + 1)(x + 1) = x^3 + 2x^2 + x + x^2 + 2x + 1$

$= x^3 + 3x^2 + 3x + 1$ cm^3

1 mark for expanding the first two (or second two) sets of brackets; 1 mark for attempting to multiply this new expression by the third set of brackets; 1 mark for a correct simplified expression. Total 3 marks.

Page 24, Factorising 1

Note that, when factorising, brackets can be written in any order.

1. a $3(2a - 5b)$ **b** $x(x + 1)$

1 mark for each correct answer.

2. a $4x(4 + 3y)$ **b** $xy(x + y)$

    c $2p(4 - 2pq + 3q)$

For each part, 1 mark for removing any common factor; 1 mark for fully factorising correctly.

3. $x^2 + 3x = x(x + 3)$ so the missing length is $x + 3$

1 mark for correct answer.

4. a $(p - 12)(p + 3)$ **b** $(x + 10)(x - 1)$

    c $(y - 7)(y - 7)$ or $(y - 7)^2$ **d** $(x + 4)(x + 4)$ or $(x + 4)^2$

For each part, 1 mark for each correct bracket.

5. $x^2 + 6x - 27 = (x + 9)(x - 3)$, so the sides of the rectangle are $x + 9$ and $x - 3$

1 mark for factorising correctly; 1 mark for giving the two sides.

Page 25, Factorising 2

1. a $(x - 7)(x + 7)$ **b** $(y - 9)(y + 9)$

    c $(2b - 1)(2b + 1)$ **d** $(p - 3q)(p + 3q)$

1 mark for each correct answer.

2. The area of a parallelogram is given by base × height. Since $x^2 - 121 = (x + 11)(x - 11)$, the base and height are $x + 11$ and $x - 11$

1 mark for factorising the area; 1 mark for writing down the base and height.

3. a $6x^2 + 5x - 4 = 6x^2 - 3x + 8x - 4$

$= 3x(2x - 1) + 4(2x - 1)$

$= (2x - 1)(3x + 4)$

1 mark for (2x − 1); 1 mark for (3x − 4).

    b $12x^2 + 20x + 3 = 12x^2 + 18x + 2x + 3$

$= 6x(2x + 3) + 1(2x + 3)$

$= (2x + 3)(6x + 1)$

1 mark for (2x + 3); 1 mark for (6x + 1).

4. Pavel is wrong because he has ignored the 2 in front of x^2. He needs to look for two numbers that multiply to make 12 and add to make 7. The correct factorisation is $(x + 2)(2x + 3)$.

1 mark for a correct explanation that references 12 and 7, or ignoring the 2 in front of x^2, or gives the correct factorisation.

5. $9x^2 + 30x + 25 = (3x + 5)^2$, so the side length is $3x + 5$ The perimeter of the square is $4(3x + 5) = 12x + 20$

1 mark for factorising correctly; 1 mark for multiplying the side length by 4; 1 mark for correct answer. Total 3 marks.

Page 26, Solving quadratic equations

1. a $(x - 8)(x + 1) = 0$ **b** $x(x + 5) = 0$

     $x = 8$ or $x = -1$ $x = 0$ or $x = -5$

    c $(x - 1)(x + 1) = 0$

     $x = 1$ or $x = -1$

For each part, 1 mark for factorising; 1 mark for correct answer from your factorisation; 1 mark for both correct answers. Total 3 marks.

2. a $x^2 - 12x + 35 = 0$

$(x - 7)(x - 5) = 0$

$x = 7$ or $x = 5$

1 mark for rearranging to equal 0; 1 mark for factorising; 1 mark for 7; 1 mark for 5. Total 4 marks.

    b $x^2 + 3x - 10 = 0$

$(x + 5)(x - 2) = 0$

$x = -5$ or $x = 2$

1 mark for rearranging to equal 0; 1 mark for factorising; 1 mark for −5; 1 mark for 2. Total 4 marks.

    c $x^2 - 144 = 0$

$(x - 12)(x + 12) = 0$

$x = 12$ or $x = -12$

1 mark for rearranging and factorising or for taking square root of 144; 1 mark for 12 and −12

3. a $6x^2 + 13x - 5 = 0$

$(3x - 1)(2x + 5) = 0$

$x = \frac{1}{3}$ or $x = -\frac{5}{2}$

1 mark for factorising correctly; 1 mark for $\frac{1}{3}$; 1 mark for $-\frac{5}{2}$. Total 3 marks.

    b $7x^2 - 19x - 6 = 0$

$(7x + 2)(x - 3) = 0$

$x = -\frac{2}{7}$ or $x = 3$

1 mark for factorising correctly; 1 mark for $-\frac{2}{7}$; 1 mark for 3. Total 3 marks.

4. a $(2x - 1)(x - 2) = 5$

$2x^2 - 5x + 2 = 5$

$2x^2 - 5x - 3 = 0$

1 mark for multiplying the two sides and writing equal to 5; 1 mark for expanding the brackets; 1 mark for rearranging to equal 0. Total 3 marks.

    b $2x^2 - 5x - 3 = 0$ $(2x + 1)(x - 3) = 0$

$x = -\frac{1}{2}$ or $x = 3$

Only $x = 3$ works in this geometric situation. The length of the shortest side is $x - 2 = 3 - 2 = 1$ cm.

1 mark for factorising the quadratic; 1 mark for $x = 3$; 1 mark for correct answer of 1 cm. Total 3 marks.

Page 27, The quadratic formula

Note, the quadratic formula used in the solutions on this page is $x = \frac{-b \pm \sqrt{b^2 - 4ac}}{2a}$

1. a Substitute $a = 3$, $b = -7$, $c = -10$ into the formula.

$x = \frac{7 \pm \sqrt{(-7)^2 - 4 \times 3 \times (-10)}}{2 \times 3} = \frac{7 \pm \sqrt{169}}{6} = \frac{7 \pm 13}{6} = \frac{10}{3}$ or -1

1 mark for substituting into the quadratic formula; 1 mark for $\frac{10}{3}$ or 3.33; 1 mark for −1. Total 3 marks.

b Substitute $a = 5$, $b = 4$, $c = -20$ into the formula.

$x = \frac{-4 \pm \sqrt{4^2 - 4 \times 5 \times (-20)}}{2 \times 5} = \frac{-4 \pm \sqrt{416}}{10} = 1.64 \text{ or } -2.44$

1 mark for substituting into the quadratic formula; 1 mark for 1.64; 1 mark for –2.44. Total 3 marks.

c Substitute $a = -2$, $b = 10$, $c = 25$ into the formula.

$x = \frac{-10 \pm \sqrt{10^2 - 4 \times (-2) \times 25}}{2 \times (-2)} = \frac{-10 \pm \sqrt{300}}{-4} = 6.83 \text{ or } -1.83$

1 mark for substituting into the quadratic formula; 1 mark for 6.83; 1 mark for –1.83. Total 3 marks.

2. a Substitute $a = 1$, $b = -10$, $c = 7$ into the formula.

$x = \frac{10 \pm \sqrt{(-10)^2 - 4 \times 1 \times 7}}{2 \times 1} = \frac{10 \pm \sqrt{72}}{2} = \frac{10 \pm 6\sqrt{2}}{2} = 5 \pm 3\sqrt{2}$

$(a = 5, b = 3, c = 2)$

1 mark for substituting into the quadratic formula; 1 mark for $5 + 3\sqrt{2}$; 1 mark for $5 - 3\sqrt{2}$. Total 3 marks.

b Substitute $a = 1$, $b = 2$, $c = -11$ into the formula.

$x = \frac{-2 \pm \sqrt{2^2 - 4 \times 1 \times (-11)}}{2 \times 1} = \frac{-2 \pm \sqrt{48}}{2} = \frac{-2 \pm 4\sqrt{3}}{2} = -1 \pm 2\sqrt{3}$

$(a = -1, b = 2, c = 3)$

1 mark for substituting into the quadratic formula; 1 mark for $-1 + 2\sqrt{3}$; 1 mark for $-1 - 2\sqrt{3}$. Total 3 marks.

c $2x^2 + 22 = 16x$ gives $2x^2 - 16x + 22 = 0$

Divide by 2 to give $x^2 - 8x + 11 = 0$ (optional)

Substitute $a = 1$, $b = -8$, $c = 11$ into the formula.

$x = \frac{8 \pm \sqrt{(-8)^2 - 4 \times 1 \times 11}}{2 \times 1} = \frac{8 \pm \sqrt{20}}{2} = \frac{8 \pm 2\sqrt{5}}{2} = 4 \pm \sqrt{5}$

$(a = 4, b = 1, c = 5)$

1 mark for rearranging and substituting into the quadratic formula; 1 mark for $4 + \sqrt{5}$; 1 mark for $4 - \sqrt{5}$. Total 3 marks.

3. a Area of trapezium $= \frac{1}{2}(a + b)h$

$a = x + 2$, $b = x + 4$ and $h = x - 1$

Area $= \frac{1}{2}(x + 2 + x + 4)(x - 1) = \frac{1}{2}(2x + 6)(x - 1)$

$\qquad = (x + 3)(x - 1)$

Since the area is 10, $(x + 3)(x - 1) = 10$

$\qquad\qquad x^2 + 3x - x - 3 = 10$

$\qquad\qquad\qquad x^2 + 2x - 13 = 0$

1 mark for substituting the lengths into the area of a trapezium formula; 1 mark for attempting to rearrange; 1 mark for a complete proof. Total 3 marks.

b Substitute $a = 1$, $b = 2$, $c = -13$ into the formula.

$x = \frac{-2 \pm \sqrt{2^2 - 4 \times 1 \times (-13)}}{2 \times 1} = \frac{-2 \pm \sqrt{56}}{2} = -1 \pm \sqrt{14}$

$\quad = 2.74\ldots \text{ or } -4.74\ldots$

The height is $x - 1$ and this cannot be negative.

Height $= 2.74\ldots - 1 = 1.74 \,\text{cm}$

1 mark for substituting into the quadratic formula; 1 mark for 2.74…; 1 mark for correct answer to 2 dp. Total 3 marks.

Page 28, Completing the square

1. a $x^2 + 6x + 5 = (x + 3)^2 - 4$

1 mark for $(x + 3)^2$; 1 mark for correct answer.

b $x^2 - 4x + 10 = (x - 2)^2 + 6$

1 mark for $(x - 2)^2$; 1 mark for correct answer.

c $x^2 - 10x = (x - 5)^2 - 25$

1 mark for $(x - 5)^2$; 1 mark for correct answer.

d $x^2 + x + 1 = \left(x + \frac{1}{2}\right)^2 + \frac{3}{4}$

1 mark for $\left(x + \frac{1}{2}\right)^2$; 1 mark for correct answer. Equivalent decimals allowed.

2. a $x^2 - 2x - 11 = (x - 1)^2 - 12$

1 mark for $(x - 1)^2$; 1 mark for correct answer.

b $x^2 - 2x - 11 = 0$

$(x - 1)^2 - 12 = 0$

$(x - 1)^2 = 12$

$x - 1 = \pm\sqrt{12}$

$x = 1 \pm \sqrt{12} = 1 \pm 2\sqrt{3} \ (a = 1, b = 2)$

1 mark for starting to rearrange to make x the subject; 1 mark for correct answer.

3. a $2x^2 + 8x + 7 = 2[x^2 + 4x] + 7$

$\qquad\qquad = 2[(x + 2)^2 - 4] + 7 = 2(x + 2)^2 - 8 + 7$

$\qquad\qquad = 2(x + 2)^2 - 1$

1 mark for factorising out 2; 1 mark for $(x + 2)^2$; 1 mark for correct answer. Total 3 marks.

b $12 + 10x - x^2 = 12 - [x^2 - 10x]$

$\qquad\qquad = 12 - [(x - 5)^2 - 25] = 12 - (x - 5)^2 + 25$

$\qquad\qquad = 37 - (x - 5)^2$

1 mark for factorising out –1; 1 mark for $(x - 5)^2$; 1 mark for correct answer (equivalent form allowed). Total 3 marks.

Page 29, Algebraic fractions 1

1. a $\frac{4x^2 - 12x}{2x} = \frac{4x(x - 3)}{2x} = \frac{2(x - 3)}{1} = 2(x - 3)$

1 mark for factorising the numerator; 1 mark for correct answer.

b $\frac{x^2 - x - 2}{x^2 - 6x + 8} = \frac{(x + 1)(x - 2)}{(x - 2)(x - 4)} = \frac{x + 1}{x - 4}$

1 mark for factorising the numerator; 1 mark for factorising the denominator; 1 mark for correct answer. Total 3 marks.

c $\frac{4x^2 - 1}{2x^2 + x} = \frac{(2x + 1)(2x - 1)}{x(2x + 1)} = \frac{2x - 1}{x}$

1 mark for factorising the numerator; 1 mark for factorising the denominator; 1 mark for correct answer. Total 3 marks.

2. a $\frac{3x - 4}{6x^2 + 7x - 20} = \frac{3x - 4}{(3x - 4)(2x + 5)} = \frac{1}{2x + 5}$

1 mark for attempting to factorise the denominator; 1 mark for correct factorisation; 1 mark for correct answer. Total 3 marks.

b $\frac{3x - 4}{6x^2 + 7x - 20} = 1$

$\frac{1}{2x + 5} = 1$

$1 = 2x + 5$

$2x = -4$

$x = -2$

1 mark for rearranging to $1 = 2x + 5$; 1 mark for correct answer.

3. $\frac{1}{x - 3} = \frac{x}{x + 5}$

$x + 5 = x(x - 3)$

$x + 5 = x^2 - 3x$

$x^2 - 4x - 5 = 0$

$(x - 5)(x + 1) = 0$

$x = 5$ or $x = -1$

1 mark for multiplying both sides by both denominators; 1 mark for rearranging to $ax^2 + bx + c = 0$; 1 mark for correct answer. Total 3 marks.

Page 30, Algebraic fractions 2

1. $\frac{2x - 8}{3x - 15} \times \frac{x - 5}{x - 3} = \frac{2(x - 4)}{3(x - 5)} \times \frac{x - 5}{x - 3} = \frac{2(x - 4)(x - 5)}{3(x - 3)(x - 5)} = \frac{2(x - 4)}{3(x - 3)}$

1 mark for factorising numerator and denominator of the first fraction; 1 mark for multiplying numerators and multiplying denominators; 1 mark for correct answer. Total 3 marks.

2. $\dfrac{x}{x^2 + 2x - 35} \div \dfrac{6x^3}{3x + 21} = \dfrac{x}{(x - 5)(x + 7)} \div \dfrac{6x^3}{3(x + 7)}$

$\qquad\qquad = \dfrac{x}{(x - 5)(x + 7)} \times \dfrac{3(x + 7)}{6x^3} = \dfrac{3x(x + 7)}{6x^3(x - 5)(x + 7)}$

$\qquad\qquad = \dfrac{1}{2x^2(x - 5)}$

1 mark for factorising where possible; 1 mark for turning the division into a correct multiplication; 1 mark for multiplying numerators and multiplying denominators; 1 mark for correct answer. Total 4 marks.

3. First, simplify the area: $\dfrac{x^2}{x^2(x + 1)} = \dfrac{1}{x + 1}$

Width = area ÷ height

$\dfrac{1}{x + 1} \div \dfrac{1}{x} = \dfrac{1}{x + 1} \times \dfrac{x}{1} = \dfrac{x}{x + 1}$

1 mark for simplifying the area; 1 mark for dividing the area by the height; 1 mark for turning the division into a correct multiplication; 1 mark for correct answer. Total 4 marks.

Note that you could divide first and then simplify at the end, and this would also get full marks.

4. $x^2 : (x - 1) = 4 : 1$ can be written $\dfrac{x^2}{x - 1} = \dfrac{4}{1}$

$x^2 = 4(x - 1); x^2 - 4x + 4 = 0; (x - 2)^2 = 0; x = 2$

1 mark for writing the equivalent ratios in an equation with fractions; 1 mark for rearranging the quadratic to equal 0; 1 mark for a method to solve the quadratic; 1 mark for correct answer. Total 4 marks.

Page 31, Algebraic fractions 3

1. a $\dfrac{2}{x} + \dfrac{3}{2x} = \dfrac{4}{2x} + \dfrac{3}{2x} = \dfrac{7}{2x}$

1 mark for the common denominator of $2x$; 1 mark for correct answer.

b $\dfrac{1}{p} - \dfrac{1}{q} = \dfrac{q}{pq} - \dfrac{p}{pq} = \dfrac{q - p}{pq}$

1 mark for the common denominator of pq; 1 mark for correct answer.

c $\dfrac{4}{x + 1} + \dfrac{3}{x + 2} = \dfrac{4(x + 2)}{(x + 1)(x + 2)} + \dfrac{3(x + 1)}{(x + 1)(x + 2)} = \dfrac{4(x + 2) + 3(x + 1)}{(x + 2)(x + 1)}$

$\qquad = \dfrac{4x + 8 + 3x + 3}{(x + 1)(x + 2)} = \dfrac{7x + 11}{(x + 1)(x + 2)}$

1 mark for the common denominator of $(x + 1)(x + 2)$; 1 mark for the correct numerator (unsimplified); 1 mark for correct answer. Total 3 marks.

d $\dfrac{x}{x - 2} - \dfrac{x - 2}{x + 3} = \dfrac{x(x + 3)}{(x - 2)(x + 3)} - \dfrac{(x - 2)(x - 2)}{(x - 2)(x + 3)}$

$\qquad = \dfrac{x(x + 3) - (x - 2)(x - 2)}{(x - 2)(x + 3)} = \dfrac{x^2 + 3x - (x^2 - 4x + 4)}{(x - 2)(x + 3)}$

$\qquad = \dfrac{x^2 + 3x - x^2 + 4x - 4}{(x - 2)(x + 3)} = \dfrac{7x - 4}{(x - 2)(x + 3)}$

1 mark for the common denominator of $(x - 2)(x + 3)$; 1 mark for the correct numerator (unsimplified); 1 mark for correct answer. Total 3 marks.

2. $\dfrac{3}{2x - 1} + \dfrac{2}{2x + 1} = 1$

$\dfrac{3(2x + 1) + 2(2x - 1)}{(2x - 1)(2x + 1)} = 1$

$\dfrac{6x + 3 + 4x - 2}{(2x - 1)(2x + 1)} = 1$

$\dfrac{10x + 1}{(2x - 1)(2x + 1)} = 1$

$10x + 1 = (2x - 1)(2x + 1)$

$10x + 1 = 4x^2 - 1$

$2x^2 - 5x - 1 = 0$

Solve with the quadratic formula to get:

$x = \dfrac{5 \pm \sqrt{(-5)^2 - 4 \times 2 \times (-1)}}{2 \times 2} = \dfrac{5 \pm \sqrt{33}}{4}$

1 mark for combining the left-hand side into one fraction; 1 mark for multiplying the denominator to the other side; 1 mark for rearranging to $ax^2 + bx + c = 0$; 1 mark for using the quadratic formula; 1 mark for correct answer. Total 5 marks.

3. Perimeter of equilateral triangle $= 3 \times \dfrac{3x - 1}{5} = \dfrac{9x - 3}{5}$

Perimeter of isosceles triangle $= \dfrac{x - 1}{5} + 2 \times \dfrac{8x + 1}{10}$

$\qquad\qquad = \dfrac{x - 1}{5} + \dfrac{8x + 1}{5}$

$\qquad\qquad = \dfrac{9x}{5}$

The difference is $\dfrac{9x}{5} - \dfrac{9x - 3}{5} = \dfrac{3}{5}$ cm

1 mark for finding the perimeter of one triangle; 1 mark for finding the perimeter for both triangles; 1 mark for subtracting one perimeter from the other (order doesn't matter); 1 mark for correct answer. Total 4 marks.

Page 32, Rearranging formulae

1. a $2x^2 - 3 = y; 2x^2 = y + 3; x^2 = \dfrac{y + 3}{2}; x = \sqrt{\dfrac{y + 3}{2}}$

1 mark for making x^2 the subject; 1 mark for correct answer (± sign before root allowed).

b $a\sqrt{x} + b = c; a\sqrt{x} = c - b; \sqrt{x} = \dfrac{c - b}{a}; x = \left(\dfrac{c - b}{a}\right)^2$

1 mark for making $\sqrt{x}$ the subject; 1 mark for correct answer.

2. $P = I^2 R; \dfrac{P}{R} = I^2; I = \sqrt{\dfrac{P}{R}}$

1 mark for making I^2 the subject; 1 mark for correct answer.

3. Fleur has made a mistake on line 3 (there should be no square root as x is not squared). It should be:

$x = \dfrac{y + b}{a^2}$

1 mark for identifying a mistake in line 3; 1 mark for correct working or correct explanation.

4. a $mp - q = ap; mp - ap = q; p(m - a) = q; p = \dfrac{q}{m - a}$

1 mark for bringing both terms with p to the same side; 1 mark for factorising; 1 mark for correct answer. Total 3 marks.

b $\dfrac{1}{p} + \dfrac{1}{r} = \dfrac{1}{t}; \dfrac{1}{p} = \dfrac{1}{t} - \dfrac{1}{r}; \dfrac{1}{p} = \dfrac{r - t}{rt}; p = \dfrac{rt}{r - t}$

1 mark for making $\dfrac{1}{p}$ the subject; 1 mark for combining two fractions; 1 mark for correct answer. Total 3 marks.

Note that there are alternative methods.

Page 33, Quadratic graphs 1

1. a

x	-2	-1	0	1	2	3
y	5	1	-1	-1	1	5

1 mark for any two answers correct; 1 mark for all four correct.

b

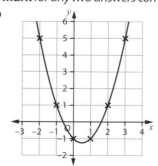

1 mark for plotting all the points correctly; 1 mark for a smooth curve drawn through the points.

c $(0.5, -1.25)$

1 mark for an answer close to $(0.5, -1.25)$.

2. a Approximately 1.4 and −1.4

1 mark for 1.4 (or close); 1 mark for −1.4 (or close).

b (0, 2)

1 mark for correct answer.

c Draw a horizontal line through −3 on the y-axis. This line cuts the graph when $x \approx -2.2$ and $x \approx 2.2$

1 mark for identifying the points where $y = -3$; 1 mark for correct answer (both solutions).

Page 34, Quadratic graphs 2

1. a $y = 16 - x^2 = (4 - x)(4 + x)$

This has roots at $x = 4$ and $x = -4$ (or $(4, 0)$ and $(-4, 0)$).

1 mark for factorising (or attempting to solve $16 - x^2 = 0$); 1 mark for correct answer.

b Since the roots are at 4 and −4, and the graph is symmetric, its turning point is on the y-axis. This graph crosses the y-axis at 16, so the turning point is (0, 16).

1 mark for correct answer.

c Since the x^2 term is negative, the parabola is 'upside-down'. This makes the turning point a maximum point.

1 mark for a correct explanation.

2. a $y = (x - 2)(x + 3) = x^2 + x - 6$

When $y = 0$, $x = 2$ or $x = -3$

When $x = 0$, $y = -6$

1 mark for the correct shape; 1 mark for the y-intercept correct; 1 mark for the roots (x-intercepts) correct. Total 3 marks.

b $y = 3x - x^2 = x(3 - x)$

When $y = 0$, $x = 0$ or $x = 3$

When $x = 0$, $y = 0$

1 mark for the correct shape; 1 mark for the graph passing through (0, 0); 1 mark for the graph passing through (3, 0). Total 3 marks.

c $y = 2x^2 + 7x + 6 = (2x + 3)(x + 2)$

When $y = 0$, $x = -\frac{3}{2} = -1.5$ or $x = -2$

When $x = 0$, $y = 6$

1 mark for the correct shape; 1 mark for the y-intercept correct; 1 mark for the roots (x-intercepts) correct. Total 3 marks.

3. a Complete the square to get $y = x^2 - 6x + 3 = (x - 3)^2 - 6$

The turning point is $(3, -6)$.

Since the turning point is below the x-axis, and the graph is a 'U shape' (positive x^2 term), it will cross the x-axis.

1 mark for completing the square; 1 mark for the turning point; 1 mark for a correct explanation for crossing the x-axis. Total 3 marks.

b Complete the square to get $y = 2x^2 + 10x + 20$

$= 2[x^2 + 5x + 10] = 2\left[\left(x + \frac{5}{2}\right)^2 + \frac{15}{4}\right] = 2\left(x + \frac{5}{2}\right)^2 + \frac{15}{2}$

The turning point is $\left(-\frac{5}{2}, \frac{15}{2}\right)$.

Since the turning point is above the x-axis, and the graph is a 'U shape' (positive x^2 term), it will not cross the x-axis.

1 mark for an attempt to complete the square; 1 mark for correctly completing the square; 1 mark for the turning point; 1 mark for a correct explanation for not crossing the x-axis. Total 4 marks.

Page 35, Quadratic inequalities

1. a $x^2 - 4 \leq -3 \Rightarrow x^2 - 1 \leq 0$

$(x - 1)(x + 1) \leq 0$

Solution is $-1 \leq x \leq 1$

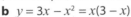

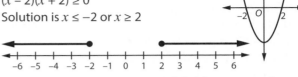

1 mark for finding −1 and 1; 1 mark for the correct solution; 1 mark for the correct number line representation. Total 3 marks.

b $7x^2 \geq 28 \Rightarrow x^2 \geq 4 \Rightarrow x^2 - 4 \geq 0$

$(x - 2)(x + 2) \geq 0$

Solution is $x \leq -2$ or $x \geq 2$

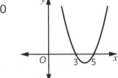

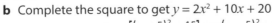

1 mark for finding −2 and 2; 1 mark for the correct solution (with the word 'or' not 'and'); 1 mark for the correct number line representation. Total 3 marks.

2. a $x^2 - 8x + 15 \leq 0 \Rightarrow (x - 5)(x - 3) \leq 0$

Roots are at 5 and 3

Solution is $3 \leq x \leq 5$

In set notation, $\{x : 3 \leq x \leq 5\}$

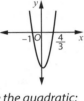

1 mark for factorising or attempting to solve the quadratic; 1 mark for finding 3 and 5; 1 mark for the correct solution shown as an inequality or on a graph; 1 mark for the correct solution in set notation. Total 4 marks.

b $3x^2 - x - 4 > 0 \Rightarrow (3x - 4)(x + 1) > 0$

Roots are at $\frac{4}{3}$ and −1

Solution is $x < -1$ or $x > \frac{4}{3}$

In set notation, $\{x : x < -1\} \cup \left\{x : x > \frac{4}{3}\right\}$ or $\left\{x : x < -1 \text{ or } x > \frac{4}{3}\right\}$

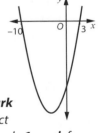

1 mark for factorising or attempting to solve the quadratic; 1 mark for finding $\frac{4}{3}$ and −1; 1 mark for the correct solution shown as an inequality or on a graph; 1 mark for the correct solution in set notation. Total 4 marks.

c $x^2 - 30 < -7x \Rightarrow x^2 + 7x - 30 < 0$

$(x + 10)(x - 3) < 0$

Roots are at −10 and 3

Solution is $-10 < x < 3$

In set notation, $\{x : -10 < x < 3\}$

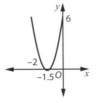

1 mark for rearranging and factorising or attempting to solve the quadratic; 1 mark for finding −10 and 3; 1 mark for the correct solution shown as an inequality or on a graph; 1 mark for the correct solution in set notation. Total 4 marks.

Page 36, Non-linear simultaneous equations

1. a $x + y = 3 \Rightarrow y = 3 - x$

Substitute into $y = x^2 + 3x - 2$:

$3 - x = x^2 + 3x - 2$; $x^2 + 4x - 5 = 0$; $(x + 5)(x - 1) = 0$

$x = -5$ or $x = 1$

Since $y = 3 - x$:

When $x = -5$, $y = 3 - (-5) = 8$

When $x = 1$, $y = 3 - 1 = 2$

Alternatively, write as $(-5, 8)$ and $(1, 2)$.

1 mark for rearranging the linear equation to make y (or x) the subject and substituting into the non-linear equation; 1 mark for rearranging the quadratic to make equal to 0; 1 mark for finding the two values of x; 1 mark for finding the corresponding two values of y. Total 4 marks.

b $y + x = 2 \Rightarrow y = 2 - x$

Substitute into $x^2 + y^2 = 10$:

$x^2 + (2 - x)^2 = 10$; $x^2 + 4 - 4x + x^2 = 10$; $2x^2 - 4x - 6 = 0$

Divide by 2: $x^2 - 2x - 3 = 0$; $(x - 3)(x + 1) = 0$

$x = 3$ or $x = -1$

Since $y = 2 - x$:

When $x = 3$, $y = 2 - 3 = -1$

When $x = -1$, $y = 2 - (-1) = 3$

Alternatively, write as $(3, -1)$ and $(-1, 3)$.

1 mark for rearranging the linear equation to make y (or x) the subject and substituting into the non-linear equation; 1 mark for expanding the brackets correctly; 1 mark for rearranging and finding the two values of x; 1 mark for finding the corresponding two values of y. Total 4 marks.

c $2y + x = 0 \Rightarrow x = -2y$

Substitute into $2x^2 + y^2 = 9$:

$2(-2y)^2 + y^2 = 9$; $2 \times 4y^2 + y^2 = 9$; $8y^2 + y^2 = 9$; $9y^2 = 9$

Divide by 9: $y^2 = 1$; $y = \pm 1$

Since $x = -2y$:

When $y = 1$, $x = -2 \times 1 = -2$

When $y = -1$, $x = -2 \times -1 = 2$

Alternatively, write as $(-2, 1)$ and $(2, -1)$.

1 mark for rearranging the linear equation to make x (or y) the subject and substituting into the non-linear equation; 1 mark for rearranging the quadratic to make equal to 0 or for reaching $y^2 = 1$; 1 mark for finding the two values of y; 1 mark for finding the corresponding two values of x. Total 4 marks.

2. a $x - y = 4 \Rightarrow x = y + 4$

Substitute into $x^2 + y^2 = 8$:

$(y + 4)^2 + y^2 = 8$; $y^2 + 8y + 16 + y^2 = 8$; $2y^2 + 8y + 8 = 0$

Divide by 2: $y^2 + 4y + 4 = 0$; $(y + 2)^2 = 0$; $y = -2$

When $y = -2$, $x = -2 + 4 = 2$, which means the only point of intersection is $(2, -2)$.

1 mark for rearranging the linear equation to make y (or x) the subject and substituting into the non-linear equation; 1 mark for expanding the brackets; 1 mark for rearranging the quadratic to make equal to 0; 1 mark for finding the value of y; 1 mark for finding the corresponding value of x and giving the final answer in coordinate form. Total 5 marks.

b $y = x - 4$ is a rearrangement of $x - y = 4$, the line from part **a**.

Since there is only one point of intersection in part **a**, this line must be a tangent (as tangents only cross curves in one place).

1 mark for identifying that $y = x - 4$ is the same line from part a; 1 mark for a correct conclusion.

Page 37, Solutions from graphs

1.

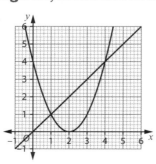

$x = 1$, $y = 1$ and $x = 4$, $y = 4$

1 mark for a correct drawing of $y = (x - 2)^2$; 1 mark for a correct drawing of $y = x$; 1 mark for 1 and 1; 1 mark for 4 and 4. Total 4 marks.

2. a

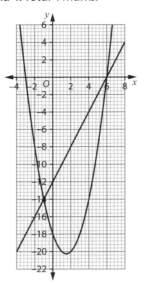

$x = -1$, $y = -14$ and $x = 6$, $y = 0$

1 mark for drawing $y = 2x - 12$ on the diagram; 1 mark for -1 and -14; 1 mark for 6 and 0. Total 3 marks.

b You are given $x^2 - 3x - 14 = 0$. Since the graph is of $y = x^2 - 3x - 18$, subtract 4 from both sides of the equation to get $x^2 - 3x - 18 = -4$. Draw the line $y = -4$ on the graph from part **a**.

The solutions are given where this line crosses the curve: approximately $x = -2.5$ and $x = 5.5$

1 mark for $x^2 - 3x - 18 = -4$ or for drawing the line $y = -4$ on the diagram; 1 mark for -2.5 (or close); 1 mark for 5.5 (or close). Total 3 marks.

Page 38, Cubic and reciprocal graphs

1. a

x	−2	−1	0	1	2
y	−15	−1	1	3	17

1 mark for two answers correct; 1 mark for all three correct.

b

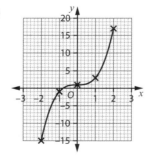

1 mark for the points plotted correctly; 1 mark for a smooth curve through the points.

c The root is approximately −0.8

1 mark for −0.8 (or close).

2. a

x	−3	−2	−1	0	1	2	3
y	$\frac{2}{3}$	−1	2	undefined	−2	−1	$-\frac{2}{3}$

1 mark for two answers correct; 1 mark for all three correct.

b

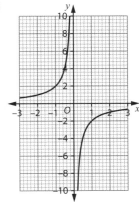

1 mark for at least three points plotted correctly; 1 mark for the correct graph drawn.

c

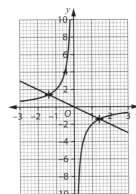

$x = 1.4$ and $y = -1.4$
$x = -1.4$ and $y = 1.4$

1 mark for the line $y = -x$ drawn on the diagram; 1 mark for the first point of intersection; 1 mark for the second point of intersection. Total 3 marks.

Page 39, Exponential graphs

1. Left graph: $y = 3^x$
Right graph: $y = \left(\frac{1}{3}\right)^x$
1 mark for each correct answer.

2.

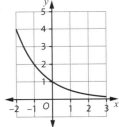

1 mark for the correct shape; 1 mark for (0, 1) labelled.

3. a When $t = 0$, $P = 200\,000 \times 1.2^0 = £200\,000$
1 mark for correct answer.

b When $t = 3$, $P = 200\,000 \times 1.2^3 = £345\,600$
1 mark for substituting $t = 3$; 1 mark for correct answer.

c

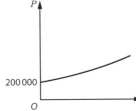

1 mark for the correct shape; 1 mark for labelling y-axis intersection.

4. Substitute the coordinates for x and y in the equation.
For $(-1, 0.4)$: $0.4 = ab^{-1}$ (1)
For $(1, 10)$: $10 = ab^1$ (2)

Divide (2) by (1): $\frac{10}{0.4} = \frac{ab}{ab^{-1}}$; $25 = b^2$; $b = 5$
Substitute $b = 5$ into (2): $10 = 5a$; $a = 2$
1 mark for substituting the coordinates into the equation; 1 mark for $b = 5$; 1 mark for $a = 2$. Total 3 marks.

Page 40, Equation of a circle

1. Substitute (1, 1) into the equation to show it does not satisfy the equation:
$1^2 + 1^2 = 2 \neq 1$, so (1, 1) does not lie on the circle.
1 mark for substituting (1, 1) into the equation; 1 mark for showing that it does not satisfy the equation.
Alternatively, draw the circle to show that (1, 1) is outside.

2. a The radius is 4, so the equation of the circle is $x^2 + y^2 = 16$
1 mark for correct answer.

b Substitute $x = 2\sqrt{2}$ and $y = 2\sqrt{2}$ into the equation:
$x^2 + y^2 = (2\sqrt{2})^2 + (2\sqrt{2})^2 = 8 + 8 = 16$, so the point lies on the circle.
1 mark for substituting into the equation; 1 mark for showing this equals 16

c $y = -4$
1 mark for correct answer.

3. Show that all the angles are right angles and that all the sides are the same length.
Points are $A(0, \sqrt{10})$, $B(\sqrt{10}, 0)$, $C(0, -\sqrt{10})$ and $D(-\sqrt{10}, 0)$.
To show ABC is a right angle, find the gradient of AB and of BC:
Gradient of $AB = \frac{\sqrt{10}}{-\sqrt{10}} = -1$
Gradient of $BC = \frac{\sqrt{10}}{\sqrt{10}} = 1$
These are perpendicular gradients, so ABC is a right angle. You can show the same thing for the other three angles. Alternatively, you can use the circle theorem that opposite angles in a cyclic quadrilateral sum to 180° to prove that if $ABC = 90°$, so does CDA. You can then use gradients to show that DAB is 90° and the circle theorem to prove that BCD is also 90°.
To show all the sides are the same length, use Pythagoras' theorem between two points:
Length $AB = BC = CD = DA = \sqrt{10 + 10} = \sqrt{20}$
Hence, $ABCD$ is a square.
1 mark for finding the coordinates of A, B, C and D; 1 mark for finding the gradient of any of AB, BC, CD or DA; 1 mark for finding the length of any of AB, BC, CD or DA; 1 mark for a full proof (which includes all sides same length, all angles 90°) and conclusion. Total 4 marks.

Alternative solution:
Show that the diagonals of the shape are perpendicular bisectors of each other and equal in length.
Points are: $A(0, \sqrt{10})$, $B(\sqrt{10}, 0)$, $C(0, -\sqrt{10})$ and $D(-\sqrt{10}, 0)$.
Since the centre is at (0, 0), OA, OB, OC and OD are all radii of the circle and are the same length.
Since AC and BD are on the y and x axes respectively, they are perpendicular to each other.
As a result, the diagonals AC and BD are equal perpendicular bisectors of each other, and $ABCD$ is a square.
1 mark for finding the coordinates of A, B, C and D; 1 mark for identifying that OA, OB, OC and OD are all the same length; 1 mark for explaining why AC and BD are perpendicular; 1 mark for a full proof and conclusion. Total 4 marks.

4. Gradient of the radius to the point $= \frac{2}{1} = 2$

The tangent is perpendicular to the radius, so the gradient of the tangent $= -\frac{1}{2}$

Equation of the tangent is of the form $y = -\frac{1}{2}x + c$

Substituting the coordinates of the point on the tangent gives $2 = -\frac{1}{2} + c$, so $c = 2.5$

Equation of tangent is $y = 2.5 - 0.5x$

1 mark for attempt to calculate gradient of radius; 1 mark for negative reciprocal for gradient of tangent, seen or implied; 1 mark for attempting to substitute into $y = mx + c$; 1 mark for attempting to solve to find c; 1 mark for correct answer (or equivalent). Total 5 marks.

Page 41, Trigonometric graphs

1. a

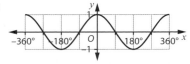

1 mark for a correct section of graph between 0° and 360°; 1 mark for a fully correct graph.

b $(180, -1)$

1 mark for correct answer.

2. a

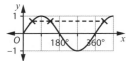

1 mark for a correct section of graph between 0° and 360°; 1 mark for a fully correct graph.

b See diagram in part **a**.

$\theta = 135°$ or $\theta = 405°$

1 mark for 135; 1 mark for 405

3. a

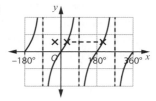

1 mark for a correct section of graph between 0° and 360°; 1 mark for a fully correct graph.

b $\tan 30° = \frac{1}{\sqrt{3}}$

1 mark for correct answer.

c See diagram in part **a**.

   i $\tan 210° = \tan 30° = \frac{1}{\sqrt{3}}$

   ii $\tan(-30)° = -\tan 30° = -\frac{1}{\sqrt{3}}$

1 mark for each correct answer.

Page 42, Graph transformations 1

1. a

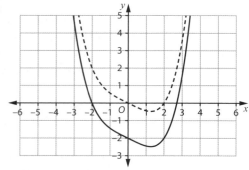

1 mark for a vertical translation; 1 mark for correct answer (translating 2 down).

b

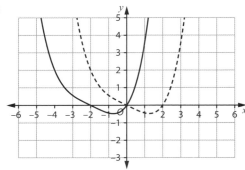

1 mark for a horizontal translation; 1 mark for correct answer (translating 2 left).

c

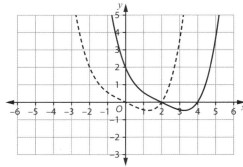

1 mark for a horizontal translation; 1 mark for correct answer (translating 3 right).

d

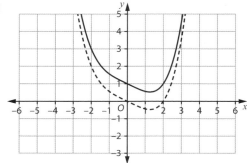

1 mark for a vertical translation; 1 mark for correct answer (translating 1 up).

2.

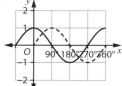

1 mark for a horizontal translation of $y = \sin x$; 1 mark for correct answer (translating 90 left).

3. a The equation shows a translation of 1 up, so the minimum point is $(2, -3)$.

1 mark for correct answer.

b

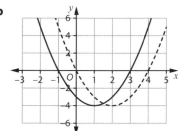

1 mark for a horizontal translation; 1 mark for correct answer (translating 1 left).

Page 43, Graph transformations 2

1.

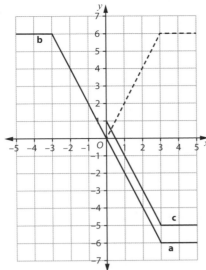

*Part **a**: **1 mark** for a reflection; **1 mark** for correct answer, reflecting in the x-axis.*

*Part **b**: **1 mark** for a reflection; **1 mark** for correct answer, reflecting in the y-axis.*

*Part **c**: **1 mark** for a reflection and translation; **1 mark** for correct answer, reflecting in the x-axis then translating one up.*

2.

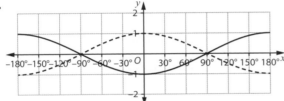

*__1 mark__ for reflecting $y = \cos x$; **1 mark** for correct answer (reflecting in the x-axis).*

3. a i (0, 0) **ii** (1, 1)

__1 mark__ for each correct answer.

b

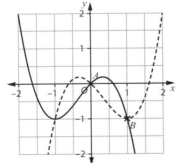

*__1 mark__ for a reflection; **1 mark** for correct answer (reflecting in the y-axis).*

c If $f(x) = x^3 - x^2 - x$, then $-f(x) = -x^3 + x^2 + x$ and
$-f(x) + 2 = -x^3 + x^2 + x + 2$

*__1 mark__ for '+ 2' on the end of any function; **1 mark** for correct answer.*

Page 44, Simple kinematic graphs

1. a The graph stops at 55 minutes, so this is when she finishes the race.

__1 mark__ for correct answer.

b 10 minutes

__1 mark__ for correct answer.

c Krystyna accelerates at a steady rate for 15 minutes until she reaches 12 km/h. She then runs at a steady pace for 30 minutes. For the last 10 minutes she runs at a steady pace of 15 km/h.

*__1 mark__ for describing the first section (using acceleration and mentioning the time and speed); **1 mark** for second section (constant speed); **1 mark** for third section (constant speed 15 km/h). Total 3 marks.*

d Distance travelled = area under graph
Split the area into a triangle, a rectangle and a taller rectangle and consider the time in hours.
Distance $= \frac{0.25 \times 12}{2} + 0.5 \times 12 + \frac{1}{6} \times 15 = 10$ km

*__1 mark__ for attempting to find the area of sections under the graph; **1 mark** for adding at least two correct sections; **1 mark** for correct answer. Total 3 marks.*

2. a You need to find the distance reached at the end of the first hour. Since distance = speed × time, distance in first hour = 25 × 1 = 25 km. This means you can label the distance axis like this. You can see that in 1.5 hours, Kai has travelled 30 km.

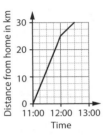

*__1 mark__ for finding the distance of 25 km in the first hour; **1 mark** for correct answer.*

b The sections marked '1' and '2' on the graph show the answer.

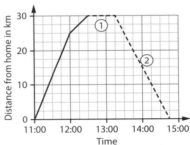

*__1 mark__ for the first horizontal section correct; **1 mark** for the second section correct.*

Page 45, Estimating areas

1. a

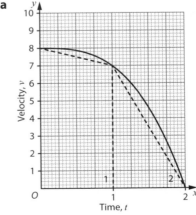

Area of trapezium $1 = \frac{1}{2}(8 + 7) \times 1 = 7.5$

Area of trapezium $2 = \frac{1}{2}(7 + 0) \times 1 = 3.5$

Total area = 7.5 + 3.5 = 11

*__1 mark__ for finding the area of one trapezium; **1 mark** for finding the area of the two correct trapezia; **1 mark** for correct answer. Total 3 marks.*

b

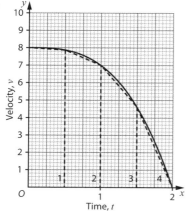

Area of trapezium 1 = $\frac{1}{2}$ (8 + 7.9) × 0.5 = 3.975

Area of trapezium 2 = $\frac{1}{2}$ (7.9 + 7) × 0.5 = 3.725

Area of trapezium 3 = $\frac{1}{2}$ (7 + 4.6) × 0.5 = 2.9

Area of trapezium 4 = $\frac{1}{2}$ (4.6 + 0) × 0.5 = 1.15

Total area = 3.975 + 3.725 + 2.9 + 1.15 = 11.75

1 mark for finding the area of one trapezium; 1 mark for finding the area of the four correct trapezia; 1 mark for correct answer from 11.7 to 11.8. Total 3 marks.

c The trapezia sit under the curve and underestimate the area. The answer to part **b** is bigger because there are more trapezia and therefore smaller gaps between them and the curve.

1 mark for a correct explanation involving the difference in the number of trapezia.

d The area under the curve represents the distance travelled (in metres).

1 mark for a correct answer mentioning distance.

2. a

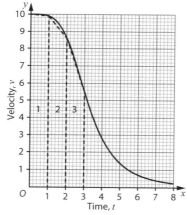

Area of trapezium 1 = $\frac{1}{2}$ (10 + 9.9) × 1 = 9.95

Area of trapezium 2 = $\frac{1}{2}$ (9.9 + 8.6) × 1 = 9.25

Area of trapezium 3 = $\frac{1}{2}$ (8.6 + 5.5) × 1 = 7.05

Total distance = 9.95 + 9.25 + 7.05 = 26.25 m

1 mark for finding the area of one trapezium; 1 mark for finding the area of the three correct trapezia; 1 mark for the correct distance (area). Total 3 marks.

b i

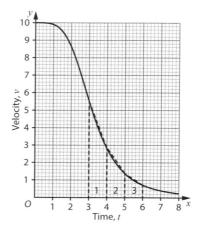

Area of trapezium 1 = $\frac{1}{2}$ (5.5 + 2.8) × 1 = 4.15

Area of trapezium 2 = $\frac{1}{2}$ (2.8 + 1.4) × 1 = 2.1

Area of trapezium 3 = $\frac{1}{2}$ (1.4 + 0.7) × 1 = 1.05

Total distance = 4.15 + 2.1 + 1.05 = 7.3 m

1 mark for finding the area of one trapezium; 1 mark for finding the area of the three correct trapezia; 1 mark for the correct distance (area). Total 3 marks.

ii This is an overestimate because the trapezia lie slightly above the curve.

1 mark for 'overestimate' and reason.

Page 46, Rates of change

1. a 3, 5, 7 and 9 (The height suddenly goes down.)

1 mark for correct answer.

b 9–12 (The gradient is the least steep here.)

1 mark for correct answer.

c It grows 2 cm in 2 weeks, so $\frac{2}{2}$ = 1 cm/week.

1 mark for correct answer.

2. Left to right in table: B, A, C

1 mark for only one correct; 1 mark for all three correct.

Page 47, Gradients of curves

1. a

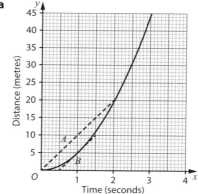

Average speed = gradient of chord = $\frac{20-0}{2-0} = \frac{20}{2} = 10$ m/s

1 mark for the chord drawn or an attempt at the gradient of the chord; 1 mark for correct answer.

b Speed = gradient of tangent $\approx \frac{10-0}{1.5-0.5} \approx \frac{10}{1} = 10$ m/s

1 mark for the tangent drawn; 1 mark for the method to find the gradient of the tangent; 1 mark for an answer between 9.5 and 10.5. Total 3 marks.

2. a

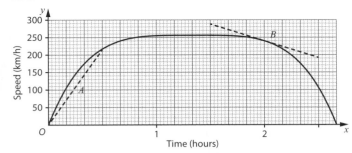

Average acceleration = gradient of chord
$$= \frac{215 - 0}{0.5 - 0} = \frac{215}{0.5} = 430 \text{ km/h}^2$$

1 mark for the chord drawn or an attempt at the gradient of the chord; 1 mark for correct answer.

b The train starts to decelerate (slow down).

1 mark for correct answer.

c Acceleration = gradient of tangent $\approx \frac{190 - 290}{2.5 - 1.5} = \frac{-100}{1}$
$$= -100, \text{ so the deceleration is } 100 \text{ km/h}^2$$

1 mark for the tangent drawn; 1 mark for the method to find the gradient of the tangent; 1 mark for an answer between 95 and 105. Total 3 marks.

Page 48, Types of sequence

1. a First 4 terms: 7, 12, 17, 22
Term-to-term rule: Add 5
Seventh term: 37
Hundredth term: 502
Type of sequence: Arithmetic

b First 4 terms: 10, 20, 40 80
Term-to-term rule: Multiply by 2
Seventh term: 640
Hundredth term: 6.3×10^{30} (to 2 sf)
Type of sequence: Geometric

c First 4 terms: −1, 0, 3, 8
Term-to-term rule: Add 1, 3, 5, … (add $2n - 1$)
Seventh term: 35
Hundredth term: 9800
Type of sequence: Quadratic

d Term-to-term rule: Add previous 2 terms
Seventh term: 13
Type of sequence: Fibonacci

1 mark for each correct answer. Total 18 marks.

2. a $8n + 3 = 51$; $8n = 48$; $n = \frac{48}{8} = 6$
The 6th term is 51

1 mark for writing the equation; 1 mark for correct answer.

b $8n + 3 = 64$; $8n = 61$
61 is not divisible by 8, so 64 is not in the sequence.

1 mark for writing the equation; 1 mark for correct answer.

c $8n + 3 > 100$; $8n > 97$; $n > \frac{97}{8}$ ($= 12.125$)
This is the 13th term. The 13th term is $8 \times 13 + 3 = 107$

1 mark for writing the inequality; 1 mark for the 13th term; 1 mark for correct answer. Total 3 marks.

3. a When $n = 4$, $n^2 - 30 = 4^2 - 30 = 16 - 30 = -14$

1 mark for substituting in 4; 1 mark for correct answer.

b $n^2 - 30 = 114$, so $n^2 = 144$. Since 144 is a square number, and $n = 12$, this is in the sequence.

1 mark for the equation; 1 mark for correct answer.

4. a

With a Fibonacci sequence, you add together the previous two terms. The sequence goes
$m, n, m + n, m + 2n, 2m + 3n, 3m + 5n, 5m + 8n, …$

i The fourth term is $m + 2n$

1 mark for correct answer.

ii The seventh term is $5m + 8n$

1 mark for finding the fifth and sixth terms; 1 mark for correct answer.

b $m = 3$
The gap between the 1st and 3rd is $(m + n) - m = n$, so $n = 5$
The 8th term is $8m + 13n = 8 \times 3 + 13 \times 5 = 89$

1 mark for finding $m = 3$ and $n = 5$; 1 mark for a method for finding the 8th term; 1 mark for correct answer. Total 3 marks.

Page 49, Arithmetic sequences

1.

	Sequence	Term-to-term rule	nth term	Tenth term
a	17, 23, 29, 35	**Add 6**	**$6n + 11$**	**71**
b	−1, 2, 5, 8	**Add 3**	**$3n - 4$**	**26**
c	4, 1, −2, −5	**Subtract 3**	**$-3n + 7$ or $7 - 3n$**	**−23**
d	20, 15, 10, 5	**Subtract 5**	**$-5n + 25$ or $25 - 5n$**	**−25**
e	3, 3.5, 4, 4.5	**Add 0.5**	**$0.5n + 2.5$**	**7.5**

1 mark for each correct answer. Total 15 marks.

2. The sequence goes 5, __, 11, …
Since it is arithmetic, it increases by the same amount each time. In two jumps, it increases by 6, so the term-to-term rule is 'add 3' and the sequence is 5, 8, 11, …
This makes the nth term $3n + 2$

1 mark for identifying the sequence; 1 mark for the nth term.

3. The sequence 12, 9, 6, 3, … has nth term $15 - 3n$
The 50th term is $15 - 3 \times 50 = -135$ and the 60th term is $15 - 3 \times 60 = -165$
The sum of these terms is $(-135) + (-165) = -300$

1 mark for finding the nth term; 1 mark for finding the 50th and 60th terms; 1 mark for correct answer. Total 3 marks.

4. From her first year salary of £24 000 to her fourth year salary of £24 900, there is a gap of three years, so the salary goes up by $\frac{900}{3} = £300$ per year.
The nth term of this sequence is $300n + 23 700$
This reaches £27 000 when $300n + 23 700 = 27 000$
$300n = 3300$; $n = \frac{3300}{300} = 11$
Gloria will reach her maximum salary in her 11th year.

1 mark for finding the difference (annual increase) of £300; 1 mark for finding the nth term and setting it equal to 27 000; 1 mark for the final answer. Total 3 marks. Note that the final two marks can be gained by simply writing out the sequence until you reach 27 000 and giving the final answer.

5. a $\frac{13}{6}$

1 mark for correct answer.

b The numerator and denominator are both following an arithmetic sequence: the numerator starts at 3 then increases by 2 with each term, whilst the numerator increases by 1 (it is always equal to n).

So the nth term is $\frac{2n+1}{n}$

1 mark for identifying the sequence of the numerator; 1 mark for identifying the sequence of the denominator; 1 mark for correct nth term. Total 3 marks.

c 6th term $= \frac{2(6)+1}{6} = \frac{13}{6}$

9th term $= \frac{2(9)+1}{9} = \frac{19}{9}$

Product $= \frac{13}{6} \times \frac{19}{9} = \frac{247}{54}$ (or 4.57 to 3 sf)

1 mark for correct 6th and 9th terms; 1 mark for correct answer.

Page 50, Quadratic sequences

1. a n^2 **b** $n^2 - 1$ **c** $3n^2$

1 mark for each correct answer.

2. a 5, 8, 13, 20, …

The difference between the terms forms an arithmetic sequence: 3, 5, 7, 9, 11, …

The next terms are 29 and 40

1 mark for each correct term.

b −2, 5, 14, 25, …

The difference between the terms forms an arithmetic sequence: 7, 9, 11, 13, 15, …

The next terms are 38 and 53

1 mark for each correct term.

3. $n^2 + 2n + 2 = 50 \Rightarrow n^2 + 2n - 48 = 0 \Rightarrow (n+8)(n-6) = 0$

So the solutions are $n = -8$ or $n = 6$

Since n is a positive number, $n = 6$

So the 6th term is 50

1 mark for writing the nth term equal to 50; 1 mark for rearranging to 0 and attempting to solve the quadratic by factorising (or using the formula or completing the square); 1 mark for correct answer. Total 3 marks.

4. a Sequence: 10, 12, 16, 22

1st difference: 2   4   6

2nd difference: 2   2

2nd difference is 2, so in the quadratic $an^2 + bn + c$, $a = \frac{2}{2} = 1$

n	1	2	3	4
	10	12	16	22
n^2	1	4	9	16
Difference	9	8	7	6

This is a linear sequence with nth term $-n + 10$

So the nth term of the sequence is $n^2 - n + 10$

1 mark for finding a = 1; 1 mark for attempting to find the second two terms of the nth term; 1 mark for correct answer. Total 3 marks.

b Sequence: −9, 2, 17, 36

1st difference: 11, 15, 19

2nd difference: 4   4

2nd difference is 4, so in the quadratic $an^2 + bn + c$, $a = \frac{4}{2} = 2$

n	1	2	3	4
	−9	2	17	36
$2n^2$	2	8	18	32
Difference	−11	−6	−1	4

This is a linear sequence with nth term $5n - 16$

So the nth term of the sequence is $2n^2 + 5n - 16$

1 mark for finding a = 2; 1 mark for attempting to find the second two terms of the nth term; 1 mark for correct answer. Total 3 marks.

5. Since n is a positive integer, n^2 will always be positive and $4n$ will always be positive, so $n^2 + 4n + 6$ will always be positive.

Alternatively, $n^2 + 4n + 6 = (n+2)^2 + 2$

Since something squared is always greater than or equal to 0, $(n+2)^2 + 2$ will always be positive.

1 mark for a correct explanation.

Page 51, Iteration 1

1. a If $x = 2$, $x^4 - 12x = -8$

If $x = 3$, $x^4 - 12x = 45$

The change of sign shows there is a solution between 2 and 3

1 mark for substituting in 2 and 3; 1 mark for a conclusion referring to change of sign.

b $x_0 = 2$

$x_1 = 2.213…, x_2 = 2.270…, x_3 = 2.284…, x_4 = 2.288…,$
$x_5 = 2.289…, x_6 = 2.289…$

The solution is 2.289 to 3 dp.

1 mark for x_1; 1 mark for at least six iterations; 1 mark for correct answer. Total 3 marks.

2. a If $x = 0.6$, $x^3 - 2x + 1 = 0.016$

If $x = 0.7$, $x^3 - 2x + 1 = -0.057$

The change of sign shows there is a solution between 0.6 and 0.7

1 mark for substituting in 0.6 and 0.7; 1 mark for a conclusion referring to change of sign.

b $x_0 = 0.6$

$x_1 = 0.609… = 0.61$ (to 2 dp)

$x_2 = 0.614… = 0.61$ (to 2 dp)

$x_3 = 0.616… = 0.62$ (to 2 dp)

1 mark for x_1; 1 mark for x_2 and x_3

c If you continue iterations (so n gets large), the x values converge to 0.618 (to 3 dp).

1 mark for a correct explanation of convergence to a fixed value.

3. a If $x = 1$, $x^2 - \sqrt{x} - 1 = -1$

If $x = 2$, $x^2 - \sqrt{x} - 1 = 1.585…$

The change of sign shows there is a solution between 1 and 2

1 mark for substituting in 1 and 2; 1 mark for a conclusion referring to change of sign.

b $x_0 = 1$

$x_1 = 2, x_2 = 1.207… = 1.21$ (to 3 sf)

$x_3 = 1.738… = 1.74$ (to 3 sf), $x_4 = 1.333… = 1.33$ (to 3 sf)

1 mark for x_1; 1 mark for x_2, x_3 and x_4

c The x values are oscillating (going up and down) but getting closer to the solution $x = 1.49$ (to 3 sf).

1 mark for a correct explanation.

Page 52, Iteration 2

1. a The roots are where the graph crosses the x-axis, so they can be found by replacing y with 0

1 mark for a correct explanation.

b $x^3 + 5x^2 - 1 = 0$; $x^3 = 1 - 5x^2$; $x = \dfrac{1 - 5x^2}{x^2}$

1 mark for making x^3 the subject; *1 mark* for correct answer.

c $x_0 = -4$

$x_1 = -4.937\ldots$, $x_2 = -4.958\ldots$, $x_3 = -4.959\ldots$

So the solution is -4.96 to 2 dp.

1 mark for x_1; *1 mark* for at least two further iterations; *1 mark* for correct answer. Total 3 marks.

d $x^3 + 5x^2 - 1 = 0$; $x^2 = \dfrac{1 - x^3}{5}$; $x = \sqrt{\dfrac{1 - x^3}{5}}$

1 mark for making x^2 the subject; *1 mark* for the correct solution.

e $x_0 = 0$

$x_1 = 0.447\ldots$, $x_2 = 0.426\ldots$, $x_3 = 0.429\ldots$, $x_4 = 0.429\ldots$

So the solution is 0.43 to 2 dp.

1 mark for x_1; *1 mark* for at least three further iterations; *1 mark* for correct answer. Total 3 marks.

f $x_0 = -1$

$x_1 = -0.4$, $x_2 = -0.532$, $x_3 = -0.432\ldots$, $x_4 = -0.499\ldots$, $x_5 = -0.450\ldots$, $x_6 = -0.484\ldots$, $x_7 = -0.459\ldots$

So the solution is -0.5 to 1 dp.

1 mark for x_1; *1 mark* for at least five further iterations; *1 mark* for correct answer. Total 3 marks.

Page 53, Functions

1. a i $f(1) = 1^2 - 2 \times 1 = -1$

ii $f(-5) = (-5)^2 - 2(-5) = 25 + 10 = 35$

iii $f(0) = 0^2 - 2 \times 0 = 0 - 0 = 0$

For each part, *1 mark* for substituting into the function; *1 mark* for correct answer.

b i $x^2 - 2x = 15$; $x^2 - 2x - 15 = 0$; $(x - 5)(x + 3) = 0$

$x = 5$, $x = -3$

1 mark for writing the function equal to 15; *1 mark* for a method of solving the quadratic; *1 mark* for the two correct answers. Total 3 marks.

ii $x^2 - 2x = 4x$; $x^2 - 6x = 0$; $x(x - 6) = 0$

$x = 0$, $x = 6$

1 mark for writing the function equal to 4x; *1 mark* for a method of solving the quadratic; *1 mark* for the two correct answers. Total 3 marks.

2. a i $f(1) = 3 \times 1 - 1 = 3 - 1 = 2$

So $gf(1) = g(2) = \dfrac{1}{2}$

ii $g\left(\dfrac{1}{2}\right) = \dfrac{1}{\frac{1}{2}} = 2$

So $fg\left(\dfrac{1}{2}\right) = f(2) = 3 \times 2 - 1 = 5$

For each part, *1 mark* for the first substitution; *1 mark* for the second substitution; *1 mark* for correct answer. Total 3 marks.

b $gf(x) = \dfrac{1}{3x - 1}$

1 mark for correct answer.

c $\dfrac{1}{3x - 1} = 2$; $1 = 2(3x - 1)$; $1 = 6x - 2$; $6x = 3$

$x = \dfrac{3}{6} = \dfrac{1}{2}$

1 mark for writing answer to part **b** equal to 2; *1 mark* for attempting to solve the equation; *1 mark* for correct answer. Total 3 marks.

Page 54, Inverse functions

1. a $y = \dfrac{x - 1}{2}$; $2y = x - 1$; $x = 2y + 1$

So $f^{-1}(x) = 2x + 1$

1 mark for starting to rearrange; *1 mark* for making x the subject; *1 mark* for correct answer. Total 3 marks.

b $y = x^2 - 4$; $y + 4 = x^2$; $\sqrt{y + 4} = x$

So $g^{-1}(x) = \sqrt{x + 4}$

1 mark for starting to rearrange; *1 mark* for making x the subject; *1 mark* for correct answer. Total 3 marks.

c $y = \dfrac{x}{2x + 3}$; $y(2x + 3) = x$; $2xy + 3y = x$;

$3y = x - 2xy$; $3y = x(1 - 2y)$; $\dfrac{3y}{1 - 2y} = x$

So $h^{-1}(x) = \dfrac{3x}{1 - 2x}$

1 mark for starting to rearrange; *1 mark* for collecting x terms together; *1 mark* for factorising; *1 mark* for correct answer. Total 4 marks.

d $y = \sqrt{x^3 + 5}$; $y^2 = x^3 + 5$; $y^2 - 5 = x^3$; $\sqrt[3]{y^2 - 5} = x$

So $k^{-1}(x) = \sqrt[3]{x^2 - 5}$

1 mark for starting to rearrange; *1 mark* for making x the subject; *1 mark* for correct answer. Total 3 marks.

2. a $y = x - 5$; $x = y + 5$; $f^{-1}(x) = x + 5$

$gf^{-1}(x) = 2^{x + 5}$

1 mark for $f^{-1}(x)$; *1 mark* for correct answer.

b $2^{x + 5} = 8$; $2^{x + 5} = 2^3$; $x + 5 = 3$; $x = -2$

1 mark for $8 = 2^3$; *1 mark* for correct answer.

c $k^{-1}(x) = \sqrt{x}$

If $k^{-1}(a) = f(a)$, $\sqrt{a} = a - 5$

$a = (a - 5)^2$; $a = a^2 - 10a + 25$; $a^2 - 11a + 25 = 0$

Using the quadratic formula,

$a = \dfrac{11 \pm \sqrt{(-11)^2 - 4 \times 1 \times 25}}{2 \times 1} = 7.79$ or 3.21 (to 2 dp)

1 mark for the correct starting equation; *1 mark* for beginning to solve by squaring both sides; *1 mark* for a method to solve the quadratic equation; *1 mark* for correct answer. Total 4 marks.

Page 55, Algebraic proof

1. Courtney is wrong because 2 is a prime number and the product of 2 and any other prime will be even.

1 mark for a correct explanation involving 2

2. $(m + n)^2 + (m - n)^2 = (m^2 + 2mn + n^2) + (m^2 - 2mn + n^2)$

$= 2m^2 + 2n^2 = 2(m^2 + n^2)$

1 mark for correctly expanding each bracket; *1 mark* for correctly simplifying (before the final factorisation); *1 mark* for the correct, factorised solution. Total 3 marks.

3. a Five consecutive integers are

$n, n + 1, n + 2, n + 3$ and $n + 4$

The sum of these is

$n + n + 1 + n + 2 + n + 3 + n + 4 = 5n + 10 = 5(n + 2)$, which is divisible by 5

1 mark for a correct (unsimplified) sum; *1 mark* for $5n + 10$; *1 mark* for factorising or showing that the simplified sum is divisible by 5, with a conclusion. Total 3 marks.

b The sum of six consecutive integers is

$n + n + 1 + n + 2 + n + 3 + n + 4 + n + 5$

$= 6n + 15 = 6(n + 2.5)$,

which is never divisible by 6

1 mark for a correct (unsimplified) sum; *1 mark* for $6n + 15$; *1 mark* for showing or explaining that the simplified sum is not divisible by 6. Total 3 marks.

c Any two even numbers are $2m$ and $2n$ (you must use two different letters here).

The sum of their squares is

$(2m)^2 + (2n)^2 = 4m^2 + 4n^2 = 4(m^2 + n^2)$,

which is divisible by 4

1 mark for a correct (unsimplified) sum; 1 mark for $4m^2 + 4n^2$; 1 mark for showing that the simplified sum is divisible by 4, with a conclusion. Total 3 marks.

d Two consecutive odd numbers could be $2n - 1$ and $2n + 1$

The sums of their squares is $(2n - 1)^2 + (2n + 1)^2$

$= (4n^2 - 4n + 1) + (4n^2 + 4n + 1) = 8n^2 + 2 = 2(4n^2 + 1)$,

which is even as it is divisible by 2

1 mark for a correct (unsimplified) sum; 1 mark for $8n^2 + 2$; 1 mark for showing that the simplified sum is divisible by 2, with a conclusion. Total 3 marks.

e Two consecutive odd numbers could be $2n - 1$ and $2n + 1$

The difference between their squares is (remembering to put the largest first)

$(2n + 1)^2 - (2n - 1)^2 = (4n^2 + 4n + 1) - (4n^2 - 4n + 1) = 8n$,

which is divisible by 8

1 mark for a correct (unsimplified) difference; 1 mark for $8n$; 1 mark for showing that the simplified difference is divisible by 8, with a conclusion. Total 3 marks.

4. The original sequence has nth term $3n - 6$

The new sequence therefore has nth term

$(3n - 6)^2 = 9n^2 - 36n + 36 = 9(n^2 - 4n + 4)$,

which is divisible by 9

1 mark for $3n - 6$; 1 mark for $(3n - 6)^2$ and an attempt to expand the brackets; 1 mark for a correct, simplified expansion; 1 mark for showing this expansion is divisible by 9. Total 4 marks.

Page 56, Ratio

1. a $x = 3$

1 mark for correct answer.

b $1 + 3 + 1 + 3 = 8$ parts

The angles in a parallelogram add up to $360°$.

$360° \div 8 = 45°$

$3 \times 45° = 135°$

Two of the angles are $45°$ and two of the angles are $135°$.

1 mark for $360 \div 8$ $(= 45)$; 1 mark for fully correct answer.

2. $5 : 12 : 13 = 1 : 2.4 : 2.6 = 2 : 4.8 : 5.2$

Perimeter $= 2 + 4.8 + 5.2 = 12$ cm

1 mark for method to find at least one of the missing sides e.g. $12 \div 5 \times 2$ $(= 4.8)$ or $13 \div 5 \times 2$ $(= 5.2)$; 1 mark for adding all three sides; 1 mark for correct answer of 12 cm. Total 3 marks.

Note that there are alternative methods.

3. $7 - 2 = 5$; 5 parts $= 90$; 1 part $= 18$

$7 \times 18 = 126$ pencils

1 mark for dividing 90 by 5 $(= 18)$; 1 mark for correct answer.

4. $AB : BC : CD = 12 : 10 : 13$

$12 + 10 + 13 = 35$

Each part $= 105$ cm $\div 35 = 3$ cm

$BC = 10 \times 3 = 30$ cm

1 mark for $12 : 10$ or $12 : 10 : 13$; 1 mark for dividing 105 by your three-ratio sum; 1 mark for correct answer. Total 3 marks.

5. Hayley $= x$, Kayleigh $= x - 2$, Bailey $= 2(x - 2) = 2x - 4$

$x + x - 2 + 2x - 4 = 38$; $4x - 6 = 38$; $4x = 44$; $x = 11$

Hayley $= 11$, Kayleigh $= 9$, Bailey $= 18$

Ratio B : H : K $= 18 : 11 : 9$

1 mark for any two correct algebraic expressions; 1 mark for equating the sum of your three algebraic expressions to 38; 1 mark for method to solve (as far as $x = \ldots$); 1 mark for correct ratio in correct order. Total 4 marks.

Page 57, Harder ratio problems

1. Carl : Friedrich $= 120 : 100 = 6 : 5$

$6 + 5 = 11$ parts; $44 \div 11 = 4$

Carl has $6 \times 4 = 24$ cards. Friedrich has $5 \times 4 = 20$ cards.

1 mark for $120 : 100$ $(= 6 : 5)$; 1 mark for $44 \div 11 \times 6$ $(= 24)$ or $44 \div 11 \times 4$ $(= 20)$; 1 mark for fully correct. Total 3 marks.

2. New ratio $= (2 \times 1.5) : (1 \times 1.25) = 3 : 1.25 = 12 : 5$

1 mark for either 1.5 or 1.25 used as a multiplier; 1 mark for $3 : 1.25$ or equivalent ratio; 1 mark for correct final answer. Total 3 marks.

3. $2x = 3y$ (1), $x + 8 = 4(y \div 2)$ (2)

Rearranging (2) and substituting into (1),

$2(2y - 8) = 3y$; $4y - 16 = 3y$; $y = 16$; $x = 24$

1 mark for forming a correct equation in any form e.g. $\frac{x}{y} = \frac{3}{2}$; 1 mark for both equations correct; 1 mark for an attempt to solve by substitution or elimination to achieve an answer for x or y; 1 mark for either x or y correct; 1 mark for fully correct. Total 5 marks.

4. $\frac{4}{7}$ of the coins are copper; $\frac{3}{7}$ of the coins are silver.

$\frac{3}{10}$ of the copper coins are small.

Fraction of all coins that are small copper:

$\frac{3}{10} \times \frac{4}{7} = \frac{12}{70} \left(= \frac{6}{35}\right)$

$\frac{1}{3}$ of the silver coins are small.

Fraction of all coins that are small silver:

$\frac{1}{3} \times \frac{3}{7} = \frac{3}{21} \left(= \frac{1}{7}\right)$

Total fraction of all coins that are small:

$\frac{6}{35} + \frac{1}{7} = \frac{11}{35}$

$\frac{11}{35}$ of the coins are small.

1 mark for $\frac{4}{7}$ or $\frac{3}{7}$; 1 mark for $\frac{3}{10}$ or $\frac{1}{3}$; 1 mark for $\frac{3}{10} \times \frac{4}{7} \left(= \frac{12}{70} = \frac{6}{35}\right)$ or $\frac{1}{3} \times \frac{3}{7} \left(= \frac{3}{21} = \frac{1}{7}\right)$; 1 mark for adding answers; 1 mark for correct final answer. Total 5 marks. Alternatively, you could use bar modelling.

5. $(2x - 5)(6 - x) = 6$; $2x^2 - 17x + 36 = 0$; $(2x - 9)(x - 4) = 0$

$x = 44.5$, $x = 4$

1 mark for forming a correct equation in any form e.g. $\frac{2x - 5}{6} = \frac{1}{6 - x}$; 1 mark for rearranging into a quadratic and equating to zero; 1 mark for factorising (or equivalent e.g. use of quadratic formula); 1 mark for both answers correct. Total 4 marks.

Page 58, Percentage change

1. 3% of £50 000 $= $ £50 000 $\div 100 \times 3 = $ £1500

New value $= $ £50 000 $+ $ £1500 $= $ £51 500

1 mark for $50\,000 + (50\,000 \div 100 \times 3)$ or equivalent e.g. $50\,000 \times 1.03$; 1 mark for correct answer of £51 500

2. Actual decrease $= 4 - 2.5 = 1.5$

% decrease $= \frac{1.5 \times 100\%}{4} = \frac{150\%}{4} = \frac{75\%}{2} = 37.5\%$

1 mark for $\frac{(4 - 2.5)}{4} \times 100\%$; 1 mark for correct answer.

3. The lengths of the sides of the squares are 4 cm and 5 cm.
   Actual increase = 5 − 4 = 1
   % increase = $\frac{1 \times 100\%}{4}$ = 25%
   1 mark *for 4 cm and 5 cm;* **1 mark** *for* $\frac{(5-4)}{4} \times 100$*;* **1 mark** *for correct answer of 25%. Total 3 marks.*

4. Total Maths score = 280
   15% of 280 (= 10% + 5%) = 28 + 14 = 42
   Total English score = 280 − 42 = 238
   Missing English score = 238 − (58 + 58 + 57)
   = 238 − 173 = 65
   1 mark *for 280;* **1 mark** *for correct method to find 15% of 280 and subtract;* **1 mark** *for subtracting 173;* **1 mark** *for correct answer of 65. Total 4 marks.*

5. Actual increase in length = 22 − 6 = 16
   % increase in length = $\frac{16 \times 100\%}{6}$ = 266.$\dot{6}$%
   Length increases by 267% to 3 sf.
   1 mark *for* $\frac{(22-6)}{6} \times 100\%$ *(= 266.6…);* **1 mark** *for correct answer to 3 sf.*

6. 3 hours 15 minutes = 195 minutes
   3 hours = 180 minutes
   Actual decrease = 195 − 180 = 15 minutes
   % decrease = $\frac{15 \times 100\%}{195}$ = 7.692…%
   The playing time decreases by 7.69%.
   1 mark *for 195 minutes;* **1 mark** *for* $\frac{(195-180) \times 100\%}{195}$*;* **1 mark** *for correct final answer (7.7% is acceptable). Total 3 marks.*

Page 59, Using multipliers

1. 40%
   1 mark *for correct answer.*

2. 44.5 grams ÷ 0.89 = 50 grams
   1 mark *for 0.89;* **1 mark** *for dividing by 0.89;* **1 mark** *for correct answer of 50 grams. Total 3 marks.*

3. Multiplier for 7% decrease is 0.93
   Next ball speed = 90 × 0.93 = 83.7 mph
   1 mark *for 0.93;* **1 mark** *for correct answer of 83.7 mph. Note other methods score no marks, as the question states that a multiplier must be used.*

4. 120% = 1.2 and 80% = 0.8
   Let the original number be x
   20% increase = $x \times 1.2 = 1.2x$
   20% decrease = $1.2x \times 0.8 = 0.96x$ $(< x)$
   Original number is x, so the answer is less than the original number. Ben is not right.
   1 mark *for either 1.2 or 0.8;* **1 mark** *for attempt to multiply any number (algebra not necessary) by 1.2 and 0.8;* **1 mark** *for complete and correct argument. Total 3 marks.*

5. Let the original number be x
   50% increase = $x \times 1.5 = 1.5x$
   25% decrease = $1.5x \times 0.75 = 1.125x$
   1.125 = 112.5%
   Original number is increased by 12.5%.
   1 mark *for either 1.5 or 0.75 used as a multiplier;* **1 mark** *for 1.125;* **1 mark** *for 12.5% as final answer. Total 3 marks.*

6. Multiplier for numerator is 1.48
   Multiplier for denominator is 1 − 0.875 = 0.125
   37 ÷ 1.48 = 25
   42 ÷ 0.125 = 336
   Original fraction is $\frac{25}{336}$

1 mark for either 1.48 or 0.125 used as a multiplier; **1 mark** *for either 25 or 336;* **1 mark** *for correct answer. Total 3 marks.*

Page 60, Growth and depreciation

1. **a** Simple interest:
   £2450 + 0.06 × £2450 × 7 = £2450 + £1029 = £3479
   Compound interest:
   £2450 × 1.06^7 = £3683.89…
   £3683.89 − £3479 = £204.89
   Jemma will have £204.89 more than Paul.
   1 mark *for 2450 + 0.06 × 2450 × 7 (= 3479);* **1 mark** *for 2450 × 1.06^7 (= 3683.89…);* **1 mark** *for subtracting answers;* **1 mark** *for correct final answer. Total 4 marks. If you use interest only, award full marks for £1233.89 − £1029 = £204.89*

   b Phoebe needs m such that $m \times 1.06^{10} \geq 5000$
   $m \geq \frac{5000}{1.06^{10}} = 2791.97…$
   Smallest m = £2792
   1 mark *for correct inequality (condone an equation for this mark);* **1 mark** *for* $\frac{5000}{1.06^{10}}$*;* **1 mark** *for 2792. Total 3 marks.*

2. 100% − 3.5% = 96.5%
   The multiplier is 0.965
   You want n such that $3\,000\,000 \times 0.965^n < 1\,500\,000$
   $0.965^n < 0.5$
   Substituting integer values for n,
   $0.965^{19} = 0.508…$
   $0.965^{20} = 0.490… < 0.5$
   Therefore, n = 20
   The population will be less than 1 500 000 at the start of the year 2040
   1 mark *for a multiplier of 0.965;* **1 mark** *for correct inequality (condone an equation for this mark);* **1 mark** *for correct answer of 2040. (Allow during the year 2039.) Total 3 marks.*

3. £4000 × (multiplier)^5 = £4300
   (multiplier)^5 = £4300 ÷ £4000 = 1.075
   multiplier = $\sqrt[5]{1.075}$ = 1.01456…
   (100 + x)% = 101.456…%
   x = 1.456…% = 1.5% to 1 dp
   1 mark *for correct equation e.g. £4000 × (multiplier)^5 = £4300;* **1 mark** *for* $\sqrt[5]{1.075}$ *(= 1.01456);* **1 mark** *for correct final answer to 1 dp. Total 3 marks.*

4. **a** 0.97 × 1.07^2 = 1.1105…
   Percentage change = 11.1% increase (to 3 sf)
   1 mark *for using 0.97 or 1.07;* **1 mark** *for 0.97 × 1.07^2;* **1 mark** *for correct answer as a percentage to 3 sf. Total 3 marks.*

   b 285 000 ÷ 1.1105… = £256 628.90
   1 mark *for dividing by 1.1105…,* **1 mark** *for correct answer.*

Page 61, Compound measures

1. Time = 2400 ÷ 20 = 120 seconds
   1 mark *for 2400 ÷ 20;* **1 mark** *for correct answer including units (or equivalent e.g. 2 minutes).*

2. Mass = density × volume = 8.94 × 0.6 = 5.364 g
   1 mark *for attempt to use correct formula;* **1 mark** *for correct answer including units.*

3. Pressure = force ÷ area = 36 ÷ 0.45 = 80 N/m² (or 80 Pa)
1 mark for attempt to use correct formula; 1 mark for correct answer including units.

4. 38 700 000 g = 38 700 kg
Density = mass ÷ volume = 38 700 ÷ 5 = 7740 kg/m³
1 mark dividing by 1000 to change g to kg; 1 mark for attempt to use correct formula; 1 mark for correct answer. Total 3 marks.

5. a 0.047 km/h = 47 m/h = 0.783… m/min
Time = distance ÷ speed = 5.64 ÷ 0.783…
= 7.2 minutes = 7 minutes and 12 seconds
1 mark for at least one of multiplying by 1000 (to change km/h to m/h) or dividing by 60 (to change m/h to m/min); 1 mark for attempt to use correct formula to find the time; 1 mark for 7.2; 1 mark for correct answer of 7 minutes and 12 seconds. Total 4 marks.
Note that there are alternative methods.

b 0.78 m/min = 46.8 m/h = 0.0468 km/h
0.047 > 0.0468, so garden snail is faster.
1 mark for at least one of multiplying by 60 (to change m/min to m/h) or dividing by 1000 (to change m/h to km/h); 1 mark for 0.0468; 1 mark for comparing correct values with correct conclusion (i.e. snail faster). Total 3 marks.

6. Time = distance ÷ speed = 6.5 ÷ 65 = 0.1 hours
0.1 hours = 6 minutes
Therefore, Florence is incorrect.
1 mark for attempt to use correct formula; 1 mark for attempt to change units; 1 mark for correct conclusion. Total 3 marks.

Page 62, Direct & inverse proportion 1

1. a

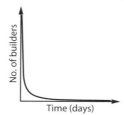

1 mark for axes drawn and labelled correctly; 1 mark for fully correct conversion graph.
b Between 135 kg and 137 kg
2 marks for correct answer (1 mark for correct lines drawn on graph).

2. 'Dogs Love Bach' sell 9 kg for £12.99
12.99 ÷ 9 = £1.44… per 1 kg
'Woof & Ready' sell 8 kg for £11.00
11.00 ÷ 8 = £1.375 per 1 kg
'Woof & Ready' offers better value.
1 mark for at least one of dividing costs by 9 or 8; 1 mark for £1.44… or £1.375; 1 mark for comparison of correct answers with correct conclusion (i.e. 'Woof & Ready' cheaper). Total 3 marks.
Note that there are alternative methods.

3. France: 58 800 ÷ 12 = 4900 euros per acre
Argentina: 4 520 000 ÷ 64.19 = 70 415.952 64 euros
70 415.952 64 ÷ 15 = 4694.39… euros per acre
Lower cost per acre in Argentina.
1 mark for 58 800 ÷ 12 (= 4900); 1 mark for 4 520 000 ÷ 64.19 (= 70 415.9…); 1 mark for 4900 and 4694(.3…) with correct conclusion (i.e. Argentina cheaper). Total 3 marks.
Note that there are alternative methods.

4. a 12 × 6 = 72 'builder days'
72 ÷ 18 = 4 days
1 mark for 12 × 6 ÷ 18 or equivalent e.g. 6 ÷ (18 ÷ 12); 1 mark for correct answer of 4 days.
b 72 ÷ 3 = 24 builders
1 mark for 12 × 6 ÷ 3 or equivalent e.g. 12 × (6 ÷ 3); 1 mark for correct answer of 24 builders.
c

1 mark for correct shape; 1 mark if graph approaches (but does not touch) both sets of axes.

Page 63, Direct & inverse proportion 2

1. (4 × 5) ÷ 8 = 2.5
1 mark for (4 × 5) ÷ 8 or equivalent e.g. 5 ÷ 2; 1 mark for correct answer.

2. a $p = kq \Rightarrow 50 = 4k \Rightarrow k = 12.5$
$p = 12.5q$
1 mark for writing p = kq and proceeding to find k = 12.5; 1 mark for correct final equation or equivalent e.g. $p = \frac{25q}{2}$
b $40 = 12.5q$
$q = 40 ÷ 12.5 = 3.2$
1 mark for substituting p = 40 into your equation from part a; 1 mark for correct answer of q = 3.2 or equivalent e.g. $q = \frac{16}{5}$

3. $y = kx^3 \Rightarrow 54 = kt^3$
When $x = 2t$, $y = k(2t)^3$
So, $y = 8kt^3 = 8 × 54 = 432$
1 mark for y = kx³; 1 mark for 54 = kt³; 1 mark for correct answer (fully justified). Total 3 marks.

4. *f* must be inversely proportional to the square of *h*, so:
$f = \frac{k}{h^2} \Rightarrow 6 = \frac{k}{0.5^2} \Rightarrow k = \frac{3}{2} \Rightarrow f = \frac{3}{2h^2}$
1 mark for describing the proportionality of f and h; 1 mark for $f = \frac{k}{h^2}$ or equivalent; 1 mark for correct value of your k; 1 mark for correct final answer of $f = \frac{3}{2h^2}$ or equivalent. Total 4 marks.

Alternative solution:
$f = \frac{k}{g} \Rightarrow 6 = \frac{k}{3} \Rightarrow k = 18 \Rightarrow f = \frac{18}{g}$
$g = ch^2 \Rightarrow 3 = 0.25c \Rightarrow c = 12 \Rightarrow g = 12h^2$
$f = \frac{18}{12h^2} = \frac{3}{2h^2}$
1 mark for $f = \frac{k}{g}$ or $g = ch^2$; 1 mark for correct substitution to find your k or your c; 1 mark for either value correct for your k or your c; 1 mark for correct final answer of $f = \frac{3}{2h^2}$ or equivalent e.g. $f = \frac{18}{12h^2}$. Total 4 marks.

5. $V = k\sqrt{E}$

Multiplier for 20% increase is 1.2, so multiply through by 1.2

$1.2V = 1.2k\sqrt{E}$

$\Rightarrow 1.2V = k\sqrt{1.44E}$

The multiplier for E is therefore 1.44

E has increased by 44%.

1 mark for attempt to use a multiplier of 1.2; 1 mark for 1.44; 1 mark for correct final answer. Total 3 marks.

Page 64, Measures

1. a $70 \div 1.6 = 43.75\,\text{mph}$

The approximate maximum speed is 44 mph to the nearest integer.

1 mark for 70 ÷ 1.6 (= 43.75); 1 mark for correct answer of 44

b 70 km ($= 70 \times 1000$) $= 70\,000\,\text{m}$

1 hour ($= 60 \times 60$) $= 3600\,\text{s}$

$70\,000 \div 3600 \left(= \frac{175}{9}\right) = 19.4\,\text{m/s}$ to 1 dp

1 mark for 70 × 1000 (= 70 000) or 60 × 60 (= 3600); 1 mark for dividing your 70 000 by your 3600 or for $\frac{175}{9}$ or 19.4…; 1 mark for correct answer to 1 dp. Total 3 marks.

2. Convert all units to kg:

UK = 75.8 kg

USA = $180.62 \div 2.2 = 82.1\,\text{kg}$

Australia = $12.25 \times 6.35 = 77.7875\,\text{kg}$

The United States has the highest average mass.

1 mark for 180.62 ÷ 2.2 (= 82.1 kg), 1 mark for 12.25 × 6.35 (= 77.7875 kg); 1 mark for three correct masses with United States as the answer. Total 3 marks.

Alternatively, you could convert all to lb (166.76 for UK; 171.1325 for Australia) or to st (11.93… for UK; 12.92… for USA) and compare.

3. a $5 \times 10^2 = 500\,\text{mm}^2$

1 mark for 5 × 10² or 5 × 100; 1 mark for correct answer.

b $2500 \div 10^3 = 2.5\,\text{cm}^3$

1 mark for 2500 ÷ 10³ or 2500 ÷ 1000; 1 mark for correct answer.

c $0.03 \times 1000^3 = 30\,000\,000\,\text{m}^3$

1 mark for 0.03 × 1000³ or 0.03 × 1 000 000 000; 1 mark for correct answer.

4. Volume of water $= \frac{1}{2} \times 110\,\text{cm} \times 2200\,\text{mm} \times \frac{9}{20}\,\text{m}$

$= \frac{1}{2} \times 110\,\text{cm} \times 220\,\text{cm} \times 45\,\text{cm}$

$= 544\,500\,\text{cm}^3$

$544\,500 \div 1000 = 544.5$ litres

1 mark for converting all lengths to the same unit; 1 mark for volume calculation; 1 mark for converting to litres; 1 mark for correct answer. Total 4 marks.

Page 65, Angle rules

1. Angle $GAB = 100°$ (Diagonally opposite angles in a parallelogram are equal.)

Angle $FAB = 75°$ (Corresponding angles are equal, $AB // GC$.)

$x = 100° - 75° = 25°$

2 marks for x = 25 or 1 mark for either GAB = 100 or FAB = 75 (can be shown on the diagram); 1 mark for full justification of all angles. Total 3 marks.

Note that there are many possible methods for this question. You could use alternate angles are equal, vertically opposite angles are equal, angles in a triangle sum to 180°, etc. Typically, 2 marks will be awarded for correct angles and 1 for correct reasons.

2.

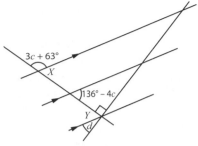

Angle $X = 136° - 4c$

(Corresponding angles are equal.)

$3c + 63° + 136° - 4c = 180°$

(Angles on a straight line sum to 180°.)

$199° - c = 180° \Rightarrow c = 19°$

$Y = 136° - 4 \times 19° = 60°$

(Alternate angles are equal.)

$d = 180° - 90° - 60° = 30°$

(Angles on a straight line sum to 180°.)

1 mark for 3c + 63 + 136 − 4c = 180; 1 mark for solving equation; 1 mark for d = 30; 1 mark for geometrical reasons given. Total 4 marks.

Note that there are alternative methods.

3. $151° - 3x + x + y + 51° = 180°$

(Angles on a straight line sum to 180°.)

$x + 53° + 2y + 36° = 180°$

(Angles on a straight line sum to 180°.)

Simplifying both equations,

$22 = 2x - y$ (1), $91 = x + 2y$ (2)

$2 \times$ (1) + (2): $135 = 5x$; $x = 27°$

Substituting into (2), $91 = 27 + 2y$; $2y = 64$; $y = 32°$

Substituting these values into each slice size, the angles are 70°, 110°, 100° and 80°. The largest slice size is 110°.

1 mark for 151 − 3x + x + y + 51 = 180 or x + 53 + 2y + 36 = 180 with reason (angles on a straight line sum to 180°); 1 mark for attempt to solve; 1 mark for correct answer for both x and y; 1 mark for 110° as final answer. Total 4 marks.

Page 66, Triangles & quadrilaterals

1. Angles on a straight line add up to 180°.

Angle $ABC = 180° - 95° = 85°$

Opposite angles of a rhombus are equal.

Therefore, $x = 85°$

1 mark for each correct reason stated; 1 mark for correct answer of 85°. Total 3 marks.

Alternative solutions may include angle rules for parallel lines (e.g. corresponding angles, alternate angles).

2. Angle $EAD = 44°$ (alternate angles)

Angle $FDE = 180° - 90° - 44° = 46°$

(Angles in triangle add up to 180°.)

1 mark for angle EAD = 44; 1 mark for 180 − 90 − angle EAD; 1 mark for correct final answer. Total 3 marks.

3. Angle STU = angle PQR = 60° (equilateral triangles)

$t = \frac{360° - (60° + 60°)}{2} = 120°$

(Opposite angles of a parallelogram are equal and angles in a quadrilateral sum to 360°.)

***2 marks** for t = 120 or **1 mark** for either STU or PQR = 60; **1 mark** for any correct geometrical reason; **1 mark** for fully correct geometrical reasons. Total 4 marks.*

Note that there are many methods for this question. You could use alternate angles, corresponding angles, vertically opposite angles, etc. Typically, 2 marks will be awarded for correct angle calculations and 2 will be awarded for geometrical reasons.

4. $x + y = 2x - y + 99°$ (from kite symmetry)

$x + y + 2x - y + 99° + y + 25 + x - 25 = 360°$

(Angles in a quadrilateral add up to 360°.)

Simplifying both equations,

$-x + 2y = 99$ (1), $4x + y = 261$ (2)

$4 \times (1) + (2)$: $9y = 657$; $y = 73°$

Substituting into (2), $4x + 73 = 261$; $4x = 188$; $x = 47°$

***1 mark** for x + y = 2x − y + 99 or x + y + 2x − y + 99 + y + 25 + x − 25 = 360; **1 mark** for attempt to eliminate either x or y and solve; **1 mark** for correct answer for x or y; **1 mark** for correct answer for both x and y. Total 4 marks.*

Page 67, Polygons

1. $360° \div 60° = 6$

The shape is a (regular) hexagon.

***1 mark** for 360 ÷ 60 (= 6) or for stating that exterior angles add to 360°; **1 mark** for hexagon.*

2. $(6 - 2) \times 180° = 720°$

$41° + 59° + 83° + 90° + 147° = 420°$

$720° - 420° = 300°$

***1 mark** for (6 − 2) × 180 (= 720); **1 mark** for adding all angles and subtracting the total from your 720; **1 mark** for correct answer of 300°. Total 3 marks.*

3. $(n - 2) \times 180° = 1620°$

$n = 1620 \div 180 + 2 = 11$

The polygon has 11 sides.

***1 mark** for (n − 2) × 180 = 1620; **1 mark** for 11.*

4. $(8 - 2) \times 180° = 1080°$

$1080° \div 8 = 135°$ (= angle in octagon)

$x = 360° - 60°$ (equilateral triangle) $- 90°$ (square) $- 135°$ (octagon) $= 75°$

(Angles around a point add up to 360°.)

***1 mark** for method to find interior angle of octagon; **1 mark** for 135; **1 mark** for subtracting your 3 angles from 360; **1 mark** for correct final answer of 75°. If no marks scored, score **1 mark** for 60 (equilateral triangle) or 90 (square). Total 4 marks.*

5. Exterior angle $= 180° - 80° = 100°$

$360° \div 100° = 3.6$

A polygon cannot have 3.6 sides, so Sophia is correct.

***1 mark** for 180 − 80 (= 100); **1 mark** for 360 ÷ 100 (= 3.6); **1 mark** for concluding that Sophia is correct with full explanation. Total 3 marks.*

Alternative solution:

An equilateral triangle (regular 3-sided polygon) has interior angles of size 60°.

A square (regular 4-sided polygon) has interior angles of size 90°.

As 60° < 80° < 90°, there can be no regular polygon with an interior angle of 80°.

***1 mark** for attempt at comparison with regular 3 and 4-sided polygons; **1 mark** for 60 and 90; **1 mark** for concluding that Sophia is correct with full explanation. Total 3 marks.*

Page 68, Circle theorems 1

1. a $x = 90°$; the angle in a semicircle is a right angle.

  b $x = 72°$; angles in the same segment are equal.

  c $x = 80°$; opposite angles in a cyclic quadrilateral sum to 180°.

  ***1 mark** for each correct answer; **1 mark** for each correct circle theorem stated. Total 6 marks.*

2. Angle $ADG = 90°$ (The angle in a semicircle is a right angle.)

Angle $CED = 49°$ (Angles in a triangle sum to 180°.)

Angle $ACB = 41°$ and angle $FEG = 49°$ (Vertically opposite angles are equal.)

Angle $EFG = 112°$ (Angles in a triangle sum to 180°.)

Angle $GAB = 180 - 112 = 68°$ (Opposite angles in a cyclic quadrilateral sum to 180°.)

$z = 68 - 21 = 47°$

***1 mark** for ADG = 90°; **1 mark** for ACB = 41° or CED = 49°; **1 mark** for a correct circle theorem used and stated; **1 mark** for z = 47°; **1 mark** for full geometrical reasons given. Total 5 marks.*

Note z = 47° without reasons given scores 3 marks maximum. Note that there are alternative methods.

3. a $y = 78°$; angle at centre is twice the angle at the circumference.

  ***1 mark** for y = 78°; **1 mark** for correct circle theorem.*

  b

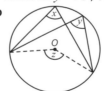

You need to prove that $x = y$

First, draw the radii (see dotted lines).

Now, you know that the angle at the centre is twice the angle at the circumference.

Applying the theorem to x and to y, you have $z = 2x$ and $z = 2y$ so $2x = 2y$ and $x = y$, as required.

***1 mark** for a diagram showing the correct theorem to be proved; **1 mark** for drawing the radii; **1 mark** for applying 'angle at the centre is twice the angle at the circumference' (must be stated clearly); **1 mark** for clearly deducing that x = y. Total 4 marks.*

Page 69, Circle theorems 2

1. a $x = 90°$; the angle between the tangent and radius is a right angle.

  b $x = 10\,cm$; two tangents to a circle from the same point are equal in length.

  c $x = 81°$; the angle between the chord and tangent is equal to the angle in the alternate segment.

  ***1 mark** for each correct answer; **1 mark** for each correct circle theorem stated. Total 6 marks.*

2.

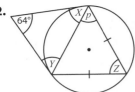

Angle X = angle Y = $(180° - 64°) \div 2 = 58°$
(Tangents to a circle from a point are equal in length, and base angles of an isosceles triangle are equal and angles in a triangle sum to 180°.)
Angle Z = angle X (= angle Y) = 58°
(The angle between the chord and tangent is equal to the angle in the alternate segment.)
$p = (180 - 58) \div 2 = 61°$
(Base angles of an isosceles triangle are equal and angles in a triangle sum to 180°.)
3 marks *for p = 61° (can be shown on the diagram) or*
1 mark *for angle X (or angle Y = 58°) (can be shown on the diagram), **1 mark** for angle Z = 58° (can be shown on the diagram) and **1 mark** for p = 61°; **1 mark** for fully correct reasons stated throughout. Total 4 marks.*

3.

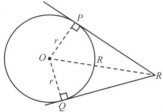

You need to prove that length PR = length QR
First, draw the radii as well as the line OR
Let $OP = OQ = r$ and let $OR = R$
Also, note that the angle between the tangent and radius is a right angle.
By Pythagoras' theorem, $PR = \sqrt{R^2 - r^2}$
Also, by Pythagoras' theorem, $QR = \sqrt{R^2 - r^2}$
So, $PR = QR$ as required.
1 mark *for a diagram showing the correct theorem to be proved and for drawing the radii, as well as line joining the centre to the exterior point; **1 mark** for stating that angle between radius and tangent is a right angle; **1 mark** for applying Pythagoras' theorem; **1 mark** for fully correct and justified conclusion. Total 4 marks.*
Note that there are alternative methods.

Page 70, Transformations

1. a Translation by vector $\binom{12}{0}$
   1 mark *for translation; **1 mark** for $\binom{12}{0}$.*
   b Reflection in the line $y = x$
   1 mark *for reflection; **1 mark** for y = x*
   c Rotation of 90° clockwise about (6, −4)
   1 mark *for rotation; **1 mark** for 90° clockwise; **1 mark** for (6, −4). Total 3 marks.*

2. a and **b**

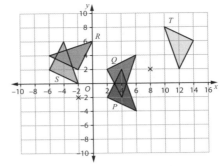

a i ***1 mark*** *for correct orientation; **1 mark** if completely correct.*
   ii ***1 mark*** *for correct orientation; **1 mark** if completely correct.*
   iii ***1 mark*** *for fully correct.*
b Rotation of 180° about (8, 2)
1 mark *for rotation; **1 mark** for 180°; **1 mark** for (8, 2). Total 3 marks.*

Page 71, Enlargement

1. a and **b**

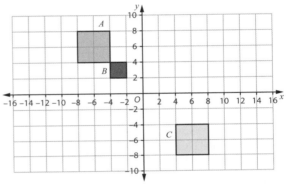

a ***1 mark*** *for correct size; **1 mark** for fully correct.*
b ***1 mark*** *for correct size; **1 mark** for fully correct.*
c Any correct transformation e.g.
   reflection in the line $y = x$, translation by vector $\binom{12}{12}$
   3 marks *for any two correct answers; deduct **1 mark** for each mistake or omission. Total 3 marks.*

2.

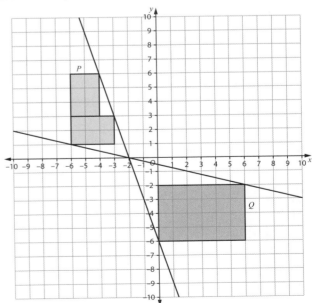

1 mark *for correct orientation after rotation; **1 mark** for fully correct rotation; **1 mark** for correct size after enlargement; **1 mark** for fully correct enlargement. Total 4 marks.*

Page 72, Congruent shapes

1. **a** 24 cm (as it corresponds to AC)

   ***1 mark** for 24 cm.*

   b 75° (as it corresponds to angle DFE)

   ***1 mark** for 75°.*

2. You are given that $AB = DE$

   Angle BDE = angle ABD (alternate angles)

   Angle AED = angle BAE (alternate angles)

   Triangles CBA and CDE are congruent because of ASA (Angle Side Angle).

   ***1 mark** for angle BDE = angle ABD with reason (alternate angles); **1 mark** for angle AED = angle BAE with reason (alternate angles); **1 mark** for all three conditions stated with reasons, along with conclusion e.g. ASA. Total 3 marks. Note that other solutions exist e.g. using vertically opposite angles.*

3.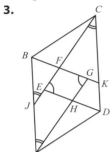

   $AB = DC$ (opposite sides of a parallelogram)

   Angle FEH = angle FGH (diagonally opposite angles of a rhombus)

   Angle GAB = angle CJB (corresponding angles) and angle CJB = angle DCE (alternate angles)

   Therefore, angle GAB = angle DCE

   Triangles ABG and CDE are congruent because of AAS (Angle Angle Side).

   ***1 mark** for $AB = DC$ with reason; **1 mark** for angle FEH = angle FGH with reason; **1 mark** for angle GAB = angle DCE with reason(s) or for angle EDC = angle GBA with reason(s); **1 mark** for all three conditions stated with reasons, along with conclusion e.g. AAS or ASA. Total 4 marks.*

Page 73, Similar shapes

1. $\frac{19.5}{13} = \frac{18}{12} = \frac{7.5}{5} = 1.5$, so scale factor is 1.5

   Therefore, triangles are similar.

   ***1 mark** for comparing ratios of at least 2 pairs of sides (also accept $\frac{13}{19.5} = \frac{12}{18} = \frac{5}{7.5} = \frac{2}{3}$); **1 mark** for scale factor 1.5 or $\frac{2}{3}$ with conclusion. Note that there are alternative methods.*

2. $\frac{AC}{AB} = \frac{AD}{AE}$

   $\frac{11.5}{9.2} = \frac{AD}{8.4}$

   $AD = \frac{11.5 \times 8.4}{9.2} = 10.5$

   $ED = AD - AE = 10.5 - 8.4 = 2.1$ cm

   ***1 mark** for comparing ratios of 2 pairs of sides e.g. $\frac{AB}{AE} = \frac{AC}{AD}$; **1 mark** for correct answer of 2.1 cm. Note that there are alternative methods.*

3. Length scale factor = 22 ÷ 10 = 2.2

   Volume scale factor = 2.2^3 = 10.648

Mass is proportional to volume.

Mass of B = 1.5 kg × 10.648 = 15.972 kg

***1 mark** for length scale factor of 2.2; **1 mark** for volume (or mass) scale factor of 10.648; **1 mark** for correct final answer. Total 3 marks.*

4. Volume scale factor = 675 ÷ 25 = 27

   Length scale factor = $\sqrt[3]{27}$ = 3

   Area scale factor = 3^2 = 9

   Smaller solid surface area = 360 ÷ 9 = 40 cm²

   ***1 mark** for length ratio of 3 : 1 or for scale factor 3 (or 1 : 3 or $\frac{1}{3}$ if considered in reverse); **1 mark** for area ratio of 9 : 1 or for scale factor 9 (or 1 : 9 or $\frac{1}{9}$ if considered in reverse); **1 mark** for correct final answer. Total 3 marks.*

Page 74, Area and perimeter

1. Large semicircle diameter = 19.3 + 4.9 = 24.2 m

   Perimeter = $\frac{\pi \times 24.2}{2} + \frac{\pi \times 19.3}{2} + \frac{\pi \times 4.9}{2} = 76.0$ m

   ***1 mark** for $\frac{\pi \times 24.2}{2}$ (= 38.013...) or $\frac{\pi \times 19.3}{2}$ (= 30.316...) or $\frac{\pi \times 4.9}{2}$ (= 7.696...); **1 mark** for adding perimeters of all 3 semicircles; **1 mark** for final answer correct to 3 sf. Total 3 marks.*

2. Area of semicircle = $\frac{\pi r^2}{2} = \frac{\pi \times 5.5^2}{2}$ (= 47.516...)

   Height of trapezium = 10 − 5.5 = 4.5

   Area of trapezium = $\frac{1}{2} \times (11 + 7) \times 4.5 = 40.5$

   Area of compound shape = 47.516… + 40.5 = 88.0 cm²

   ***1 mark** for $\frac{\pi \times 5.5^2}{2}$ (= 47.516...); **1 mark** for finding the trapezium height; **1 mark** for $\frac{1}{2} \times (11 + 7) \times 4.5$ (= 40.5); **1 mark** for correct answer to 1 dp. Total 4 marks.*

3. Triangle area = $\frac{1}{2} \times 12.8 \times 17.9$ (= 114.56 cm²)

   Trapezium area = $\frac{1}{2} \times (x + 9.4) \times 12.8$

   $\frac{1}{2} \times 12.8 \times 17.9 = \frac{1}{2} \times (x + 9.4) \times 12.8$

   $17.9 = x + 9.4$

   $x = 8.5$ cm

   ***1 mark** for $\frac{1}{2} \times 12.8 \times 17.9$ (= 114.56 cm²) or $\frac{1}{2} \times (x + 9.4) \times 12.8$; **1 mark** for an algebraic equation representing 'triangle area' = 'trapezium area'; **1 mark** for correct answer. Total 3 marks.*

4. Shaded area = (area of quarter circle × 2) − area of square

   $= \frac{\pi \times 10^2}{4} \times 2 - 10^2 = (50\pi - 100)$ cm²

   ***1 mark** for attempt to find area of a quarter (or half) circle and the area of the square; **1 mark** for 25π (or 50π) and 100; **1 mark** for correct final answer or equivalent e.g. 50(π − 2). Answer must be exact; not rounded. Total 3 marks. Note that there are alternative methods.*

Page 75, Plans and elevations

1.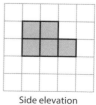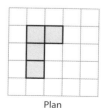

   Front elevation   Side elevation   Plan

   ***1 mark** for each correct diagram; note the plan can be in any orientation as long as it's from above. Total 3 marks.*

2. a

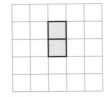

1 mark for correct diagram in any orientation.

b

1 mark for a correct 3D drawing of an 'L-shape'; 1 mark for fully correct diagram (may be facing left or right).

c i 12 vertices   **ii** 18 edges   **iii** 8 faces

1 mark for each correct answer.

Page 76, Prisms and cylinders

1. a Volume $= \pi \times 4^2 \times 11 = 176\pi \text{ cm}^3$

1 mark for $\pi \times 4^2 \times 11$; 1 mark for 176π.

b Curved surface area $= 2 \times \pi \times 4 \times 11 = 88\pi$

Area of circular base $= \pi \times 4^2 = 16\pi$

Total surface area $= 88\pi + 16\pi + 16\pi = 120\pi$

$= 376.99\ldots = 377 \text{ cm}^2$ to 3 sf

1 mark for $2 \times \pi \times 4 \times 11 (= 88\pi)$; 1 mark for $\pi \times 4^2 (= 16\pi)$; 1 mark for adding all 3 surfaces (120π or $376.99\ldots$); 1 mark for correct answer of 377. Total 4 marks.

2. Use cm.

First prism $= \frac{1}{2} \times 1.6 \times 1.8 \times 11 = 15.84$

Second prism $= \frac{1}{2} \times 2.4 \times h \times 4 = 4.8h$

$15.84 = 4.8h; h = \frac{15.84}{4.8} = 3.3 \text{ cm}$

1 mark for $\frac{1}{2} \times 1.6 \times 1.8 \times 11 (= 15.84)$ or $\frac{1}{2} \times 2.4 \times h \times 4$ $(= 4.8h)$ or either without $\frac{1}{2}$; 1 mark for $15.84 = 4.8h$ or $31.68 = 9.6h$; 1 mark for 3.3; 1 mark for cm. Total 4 marks. Note that you could use mm as an alternative method.

3. Length of cube $= \sqrt[3]{2\sqrt{2}} = \sqrt{2} \text{ m}$

Exterior surface area $= 6 \times (\sqrt{2})^2 - 2 \times \pi \times 0.25^2$

$= \left(12 - \frac{\pi}{8}\right) \text{cm}^2$

1 mark for length of cube $= \sqrt[3]{2\sqrt{2}}$ $(= \sqrt{2})$; 1 mark for $6 \times (\text{your length})^2 - 2 \times \pi \times 0.25^2$; 1 mark for $\left(12 - \frac{\pi}{8}\right)$ or equivalent e.g. $\frac{96 - \pi}{8}$. Total 3 marks.

4. a Total number of parts $= 2 + 1 = 3$

$2400\pi \div 3 = 800\pi$

Volume of larger jug $= 800\pi \times 2 = 1600\pi$

$\pi \times 12^2 \times h = 1600\pi$

$h = 11.11\ldots = 11.1 \text{ cm}$ to 3 sf

1 mark for calculating volume of larger jug; 1 mark for use of correct formula; 1 mark for attempt to find height; 1 mark for correct answer to 3 sf. Total 4 marks.

b Volume of smaller jug $= 800\pi$

$h = r$

$\pi \times r^2 \times r = 800\pi$

$r^3 = 800$

$r = 9.283\ldots = 9.28 \text{ cm}$ to 3 sf

1 mark for use of correct formula; 1 mark for attempt to find height by substituting $h = r$; 1 mark for correct answer to 3 sf. Total 3 marks.

Page 77, Spheres and pyramids

1. Area of base $= 230 \times 230 = 52\,900$

Volume $= \frac{1}{3} \times 52\,900 \times 147 = 2\,592\,100 \text{ m}^3$

$= 2\,600\,000 \text{ m}^3$ to 2 sf

1 mark for $230 \times 230 (= 52\,900)$; 1 mark for $\frac{1}{3} \times 52\,900 \times 147 (= 2\,592\,100)$; 1 mark for $2\,600\,000$. Total 3 marks.

2. $4 \times \pi \times r^2 = 400\pi$

$r^2 = 100$

$r = 10 \text{ cm}$

1 mark for $4 \times \pi \times r^2 = 400\pi$ or $r^2 = 100$; 1 mark for correct answer.

3.

Area of one face $= \frac{1}{2} \times 8 \times 8 \sin 60° = 16\sqrt{3}$

Surface area $= 4 \times 16\sqrt{3} = 64\sqrt{3} \text{ cm}^2$

1 mark for $60°$; 1 mark for attempt to use $\frac{1}{2}ab \sin C$ (or for $16\sqrt{3}$); 1 mark for $64\sqrt{3}$; 1 mark for cm^2. Total 4 marks.

Alternative solution:

Height of triangle $= \sqrt{8^2 - 4^2} = \sqrt{48} = 4\sqrt{3}$ (Pythagoras)

Area of one face $= \frac{1}{2} \times 8 \times 4\sqrt{3} = 16\sqrt{3}$

Surface area $= 4 \times 16\sqrt{3} = 64\sqrt{3} \text{ cm}^2$

1 mark for attempt to use Pythagoras to find the height (or for $\sqrt{48}$ or $4\sqrt{3}$); 1 mark for attempt to use $\frac{1}{2} \times 8 \times$ your height (or for $16\sqrt{3}$); 1 mark for $64\sqrt{3}$; 1 mark for cm^2. Total 4 marks.

4. Volume $= \frac{4}{3}\pi r^3 \div 2 = \frac{2}{3}\pi r^3 = \frac{2}{3} \times \pi \times 25^3 = \frac{31\,250\pi}{3}$

$= 32\,724.923\ldots = 32\,700 \text{ cm}^3$ to 3 sf

1 mark for $\frac{2}{3} \times \pi \times 25^3$ or $\left(\frac{\frac{4}{3} \times \pi \times 25^3}{2}\right)$; 1 mark for $\frac{31\,250\pi}{3}$ or $32\,724.923\ldots$; 1 mark for $32\,700$. Total 3 marks.

Page 78, Cones and frustums

1. a Volume $= \frac{1}{3} \times \pi \times 10^2 \times 24 = 800\pi \text{ cm}^3$

1 mark for $\frac{1}{3} \times \pi \times 10^2 \times 24$; 1 mark for correct answer.

b Slant height of cone $= \sqrt{10^2 + 24^2} = 26 \text{ cm}$

Curved surface area $= \pi \times 10 \times 26 = 260\pi$

Base area $= \pi \times 10^2 = 100\pi$

Total surface area $= 260\pi + 100\pi = 360\pi \text{ cm}^2$

1 mark for attempt to use Pythagoras to find the slant height ($= 26 \text{ cm}$); 1 mark for $\pi \times 10 \times$ your slant height ($= 260\pi$); 1 mark for $\pi \times 10^2 (= 100\pi)$; 1 mark for correct final answer. Total 4 marks.

2. Let height of the small cone (cut-off) be h

$\frac{24}{18} = \frac{36 + h}{h}$ since cones are similar.

$24h = 648 + 18h; 6h = 648; h = 108 \text{ mm}$

Radius of large cone $= 24 \div 2 = 12$

Radius of small cone $= 18 \div 2 = 9$

Volume of large cone $= \frac{1}{3} \times \pi \times 12^2 \times (36 + 108) = 6912\pi$

Volume of small cone $= \frac{1}{3} \times \pi \times 9^2 \times 108 = 2916\pi$

Volume of frustum $= 6912\pi - 2916\pi = 3996\pi \text{ mm}^3$

1 mark for attempt to find h by equating ratios of corresponding lengths; 1 mark for solving to find h; 1 mark for using your value of h to find the volume of either the small cone or the large cone; 1 mark for finding both volumes and subtracting; 1 mark for correct final answer in terms of π. Total 5 marks.

3. Volume of cone $= \frac{1}{3} \times \pi \times 6^2 \times 15 = 180\pi$

Volume of hemisphere $= \frac{2}{3} \times \pi \times 6^3 = 144\pi$

Total volume $= 180\pi + 144\pi = 324\pi\,\text{cm}^3$

1 mark for calculating volume of cone; 1 mark for calculating volume of hemisphere; 1 mark for adding volumes and giving correct answer in terms of π. Total 3 marks.

Page 79, Constructing triangles

1. a B (The sum of two sides must be more than the third side.)

1 mark for correct answer.

b

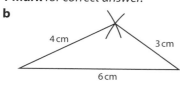

1 mark for one side correctly drawn; 1 mark for second side; 1 mark for fully correct diagram (any orientation). Total 3 marks.

2. SAS known, so use ruler and protractor.

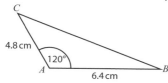

1 mark for 120° angle correctly drawn; 1 mark for either 6.4 cm line or 4.8 cm line correctly drawn; 1 mark for fully correct diagram (this includes a reflection or rotation of the one shown). Total 3 marks.

3. $EF = 66 \div 3 \times 2 = 44\,\text{mm}$

$FD = 44 \div 4 \times 3 = 33\,\text{mm}$

SSS known, so use ruler and compasses.

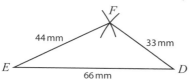

1 mark for each line (correct to 1 mm). Total 3 marks.

Page 80, Perpendiculars and bisectors

1. a

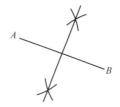

1 mark for intersecting construction arcs either side of line segment; 1 mark for fully correct diagram.

b

1 mark for construction arc(s) intersecting DC and DE or for second set of construction arcs (intersecting between C and E); 1 mark for fully correct diagram.

2.

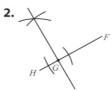

1 mark for construction arcs both sides of G; 1 mark for second set of intersecting construction arcs either side of line segment (either above the line FH as shown, or below); 1 mark for fully correct diagram. Total 3 marks.

3. First construct a right angle.

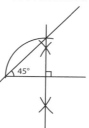

1 mark for construction arcs either side of a line segment and perpendicular line drawn; 1 mark for arc intersecting perpendicular line; 1 mark for fully correct diagram with angle labelled. Total 3 marks.

Full marks also given if instead of using the arc to make a triangle, you correctly bisected the 90° angle constructed.

Page 81, Loci

1.

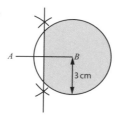

1 mark for construction arcs either side of AB and perpendicular bisector drawn; 1 mark for circle centre B; 1 mark for 3 cm radius; 1 mark for correctly shaded region. Total 4 marks.

2.

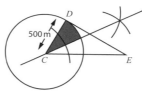

1 mark for construction arc(s) intersecting CD and CE and pair of intersecting arcs in the space between D and E; 1 mark for angle bisector drawn; 1 mark for circle or arc centre C with radius of CD; 1 mark for correct shaded region. Total 4 marks.

3.

$2.5\,\text{m} = 250\,\text{cm}$

$250 \div 125 = 2$

The locus needs to be 2 cm from the track.

1 mark for attempt to use the ratio to calculate the distance from the track (= 2 cm); 1 mark for any correct straight line 2 cm from the T or any semicircle in correct position with 2 cm radius; 1 mark for fully correct locus. Total 3 marks.

Page 82, Pythagoras' theorem

1. D (Pythagoras' theorem holds true: $7^2 + 24^2 = 25^2$)
1 mark for correctly checking if the sum of squares of opposite and adjacent sides equals square of hypotenuse for any of the triangles; **1 mark** for correct answer.

2.

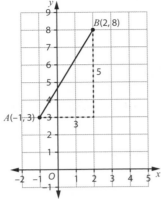

From the diagram,
$(AB)^2 = 5^2 + 3^2 = 34$
$AB = 5.83... = 5.83$ to 3 sf
1 mark for identifying at least one of 3 and 5 as sides of a right-angled triangle; **1 mark** for squaring and adding; **1 mark** for taking the square root of your answer; **1 mark** for correct answer to 3 sf. Total 4 marks.

3.

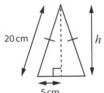

From the diagram,
$h^2 = 20^2 - 5^2 = 375$
$h = 19.364... = 19.4$ cm to 1 dp
1 mark for splitting into two right-angled triangles with side 5 and squaring and subtracting; **1 mark** for taking the square root of your answer; **1 mark** for correct answer to 1 dp. Total 3 marks.

4. $(3h)^2 = 90^2 - 60^2 = 4500$
$3h = 67.082...$
$h = 22.360... = 22.4$ cm to 1 dp
1 mark for squaring and subtracting; **1 mark** for taking the square root of your answer; **1 mark** for dividing by 3; **1 mark** for correct answer to 1 dp. Total 4 marks.
Alternatively, work with a triangle with one-third of these measurements.

Page 83, Trigonometry 1

1. a $x = 16 \cos 35° = 13.1$ cm to 1 dp
1 mark for 16 cos 35; **1 mark** for correct answer to 1 dp.
b $x = \frac{14}{\sin 67°} = 15.2$ cm to 1 dp
1 mark for $\frac{14}{\sin 67}$; **1 mark** for correct answer to 1 dp.

2. The trapezium can be split into a rectangle 24 cm by h cm and a right-angled triangle of height h
Base of triangle = 40 − 24 = 16 cm
$h = 16 \tan 50° = 19.1$ cm to 3 sf
1 mark for 40 − 24 (= 16); **1 mark** for 16 tan 50; **1 mark** for correct answer to 3 sf. Total 3 marks.

3. Distance $= \frac{1000}{\sin 26°} = 2281.17... = 2300$ m to 2 sf
1 mark for $\frac{1000}{\sin 26}$; **1 mark** for correct answer to 2 sf.

4. Using the left triangle in the diagram,
the common side $= \frac{6.4}{\tan 52°} = 5.0002...$ cm
Using the right triangle in the diagram,
$b = \frac{5.0002...}{\tan 31°} = 8.3$ cm to 1 dp
1 mark for $\frac{6.4}{\tan 52}$ (= 5.0002...); **1 mark** for dividing your answer by tan 31; **1 mark** for correct answer to 1 dp. Total 3 marks.

Page 84, Trigonometry 2

1. a $\sin x = \frac{4}{7}$
$x = \sin^{-1}\left(\frac{4}{7}\right) = 34.8°$ to 1 dp
1 mark for $\sin x = \frac{4}{7}$; **1 mark** for correct answer to 1 dp.
b $\tan x = \frac{10}{11}$
$x = \tan^{-1}\left(\frac{10}{11}\right) = 42.3°$ to 1 dp
1 mark for $\tan x = \frac{10}{11}$; **1 mark** for correct answer to 1 dp.
c $\cos x = \frac{13}{20}$
$x = \cos^{-1}\left(\frac{13}{20}\right) = 49.5°$ to 1 dp
1 mark for $\cos x = \frac{13}{20}$; **1 mark** for correct answer to 1 dp.

2.

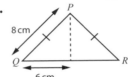

$\cos PQR = \frac{6}{8}$
$PQR = \cos^{-1}\left(\frac{6}{8}\right) = 41.4°$ to 1 dp
1 mark for 12 ÷ 2 (= 6); **1 mark** for $\cos PQR = \frac{6}{8}$; **1 mark** for correct answer to 1 dp. Total 3 marks.

3.

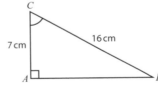

$\cos BAC = \frac{7}{16}$
$BAC = \cos^{-1}\left(\frac{7}{16}\right) = 64.1°$ to 1 dp
1 mark for a correctly labelled sketch (angle BAC does not need to be indicated); **1 mark** for $\cos BAC = \frac{7}{16}$; **1 mark** for correct answer. Total 3 marks.

4.

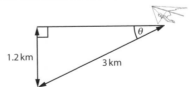

Let the required angle be θ
$\sin \theta = \frac{1.2}{3}$
$\theta = \sin^{-1}\left(\frac{1.2}{3}\right) = 23.6°$ to 3 sf
1 mark for identifying the correct angle (could be on the diagram or could be implied by a correct calculation); **1 mark** for $\sin \theta = \frac{1.2}{3}$; **1 mark** for correct answer to 3 sf. Total 3 marks.

Page 85, Bearings

1.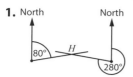

North ... North
80° ... H ... 280°

1 mark for either 080° bearing or 280° bearing drawn correctly; 1 mark for both bearings drawn correctly; 1 mark for correct lines intersecting and labelled H. Total 3 marks.

2.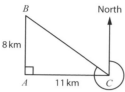

B ... North
8 km
A ... 11 km ... C

$\tan BCA = \dfrac{8}{11}$

$BAC = \tan^{-1}\left(\dfrac{8}{11}\right) = 36.027\ldots = 36°$ to the nearest degree

Bearing of B from C is $270° + 36° = 306°$

1 mark for $\tan BCA = \dfrac{8}{11}$; 1 mark for $36.027\ldots$; 1 mark for $270 +$ your BCA; 1 mark for correct answer to nearest degree. Total 4 marks.

3.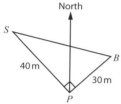

North
S
40 m ... B
30 m
P

By Pythagoras' theorem,

$SB = \sqrt{30^2 + 40^2} = \sqrt{2500} = 50$ m

1 mark for a sketch showing a right-angled triangle; 1 mark for attempt to use Pythagoras' theorem; 1 mark for $\sqrt{2500}$; 1 mark for correct final answer. Total 4 marks.

Page 86, Exact values of sin, cos, tan

1. a $x = 4\sin 30° = 4 \times \dfrac{1}{2} = 2$ cm

1 mark for $4\sin 30$; 1 mark for $\sin 30 = \dfrac{1}{2}$; 1 mark for correct final answer. Total 3 marks.

b $x = 1 \times \tan 45° = 1 \times 1 = 1$ cm

1 mark for $1 \times \tan 45$; 1 mark for $\tan 45 = 1$; 1 mark for correct final answer. Total 3 marks.

c $x = \dfrac{6}{\cos 60°} = \dfrac{6}{\frac{1}{2}} = 12$ cm

1 mark for $\dfrac{6}{\cos 60}$; 1 mark for $\cos 60 = \dfrac{1}{2}$; 1 mark for correct final answer. Total 3 marks.

2. a

	0°	30°	45°	60°	90°
sin	0	$\dfrac{1}{2}$	$\dfrac{1}{\sqrt{2}}$	$\dfrac{\sqrt{3}}{2}$	⓪
cos	1	$\dfrac{\sqrt{3}}{2}$	$\dfrac{\sqrt{3}}{2}$	$\dfrac{1}{2}$	0
tan	0	$\sqrt{3}$	1	$\dfrac{\sqrt{3}}{2}$	undefined

1 mark for each correct answer circled. (Note: 1 mark deducted for each incorrect answer circled.) Total 4 marks.

b $\sin 90° = 1$ ... $\tan 30° = \dfrac{1}{\sqrt{3}}$ or $\dfrac{\sqrt{3}}{3}$

$\cos 45° = \dfrac{1}{\sqrt{2}}$ or $\dfrac{\sqrt{2}}{2}$ ... $\tan 60° = \sqrt{3}$

1 mark for each correct answer. Total 4 marks.

3. a $\cos x = \dfrac{1+\sqrt{2}}{2+\sqrt{2}} = \dfrac{1+\sqrt{2}}{2+\sqrt{2}} \times \dfrac{(2-\sqrt{2})}{(2-\sqrt{2})} = \dfrac{1}{\sqrt{2}}$

$x = \cos^{-1}\left(\dfrac{1}{\sqrt{2}}\right) = 45°$

1 mark for $\cos x = \dfrac{1+\sqrt{2}}{2+\sqrt{2}}$; 1 mark for $\cos x = \dfrac{1}{\sqrt{2}}$; 1 mark for correct final answer. Total 3 marks.

b $\tan 60° = \dfrac{x\sqrt{6}}{2-\sqrt{3}}$

$\sqrt{3} = \dfrac{x\sqrt{6}}{2-\sqrt{3}}$

$x = \dfrac{\sqrt{3}(2-\sqrt{3})}{\sqrt{6}} = \dfrac{2\sqrt{2}-\sqrt{6}}{2}$ cm

1 mark for $\tan 60 = \dfrac{x\sqrt{6}}{2-\sqrt{3}}$; 1 mark for $\tan 60 = \sqrt{3}$; 1 mark for correct final answer. Total 3 marks.

Page 87, Pythagoras' theorem in 3D

1. $12^2 + 3^2 + h^2 = 13^2$

$144 + 9 + h^2 = 169$

$h^2 = 16$

$h = 4$ cm

1 mark for $12^2 + 3^2 + h^2 = 13^2$; 1 mark for attempt to solve for h; 1 mark for final answer of 4. Total 3 marks.

2. Same method as for a 2 cm × 2 cm × 1 cm cuboid.

Length $PQ = \sqrt{2^2 + 2^2 + 1^2} = 3$ cm

1 mark for $\sqrt{2^2 + 2^2 + 1^2}$; 1 mark for correct final answer.

3. Let the centre of the base be O and let the midpoint of AB be M

Using triangle AOM,

$AO = \sqrt{\left(\dfrac{\sqrt{2}}{2}\right)^2 + \left(\dfrac{\sqrt{2}}{2}\right)^2} = 1$ cm

O ... E
$\dfrac{\sqrt{2}}{2}$ ... $\sqrt{3}$ ... h
A ... $\dfrac{\sqrt{2}}{2}$ ... M ... A ... 1 ... O

Using triangle AEO,

$h = \sqrt{(\sqrt{3})^2 - 1^2} = \sqrt{2}$ cm

1 mark for $(AO =) \sqrt{\left(\dfrac{\sqrt{2}}{2}\right)^2 + \left(\dfrac{\sqrt{2}}{2}\right)^2} (= 1)$; 1 mark for $\sqrt{(3)^2 - AO^2}$; 1 mark for correct answer. Total 3 marks.

4. Let h cm be the height of the container.

The volume of the prism in terms of h

$= \dfrac{1}{4} \times \pi \times \left(\dfrac{11}{2}\right)^2 \times h = \dfrac{121}{16}\pi h$

Using Pythagoras, the length of the prism

$= \sqrt{14^2 - 4^2} = \sqrt{180} = 6\sqrt{5}$

The base of the prism is equilateral, so its angles are 60°.

Area of the base of the prism

$= \dfrac{1}{2} \times 4 \times 4 \times \sin 60° = 8 \times \dfrac{\sqrt{3}}{2} = 4\sqrt{3}$

Volume of prism $= (4\sqrt{3}) \times 6\sqrt{5} = 24\sqrt{15}$

Equating the two expressions for volume gives

$h = 24\sqrt{15} \times \dfrac{16}{121\pi} = 3.9123\ldots$

The height of the container is 3.91 cm (to 3 sf).

1 mark for using volume of a cylinder; 1 mark for using Pythagoras to work out prism length; 1 mark for area of triangle multiplied by length to work out prism volume; 1 mark for equating two expressions for volume and rearranging; 1 mark for correct rounded answer. Total 5 marks.

Page 88, Trigonometry in 3D

1. Let M be the midpoint of WX

Using triangle MOX,

$$OX = \frac{1.5}{\cos 30°} = \sqrt{3}$$

(Angle $OXM = 30°$ since OX bisects angle VXW which is $60°$ as VXW is an equilateral triangle.)

Using triangle YOX,

$$\cos \alpha = \frac{\sqrt{3}}{3} \Rightarrow \alpha = 54.735\ldots = 55° \text{ to the nearest degree}$$

***1 mark** for attempt to use 90°, 60°, 30° triangle;*
***1 mark** for $(OX =) \frac{1.5}{\cos 30} \ (= \sqrt{3})$; **1 mark** for $\cos OXY = \frac{OX}{3}$;*
***1 mark** for 55 to nearest degree. Total 4 marks.*

2. Let h be the height of the office block and d be Graham's original distance from the block.

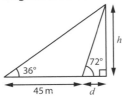

$h = d \tan 72$
$h = (45 + d) \tan 36°$
So, $d \tan 72° = (45 + d) \tan 36°$
$d(\tan 72° - \tan 36°) = 45 \tan 36°$

Hence, $h = \left(\frac{45 \tan 36°}{\tan 72° - \tan 36°}\right) \tan 72°$

$= 42.8\,\text{m}$ (to 3 sf)

The office block is 42.8 m tall (to 3 sf).

***1 mark** for a correct equation using tan 72; **1 mark** for a correct equation using tan 36; **1 mark** for equating and attempting to rearrange; **1 mark** for correct final answer for height. Total 4 marks.*

3. Let θ be the angle of elevation.

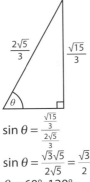

$\sin \theta = \frac{\frac{\sqrt{15}}{3}}{\frac{2\sqrt{5}}{3}}$

$\sin \theta = \frac{\sqrt{3}\sqrt{5}}{2\sqrt{5}} = \frac{\sqrt{3}}{2}$

$\theta = 60°, 120°, \ldots$

However, since one of the angles in the triangle is 90° and the angle sum for the triangle is 180°, θ is between 0 and 90°.

Therefore, θ is 60°.

***1 mark** for using sin; **1 mark** for attempt to simplify fractions; **1 mark** for $\frac{\sqrt{3}}{2}$; **1 mark** for explanation of 60° being only answer. Total 4 marks.*

Page 89, Sine and cosine rules

1. a Using the cosine rule,

$\quad x^2 = 14^2 + 11^2 - 2 \times 14 \times 11 \times \cos 42° = 88.111\ldots$
$\quad x = 9.386\ldots = 9.4\,\text{cm}$ to 1 dp

***1 mark** for $14^2 + 11^2 - 2 \times 14 \times 11 \times \cos 42$; **1 mark** for 88.111…; **1 mark** for 9.4 to 1 dp. Total 3 marks.*

b Using the sine rule,

$\quad \dfrac{x}{\sin 34°} = \dfrac{2.7}{\sin 21°}$

$\quad\quad x = \dfrac{2.7 \times \sin 34°}{\sin 21°} = 4.213\ldots = 4.2\,\text{cm}$ to 1 dp

***1 mark** for $\frac{x}{\sin 34} = \frac{2.7}{\sin 21}$; **1 mark** for $\frac{2.7 \times \sin 34}{\sin 21}$ (= 4.213…); **1 mark** for 4.2 to 1 dp. Total 3 marks.*

2. a Using the cosine rule,

$\quad \cos x = \dfrac{10.8^2 + 16.3^2 - 8.2^2}{2 \times 10.8 \times 16.3} = 0.894\ldots$

$\quad x = 26.499\ldots = 26.5°$ to 1 dp

***1 mark** for $\frac{10.8^2 + 16.3^2 - 8.2^2}{2 \times 10.8 \times 16.3}$; **1 mark** for 0.894…; **1 mark** for 26.5 to 1 dp. Total 3 marks.*

b Using the sine rule,

$\quad \dfrac{\sin x}{13} = \dfrac{\sin 67°}{19}$

$\quad \sin x = \dfrac{13 \times \sin 67°}{19} = 0.6298\ldots$

$\quad x = 39.036\ldots = 39.0°$ to 1 dp

***1 mark** for $\frac{\sin x}{13} = \frac{\sin 67}{19}$; **1 mark** for $\frac{13 \times \sin 67}{19}$ (= 0.6298…); **1 mark** for 39.0 to 1 dp. Total 3 marks.*

3.

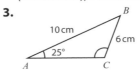

Using the sine rule,

$\quad \dfrac{\sin ACB}{10} = \dfrac{\sin 25°}{6}$

$\quad \sin ACB = \dfrac{10 \times \sin 25°}{6} = 0.704\ldots$

$\quad\quad ACB = 44.778\ldots$

ACB is obtuse, so $ACB = 180° - 44.778\ldots° = 135.2°$ to 1 dp

***1 mark** for $\frac{\sin ACB}{10} = \frac{\sin 25}{6}$; **1 mark** for $\frac{10 \times \sin 25}{6}$ (= 0.704…); **1 mark** for 44.778…; **1 mark** for correct obtuse angle (i.e. 135.2) to 1 dp. Total 4 marks.*

4. Triangle ABD

Using the sine rule,

$\quad \dfrac{BD}{\sin 70°} = \dfrac{16}{\sin 37°}$

$\quad BD = \dfrac{16 \times \sin 70°}{\sin 37°} = 24.982\ldots$

Triangle BCD

Using the cosine rule,

$\quad BC^2 = 18^2 + BD^2 - 2 \times 18 \times BD \times \cos 43°$

$\quad\quad\quad = 290.377\ldots$

$\quad BC = 17.040\ldots = 17.0\,\text{cm}$ to 1 dp

***1 mark** for $\frac{BD}{\sin 70} = \frac{16}{\sin 37}$; **1 mark** for $\frac{16 \times \sin 70}{\sin 37}$ or 24.982…; **1 mark** for $BC^2 = 18^2 + BC^2 - 2 \times 18 \times BD \times \cos 43$; **1 mark** for 290.377…; **1 mark** for 17.0 to 1 dp. Total 5 marks.*

Page 90, Area of a triangle

1. a $\frac{1}{2} \times 6 \times 9 \times \sin 32° = 14.3078\ldots = 14.31\,\text{cm}$ to 2 dp
***1 mark** for $\frac{1}{2} \times 6 \times 9 \times \sin 32$; **1 mark** for 14.31 to 2 dp.*

b $\frac{1}{2} \times 10.21 \times 13.64 \times \sin 80° = 68.5743... = 68.57\,\text{cm}$ to 2 dp

1 mark *for* $\frac{1}{2} \times 10.21 \times 13.64 \times \sin 80$; ***1 mark*** *for 68.57 to 2 dp.*

2. First sketch the triangle.

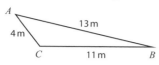

Using the cosine rule,

$\cos CAB = \frac{4^2 + 13^2 - 11^2}{2 \times 4 \times 13} = \frac{8}{13}$

Angle $CAB = \cos^{-1} \frac{8}{13} = 52.0201...$

Area of triangle $= \frac{1}{2} \times 4 \times 13 \times \sin 52.0201°$

$= 20.4939... = 20.5\,\text{m}^2$ to 3 sf

1 mark *for correct use of cosine rule;* ***1 mark*** *for 52.0201...;* ***1 mark*** *for correct use of area of triangle formula;* ***1 mark*** *for correct answer to 3 sf. Total 4 marks. Note that there are alternative methods.*

3. Draw a sketch (yours may have CD and AD swapped round but the area will be the same).

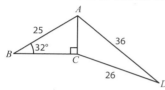

Work out the areas of triangles ABC and ACD separately and sum for the area of $ABCD$

$AC = 25 \sin 32° = 13.2479...$

$BC = 25 \cos 32° = 21.2012...$

Area of $ABC = \frac{1}{2} \times$ base $\times$ height $= \frac{1}{2} \times AC \times BC$

$= 140.4365...$

You need to work out one of the angles in ACD

Using the cosine rule,

$AC^2 = 36^2 + 26^2 - 2 \times 36 \times 26 \times \cos ADC$

$ADC = \cos^{-1} \left(\frac{36^2 + 26^2 - 13.2479...^2}{2 \times 36 \times 26} \right) = 16.3288...°$

Area of $ACD = \frac{1}{2} \times AD \times DC \times \sin ADC$

$= \frac{1}{2} \times 36 \times 26 \times \sin 16.3288...°$

$= 131.5779...$

Total area $= 140.4365... + 131.5779...$

$= 272.0145...$

Area of shape $ABCD = 272.0\,\text{m}^2$ (to 1 dp)

1 mark *for base or height of* ABC; ***1 mark*** *for correct area of* ABC; ***1 mark*** *for attempt to use cosine rule to find an angle of* ADC *(the other angles are 33.5° and 130.2°);* ***1 mark*** *for use of area formula;* ***1 mark*** *for correct rounded final answer. Total 5 marks.*

Page 91, Sectors, arcs & segments

1. a Area $= \pi r^2 \times \frac{\theta}{360°} = \pi \times 15^2 \times \frac{50°}{360°} = 98.2\,\text{cm}^2$

1 mark *for* $\pi \times 15^2 \times \frac{50}{360}$; ***1 mark*** *for correct answer to 1 dp;* ***1 mark*** *for correct units. Total 3 marks.*

b Arc length $= 2\pi r \times \frac{\theta}{360°} = 2 \times \pi \times 15 \times \frac{50°}{360°} = 13.1\,\text{cm}$

1 mark *for* $2 \times \pi \times 15 \times \frac{50}{360}$; ***1 mark*** *for correct answer to 1 dp;* ***1 mark*** *for correct units. Total 3 marks.*

2. Arc length $= 90 - 12 - 12 = 66\,\text{cm}$

Sector angle cut out $= \theta$

Let $x = 360° - \theta$

$\frac{x}{360°} = \frac{\text{arc length}}{\text{circumference}} = \frac{66}{2 \times \pi \times 12}$

$x = \frac{66 \times 360°}{2 \times \pi \times 12} = 315.126...$

$\theta = 360 - 315.126... = 44.873... = 45°$ to nearest degree

1 mark *for arc length of 66 cm;* ***1 mark*** *for* $\frac{angle}{360} = \frac{66}{2 \times \pi \times 12}$; ***1 mark*** *for angle* $= \frac{66 \times 360}{2 \times \pi \times 12} (= 315.126...)$; ***1 mark*** *for 360 – angle;* ***1 mark*** *for correct answer to nearest degree. Total 5 marks.*

3. a Equilateral triangle, so angle $DOC = 60°$

Area of triangle $OAB = \frac{1}{2} \times 8 \times 8 \times \sin 60° = 16\sqrt{3}\,\text{cm}^2$

Radius of circle $= 8 \div 2 = 4$

Area of sector $= \frac{60°}{360°} \times \pi \times 4^2 = \frac{8\pi}{3}\,\text{cm}^2$

Shaded area $= \left(16\sqrt{3} - \frac{8\pi}{3} \right)\,\text{cm}^2$

1 mark *for 60°;* ***1 mark*** *for* $\frac{1}{2} \times 8 \times 8 \times \sin 60 (= 16\sqrt{3})$; ***1 mark*** *for* $\frac{60}{360} \times \pi \times 4^2 \left(= \frac{8\pi}{3} \right)$; ***1 mark*** *for correct final answer or equivalent e.g.* $\frac{48\sqrt{3} - 8\pi}{3}$. *Total 4 marks.*

b

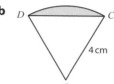

Use sector area from part **a** $= \frac{8\pi}{3}\,\text{cm}^2$

Triangle area $= \frac{1}{2} \times 4 \times 4 \times \sin 60°$

$= 4\sqrt{3}\,\text{cm}^2$

Segment area $= \frac{8\pi}{3} - 4\sqrt{3} = 1.4493...$

$= 1.4\,\text{cm}^2$ to 1 dp

1 mark *for triangle area formula;* ***1 mark*** *for subtracting from sector area;* ***1 mark*** *for final answer to 1 dp. Total 3 marks.*

Page 92, Vectors 1

1. a $\overrightarrow{OT} = \overrightarrow{QO} = -3\mathbf{b}$

1 mark *for correct answer.*

b $\overrightarrow{PQ} = \overrightarrow{PO} + \overrightarrow{OQ} = -2\mathbf{a} + 3\mathbf{b}$

1 mark *for correct answer (also accept 3**b** –2**a**).*

c $\overrightarrow{OU} = \overrightarrow{OP} + \overrightarrow{PU} = 2\mathbf{a} - 3\mathbf{b}$

1 mark *for correct answer (also accept –3**b** +2**a**).*

d $\overrightarrow{UQ} = \overrightarrow{UP} + \overrightarrow{PQ} = 3\mathbf{b} - 2\mathbf{a} + 3\mathbf{b} = 6\mathbf{b} - 2\mathbf{a}$

1 mark *for correct answer (also accept –2**a** + 6**b**).*

2.

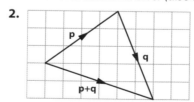

1 mark *for each of vectors **p** and **q** drawn correctly (with arrows in correct direction);* ***1 mark*** *for creating a triangle with your **p** and **q** (with arrow in correct direction);* ***1 mark*** *for fully correct diagram. Total 4 marks.*

3.

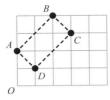

$\overrightarrow{OC} = \begin{pmatrix} 3 \\ 3 \end{pmatrix}$

1 mark for C plotted in correct position or correct rectangle drawn; 1 mark for correct column vector.

Page 93, Vectors 2

1. $\overrightarrow{AB} = \overrightarrow{AO} + \overrightarrow{OB} = \mathbf{b} - \mathbf{a}$

$\overrightarrow{MN} = \overrightarrow{MA} + \overrightarrow{AN} = \frac{1}{2}\overrightarrow{OA} + \frac{4}{5}\overrightarrow{AB} = \frac{1}{2}\mathbf{a} + \frac{4}{5}(\mathbf{b} - \mathbf{a})$

$= \frac{4}{5}\mathbf{b} - \frac{3}{10}\mathbf{a}$

1 mark for $\overrightarrow{AB} = \mathbf{b} - \mathbf{a}$; 1 mark for $\overrightarrow{MN} = \frac{1}{2}\overrightarrow{OA} + \frac{4}{5}\overrightarrow{AB}$; 1 mark for either $\frac{4}{5}\mathbf{b}$ or $-\frac{3}{10}\mathbf{a}$ correct; 1 mark for both correct. Total 4 marks.

Alternatively, you could use $\overrightarrow{MN} = \overrightarrow{MO} + \overrightarrow{OB} + \overrightarrow{BN}$ to get the same answer.

2. $\overrightarrow{PQ} = \overrightarrow{PO} + \overrightarrow{OQ} = \mathbf{q} - \mathbf{p}$

If $PQ:QR = 2:3$,

then $\overrightarrow{PR} = \frac{5}{2}\overrightarrow{PQ} = \frac{5}{2}(\mathbf{q} - \mathbf{p})$

$\overrightarrow{OR} = \overrightarrow{OP} + \overrightarrow{PR} = \mathbf{p} + \frac{5}{2}(\mathbf{q} - \mathbf{p}) = \frac{5}{2}\mathbf{q} - \frac{3}{2}\mathbf{p} = \frac{1}{2}(5\mathbf{q} - 3\mathbf{p})$

which is a multiple of $5\mathbf{q} - 3\mathbf{p}$ so parallel.

1 mark for $\overrightarrow{PQ} = \mathbf{q} - \mathbf{p}$; 1 mark for $\overrightarrow{PR} = \frac{5}{2}\overrightarrow{PQ}$ $(= \frac{5}{2}(\mathbf{q} - \mathbf{p}))$; 1 mark for either $\frac{5}{2}\mathbf{q}$ or $-\frac{3}{2}\mathbf{p}$ correct; 1 mark for both correct; 1 mark for valid conclusion. Total 5 marks.

Alternatively, you could use $\overrightarrow{OR} = \overrightarrow{OQ} + \overrightarrow{QR}$ to get the same answer.

3. $\overrightarrow{XY} = \overrightarrow{XO} + \overrightarrow{OY} = \mathbf{y} - \mathbf{x}$

If $XN:NY = 5:2$

then $\overrightarrow{XN} = \frac{5}{7}\overrightarrow{XY} = \frac{5}{7}(\mathbf{y} - \mathbf{x})$

$\overrightarrow{MN} = \overrightarrow{MX} + \overrightarrow{XN}$

$= \frac{1}{2}\mathbf{x} + \frac{5}{7}(\mathbf{y} - \mathbf{x}) = \frac{5}{7}\mathbf{y} - \frac{3}{14}\mathbf{x}$

$\overrightarrow{MZ} = \overrightarrow{MO} + \overrightarrow{OZ} = -\frac{1}{2}\mathbf{x} + k\mathbf{y}$

Comparing $\overrightarrow{MN}$ with $\overrightarrow{MZ}$,

$\overrightarrow{MN} = \frac{3}{7}\overrightarrow{MZ}$ (as $-\frac{3}{14} = \frac{3}{7} \times -\frac{1}{2}$)

$\frac{5}{7} = \frac{3}{7} \times k \Rightarrow k = \frac{5}{3}$

1 mark for $\overrightarrow{XY} = \mathbf{y} - \mathbf{x}$; 1 mark for $\overrightarrow{XN} = \frac{5}{7}\overrightarrow{XY}$ $(= \frac{5}{7}(\mathbf{y} - \mathbf{x}))$; 1 mark for both $\frac{5}{7}\mathbf{y}$ and $-\frac{3}{14}\mathbf{x}$ correct; 1 mark for comparing $\overrightarrow{MZ}$ with $\overrightarrow{MN}$; 1 mark for final answer. Total 5 marks.

Page 94, Sampling

1. a Quantitative secondary data
   1 mark for quantitative; 1 mark for secondary.
   b Data not current, out-of-date etc.
   1 mark for suitable reason.

2. a Convenient, cheap
   1 mark for any correct answer.
   b Unreliable
   1 mark for correct answer.

3. a $8 \div 40 \times 180 = 36$
   1 mark for $8 \div 40 \times 180$ or $180 \div 5$; 1 mark for correct answer.
   b Sample is representative, random sample, there is no bias etc.
   1 mark for suitable reason.

4. a Every item has an equal chance of selection.
   1 mark for any correct answer.
   b i All pupils at the school
   ii The five friends who were chosen
   1 mark for each correct answer.
   c Not every pupil had an equal chance of selection so the sample isn't random.
   1 mark for correct answer.
   d Take a larger sample, use a random method of selection
   1 mark for each correct answer.

Page 95, Capture-recapture method

1. a $N = \frac{50 \times 234}{18} = 650$
   Estimate the total number of gulls to be 650
   1 mark for proportion used (e.g. $\frac{18}{50}$ or $\frac{18}{234}$ seen); 1 mark for $\frac{50 \times 234}{18}$; 1 mark for correct answer. Total 3 marks.
   b Samples are random, the tagged/untagged gulls have mixed up, the population hasn't changed within a day, tags are all still intact etc.
   1 mark for any sensible assumption.

2. a $N = \frac{12 \times 40}{3} = 160$
   Estimate the total number of grasshoppers to be 160
   1 mark for proportion used (e.g. $\frac{3}{12}$ or $\frac{3}{40}$ seen); 1 mark for $\frac{12 \times 40}{3}$; 1 mark for correct answer. Total 3 marks.
   b Grasshoppers might not stay in the same field.
   1 mark for any sensible reason.

3. $N = \frac{15 \times 136}{4} = 510$
   Estimate the total amount to be £5.10
   1 mark for proportion used (e.g. $\frac{4}{15}$ or $\frac{4}{136}$ seen); 1 mark for $\frac{15 \times 136}{4}$; 1 mark for correct answer in context i.e. £5.10 or 510p. Total 3 marks.

4. Let the number of tagged dolphins $= n$
   Then $1000 = \frac{n \times 440}{22}$
   So $n = \frac{22 \times 1000}{440} = 50$
   50 dolphins were tagged.
   1 mark for proportion used (e.g. $\frac{22}{440}$ or $\frac{22}{n}$ seen); 1 mark for $\frac{22 \times 1000}{440}$; 1 mark for correct answer of 50. Total 3 marks.

Page 96, Averages and spread

1. a

Score on dice	Tally	Frequency
1	IIII	4
2	II	2
3	IIII I	6
4	II	2
5	III	3
6	III	3

1 mark for at most 2 errors; 1 mark for fully correct table.

b i 3   **ii** $6 - 1 = 5$
     iii Value half-way between 10th and 11th value = 3
1 mark for each correct answer.

2. $63 \times 10 = 630$ (total of all 10 numbers)
  $51 \times 4 = 204$ (total of 4 of the numbers)
  $630 - 204 = 426$ (total of remaining 6 numbers)
  Mean of remaining 6 numbers is $426 \div 6 = 71$
1 mark for 630 or 204; 1 mark for subtracting your 204 from your 630 and dividing by 6; 1 mark for correct answer of 71. Total 3 marks.

3. a

Number of goals, g	Frequency, f	$g \times f$
0	5	0
1	6	6
2	5	10
4	4	12
Total	20	28

From table, mean = $28 \div 20 = 1.4$
1 mark for attempt to multiply number of goals by frequency (i.e. any correct value in the final column); 1 mark for either total correct (20 or 28) or for dividing your column 3 total by your column 2 total; 1 mark for correct answer. Total 3 marks.

b i Highest number of goals scored is 2
     Lowest number of goals scored is 1
     So range = $2 - 1 = 1$
1 mark for correct answer of 1
  ii Mean for Fermat United is 1.4
     Mean for Gauss Town is 1.4
     So they score the same number of goals per match on average.
1 mark for comparing means; 1 mark for comparing means with correct conclusion.
  iii Range for Fermat United is 1
     Range for Gauss Town is $3 - 0 = 3$
     Fermat United have the lower range and so are more consistent.
1 mark for comparing your ranges or for stating that the range for Gauss Town = 3; 1 mark for comparing ranges with correct conclusion.

Page 97, Grouped data

1. a

Length (x cm)	Frequency, f	Midpoint	$f \times$ Midpoint
$0 < x \leq 8$	50	4	200
$8 < x \leq 16$	30	12	360
$16 < x \leq 24$	20	20	400
Total	100		960

1 mark for 20 or 360 or 960; 1 mark for fully correct table.
b $0 < x \leq 8$
1 mark for correct answer.
c Estimated mean length = $960 \div 100 = 9.6$ cm
1 mark for dividing the final column total by 100; 1 mark for 9.6 cm.

2. a $\frac{71 + 1}{2} = 36$
  The median is the 36th value
  Median class = $30 < t \leq 35$
1 mark for $\frac{71+1}{2}$ (=36); 1 mark for $30 < t \leq 35$
b

Time (t minutes)	Frequency	Midpoint	Frequency × midpoint
$20 < t \leq 25$	10	22.5	225
$25 < t \leq 30$	17	27.5	467.5
$30 < t \leq 35$	24	32.5	780
$35 < t \leq 40$	11	37.5	412.5
$40 < t \leq 45$	9	42.5	382.5
	71		2267.5

Estimate for mean = $2267.5 \div 71 = 31.93\ldots$
This is 32 minutes to the nearest minute.
1 mark for multiplying frequencies by your midpoints; 1 mark for dividing your final column total by 71 or for 31.93…; 1 mark for correct answer to nearest minute. Total 3 marks.
c You don't know the actual data values, so you can only provide an estimate by using midpoints.
1 mark for clear explanation.

3.

Score (x)	Frequency	Midpoint	Frequency × midpoint
$0 < t \leq 4$	$3y$	2	$6y$
$4 < t \leq 8$	$7y$	6	$42y$
	$10y$		$48y$

Estimate for mean = $48y \div 10y = 4.8$
1 mark for multiplying frequencies by your midpoints; 1 mark for dividing your final column total by your frequency total; 1 mark for correct answer of 4.8. Total 3 marks.
Note that if calculations do not contain y, then full marks can still be awarded for this question.

Page 98, Interquartile range

1. The position of the lower quartile is $\frac{1}{4}(11 + 1) = 3$
3rd value is 16
The position of the upper quartile is $\frac{3}{4}(11 + 1) = 9$
9th value is 25
Interquartile range = $25 - 16 = 9$
1 mark for correct method for either lower or upper quartile; 1 mark for subtracting your quartiles; 1 mark for correct final answer. Total 3 marks.

2. a Mean = $(11 + 12 + \ldots + 47 + 47) \div 19 = 542 \div 19$
         = 28.5 to 1 dp
1 mark for adding all values and dividing by 19; 1 mark for correct answer to 1 dp.
b $\frac{1}{2}(19 + 1) = 10$; 10th value is 22
  The median is 22
1 mark for $\frac{1}{2}(19 + 1)$ or for clear method to find the median; 1 mark for correct final answer.

c The position of the lower quartile is $\frac{1}{4}(19 + 1) = 5$

5th value is 19

The position of the upper quartile is $\frac{3}{4}(19 + 1) = 15$

15th value is 45

Interquartile range = 45 − 19 = 26

1 mark for correct method for either lower or upper quartile;
1 mark for correct final answer.

3. The position of the upper quartile is $\frac{3}{4}(7 + 1) = 6$

6th value is 8

The position of the lower quartile is $\frac{1}{4}(7 + 1) = 2$

2nd value is the missing number

3 = 8 − missing number

So missing number is 5

1 mark for correct method to find either quartile; 1 mark for correct final answer.

4. Physics:

The position of the median is $\frac{1}{2}(15 + 1) = 8$

8th value is 71

The position of the lower quartile is $\frac{1}{4}(15 + 1) = 4$

4th value is 54

The position of the upper quartile is $\frac{3}{4}(15 + 1) = 12$

12th value is 72

Interquartile range = 72 − 54 = 18

Maths:

The position of the median is $\frac{1}{2}(15 + 1) = 8$

8th value is 67

The position of the lower quartile is $\frac{1}{4}(15 + 1) = 4$

4th value is 56

The position of the upper quartile is $\frac{3}{4}(15 + 1) = 12$

12th value is 78

Interquartile range = 78 − 56 = 22

The median score for physics is higher than for maths.
The IQR for physics is lower so the physics scores are more consistent.

1 mark for correct method for either median or either lower or upper quartile for either maths or physics; 1 mark for subtracting your quartiles for either maths or physics; 1 mark for correct final answer for either maths or physics; 1 mark for both correct answers; 1 mark for correct conclusion e.g. higher and more consistent scores in physics. Total 5 marks.

Page 99, Simple charts

1. Number of tulips $= \frac{117}{360} \times 400 = 130$

So number of hyacinths = 400 − 180 − 130 = 90

So missing pie chart values are $\frac{180}{400} \times 360 = 162°$ for daffodils and $\frac{90}{400} \times 360 = 81°$ for hyacinths.

1 mark for correct number of tulips; 1 mark for correct number of hyacinths; 1 mark for correctly completed pie chart. Total 3 marks.

2. a

Mass (*m* kg)	Frequency
$0 < m \le 5$	**4**
$5 < m \le 10$	12
$10 < m \le 15$	6
$15 < m \le 20$	**18**
$20 < m \le 25$	3

1 mark for at least 3 cells correctly completed; 1 mark for fully correct.

b Estimate of total mass
$= (2.5 \times 4) + (7.5 \times 12) + (12.5 \times 6) + (17.5 \times 18) + (22.5 \times 3)$
$= 10 + 90 + 75 + 315 + 67.5 = 557.5$

Total frequency = 4 + 12 + 6 + 18 + 3 = 43

Estimate of mean = 557.5 ÷ 43 = 12.965…
= 13 kg to nearest kg

1 mark for use of frequency midpoint; 1 mark for complete method to find estimate of total mass (= 557.5); 1 mark for attempt to find total frequency (= 43); 1 mark for correct answer to nearest kg. Total 4 marks.

Page 100, Scatter graphs

1. a

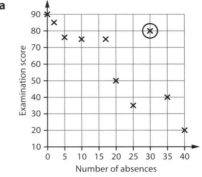

1 mark for at most one error in points plotted; 1 mark if all correct.

b Outlier at (30, 80) circled on graph (see above).
Possible reason: recording error, very bright student.

1 mark for correct answer; 1 mark for sensible reason.

c Negative

1 mark for correct answer.

2. Cooper is not correct. The first graph shows a linear relationship and the second graph shows a non-linear relationship.

1 mark for clear explanation that Cooper is wrong.

Page 101, Lines of best fit

1. Both are affected by warm weather but not by each other.

1 mark for suitable explanation.

2. a Including an outlier would mean the line doesn't follow the general trend of the rest of the data.

1 mark for clear explanation.

b Negative correlation

1 mark for correct answer

c

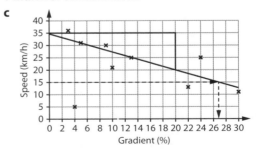

1 mark for line of best fit drawn as above.

d 26.5% (see graph)

1 mark for a value between 24 and 28

e Gradient of line of best fit is approximately
−15 ÷ 20 = −0.75
The speed decreases by around 0.75 km/h for every 1% gradient increase.
1 mark for attempt to find the gradient of the line of best fit; 1 mark for answer between 0.7 and 0.8

f Unreliable as outside range of data values (extrapolation)
1 mark for suitable explanation.

Page 102, Time series

1. As time passes, the price is decreasing.
1 mark for correct answer.

2. a

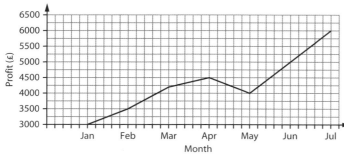

1 mark for any 6 points correctly plotted and joined with straight lines; 1 mark for all points correctly plotted.

b The general trend is increasing.
1 mark for 'increasing'.

c The vertical axis does not start at zero.
1 mark for correct answer.

3. a The general trend is decreasing.
1 mark for 'decreasing'.

b Week 1 and Week 4
1 mark for both correct.

c 150 approximately
1 mark for anything between 100 and 200

Page 103, Box plots

1. Lengths in order: 0.8 0.8 0.8 0.9 1.0 1.1 1.1 1.1 1.3 1.3 1.4
1.4 1.4 1.5 1.5 1.6 1.7 1.7 1.7 1.8 1.8 1.9 1.9 2.0 2.0
Minimum = 0.8
Maximum = 2.0
Median = $\frac{1}{2}$(25 + 1) = 13; 13th value = 1.4
Lower quartile = $\frac{1}{4}$(25 + 1) = 6.5
Mean of 6th and 7th values = 1.1
Upper quartile = $\frac{3}{4}$(25 + 1) = 19.5
Mean of 19th and 20th values = 1.75

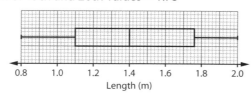

1 mark for correct method to find median or either quartile (or for 1.4, 1.1 or 1.75 correct); 1 mark for median and both quartiles correct; 1 mark for your median and quartiles plotted correctly to form the box; 1 mark for fully correct box plot. Total 4 marks.

2. a

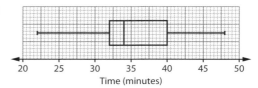

1 mark for median and quartiles plotted correctly to form the box; 1 mark for fully correct.

b For Y10, median = 34 and IQR = 8
For Y11, median = 37.5 and IQR = 42 − 32.5 = 9.5
The median and IQR are both higher for Y11. This shows that, on average, they spend longer doing their homework, but there is also a greater variation in the times.
1 mark for median = 37.5; 1 mark for IQR = 9.5; 1 mark for comparing medians and IQRs correctly. Total 3 marks.

Page 104, Cumulative frequency

1. a

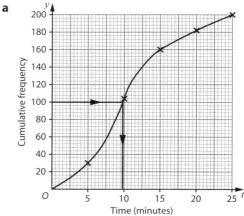

1 mark for plotting upper boundaries against cumulative; 1 mark if all plotted correctly and curve drawn.

b Median is approximately 9.7 minutes
1 mark for correct answer.

2.

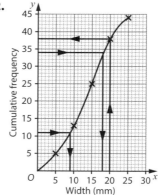

a Lower quartile (25% of 44 = 11) is approximately 9 mm
Upper quartile (75% of 44 = 33) is approximately 18 mm
So IQR = 18 − 9 = 9 mm
1 mark for lines drawn (as above) for lower quartile or upper quartile or for 8.5 to 9.5 or 17.5 to 18.5; 1 mark for IQR between 8 and 10

b 44 − 38 = 6
1 mark for line drawn as on graph; 1 mark for correct answer.

Page 105, Histograms

1. a

Speed (s km/h)	Frequency	Frequency density
$65 < s \le 70$	25	5.0
$70 < s \le 80$	**44**	4.4
$80 < s \le 85$	21	4.2
$85 < s \le 100$	**18**	1.2

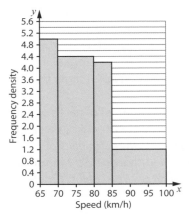

1 mark for either 25 or 21; 1 mark for both frequency table entries correct; 1 mark for a correct frequency density calculated (4.4 or 1.2) or for one bar correct; 1 mark for histogram fully correct. Total 4 marks.

b Mean = [67.5 × 25 + 75 × 44 + 82.5 × 21 + 92.5 × 18] ÷
[25 + 44 + 21 + 18]
= 77.6 km/h to 3 sf

1 mark for using correct midpoints or correct frequencies; 1 mark for attempting to use correct formula for mean; 1 mark for correct answer. Total 3 marks.

c There are 25 + 44 + 21 + 18 = 108 cars, so the median is the 54.5th value.
This lies in the $70 < s \le 80$ class interval.

1 mark for finding the position of the median; 1 mark for correct answer.

2. a Frequency density for 10 to 20 class = 27 ÷ 10 = 2.7
This gives the vertical scale and the other frequency densities: 3.2, 1.8, 0.7
Estimate for players who took more than 30 seconds
= (5 × 1.8) + (15 × 0.7) = 9 + 10.5
= 19.5 players i.e. 20 players

1 mark for 2.7 frequency density or correct scale seen or implied; 1 mark for 5 × 1.8 (= 9) or 15 × 0.7 (= 10.5); 1 mark for correct final answer. Total 3 marks.

b 30 is in the middle of a class. Assumed that the times are equally spaced within each class.

1 mark for correct answer.

Page 106, Theoretical probability

1. $x + x + \frac{1}{2} = 1$; $2x = \frac{1}{2}$; $x = \frac{1}{4}$

1 mark for $x + x + \frac{1}{2} = 1$ or $2x = \frac{1}{2}$; 1 mark for correct answer of $\frac{1}{4}$ or 0.25

2. a $1 - (0.3 + 0.15 + 0.26) = 1 - 0.71 = 0.29$

1 mark for $1 - (0.3 + 0.15 + 0.26)$ or $1 - 0.71$; 1 mark for correct answer of 0.29 or $\frac{29}{100}$

b P(not white or orange)
= P(yellow or pink) = 0.15 + 0.26 = 0.41

1 mark for 0.15 + 0.26; 1 mark for correct answer of 0.41 or $\frac{41}{100}$

Alternative solution:
P(not white or orange) = 1 – P(white or orange)
= 1 – (0.3 + 0.29) = 1 – 0.59
= 0.41

1 mark for 1 – (0.3 + 0.29) or 1 – 0.59; 1 mark for correct answer.

c P(yellow) = 0.15
0.15 × 200 = 30

1 mark for 0.15 × 200; 1 mark for correct answer of 30

Alternative solution:
P(yellow) = $0.15 = \frac{15}{100} = \frac{30}{200}$
So 30 counters are yellow.

1 mark for $\frac{30}{200}$; 1 mark for correct answer of 30

3. a 0

1 mark for correct answer.

b There are 6 + 5 = 11 non-red counters. So for the probability to be half, there must also be 11 red counters. 11 – 4 = 7, so she adds 7 red counters.

1 mark for determining the number of red counters required in total; 1 mark for correct answer.

Page 107, Outcomes and possibility spaces

1. a $\frac{1}{36}$ **b** $\frac{10}{36}$ or $\frac{5}{18}$ **c** $\frac{18}{36}$ or equivalent e.g. $\frac{1}{2}$

1 mark for each correct answer.

2. a Choices for 1st digit are 1, 2, 3, 4, 5, 6, 7, 8 and 9 i.e. 9 choices.
Choices for 2nd digit are 1, 3, 5, 7 and 9 i.e. 5 choices.
So number of ways = 9 × 5 = 45

1 mark for multiplying two integers where at least one of them is 9 or 5; 1 mark for correct answer.

b Choices are 11, 33, 55, 77 and 99 i.e. 5 choices.
So probability = $\frac{5}{45} = \frac{1}{9}$

1 mark for numerator of 5 or denominator of 45; 1 mark for correct answer (does not have to be simplified).

3. a 13 choices for 1st ball and 12 choices for 2nd ball.
So number of ways = 13 × 12 = 156

1 mark for product with at least one of 13 and 12; 1 mark for correct answer.

b For red followed by yellow:
6 choices for 1st ball and 7 choices for 2nd ball.
So number of ways = 6 × 7 = 42
For yellow followed by red:
7 choices for 1st ball and 6 choices for 2nd ball.
So number of ways = 7 × 6 = 42
Total number of ways = 42 + 42 = 84

1 mark for product with at least one of 7 and 6; 1 mark for 42; 1 mark for correct final answer. Total 3 marks.

4. For heart, not heart, heart:
13 choices for 1st card, 39 choices for 2nd card and 12 choices for 3rd card.
So number of ways = 13 × 39 × 12 = 6084
For heart, heart, heart:
13 choices for 1st card, 12 choices for 2nd card and 11 choices for 3rd card.
So number of ways = 13 × 12 × 11 = 1716
Total number of ways = 6084 + 1716 = 7800

1 mark for at least one of 13 × 39 × 12 or 13 × 12 × 11; 1 mark for either 6084 or 1716; 1 mark for adding answers to both calculations; 1 mark for correct final answer. Total 4 marks.

Page 108, Probability experiments

1. a

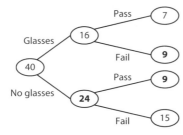

1 mark for no more than 1 error; *1 mark* for fully correct.

b $\frac{7}{40}$

1 mark for correct answer.

2. a

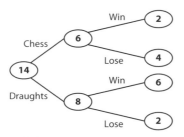

1 mark for no more than 2 errors; *1 mark* for fully correct.

b $\frac{4}{14}$ or $\frac{2}{7}$

1 mark for correct answer.

3. a

Outcome	Right way up	On its side	Upside down
Frequency	8	22	20
Relative frequency	0.16	0.44	0.4

1 mark for one value correctly filled in; *1 mark* for all correct values.

b Probability in first experiment = 0.4
Probability in second experiment = 36 ÷ 100 = 0.36
So probability was higher in first experiment.

1 mark for attempting to find probabilities for 'upside down' in both experiments; *1 mark* for correct answer with comparison.

*Allow full marks if an incorrect answer from part **a** is used as the probability, but the comparison is justified.*

Page 109, Expected results

1. a 0.85 × 60 = 51
Expect 51 reports on time.

1 mark for 0.85 × 60 or $\frac{51}{60}$; *1 mark* for correct answer.

b 0.85 × 170 = 144.5
160 > 144.5, so more than expected.

1 mark for 0.85 × 170; *1 mark* for correct answer.

Alternative solution:
$\frac{160}{170}$ = 0.94…
0.94… > 0.85, so more than expected.

1 mark for 0.94; *1 mark* for correct answer.

2. a $\frac{3}{8}$ or 0.375

1 mark for correct answer.

b $\frac{2}{8}$ × 40 = 10
Expect it 10 times.

1 mark for $\frac{2}{8}$ × 40 or $\frac{10}{40}$; *1 mark* for correct answer.

c 36 ÷ 3 × 8 = 96
Expect 96 throws.

1 mark for 36 ÷ 3 × 8 or $\frac{36}{96}$; *1 mark* for correct answer.

3. P(lands on 5) = 1 – (0.2 + 0.4 + 0.16 + 0.13) = 0.11
2500 × 0.11 = 275
Expect 275 times.

1 mark for 1 – (0.2 + 0.4 + 0.16 + 0.13) or 0.11; *1 mark* for 2500 × your probability of the spinner landing on 5; *1 mark* for correct answer. Total 3 marks.

4. The probability of one bulb lasting longer than 25 000 and another one not is 0.92 × 0.08 = 0.0736
There are two ways of achieving this configuration in a pack of two bulbs, so the probability of a pack having exactly one bulb that lasts longer than 25 000 hours is 0.0736 × 2 = 0.1472
So the expected number of packs out of 500 is 0.1472 × 500 = 73.6 = 74 packs (to nearest whole number).

1 mark for finding the probability of getting 1 bulb that lasts longer and 1 that doesn't; *1 mark* for calculating this probability for a pack of 2 bulbs; *1 mark* for correct answer. Total 3 marks.

Page 110, Tree diagrams

1.

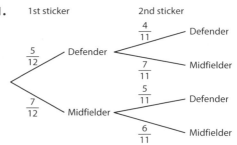

a P(both midfielders) = $\frac{7}{12} \times \frac{6}{11} = \frac{42}{132} = \frac{7}{22}$
1 mark for multiplying along correct two branches; *1 mark* for correct answer.

b P(different positions) = $\frac{5}{12} \times \frac{7}{11} + \frac{7}{12} \times \frac{5}{11} = \frac{70}{132} = \frac{35}{66}$
1 mark for multiplying along any correct two branches; *1 mark* for multiplying along two sets of branches and adding; *1 mark* for correct answer. Total 3 marks.

2. a P(win backgammon) = $\frac{1}{2} \div \frac{2}{3} = \frac{1}{2} \times \frac{3}{2} = \frac{3}{4}$
P(lose backgammon) = $\frac{1}{4}$
1 mark for $\frac{1}{2} \div \frac{2}{3}$; *1 mark* for $\frac{3}{4}$ on correct branch; *1 mark* for $\frac{1}{4}$ on correct branch. Total 3 marks.

b P(friend wins at most one game)
= P(Nkem wins at least one game)
= $\frac{2}{3} \times \frac{3}{4} + \frac{2}{3} \times \frac{1}{4} + \frac{1}{3} \times \frac{2}{5} = \frac{4}{5}$
1 mark for multiplying along at least 2 sets of branches and adding; *1 mark* for multiplying along 3 sets and adding; *1 mark* for correct answer. Total 3 marks.

Alternative solution:
P(friend wins at most one game)
= 1 – P(Nkem wins no games)
= $1 - \frac{1}{3} \times \frac{3}{5} = 1 - \frac{1}{5} = \frac{4}{5}$
1 mark for multiplying along correct branch only; *1 mark* for subtracting from 1; *1 mark* for correct answer. Total 3 marks.

3.

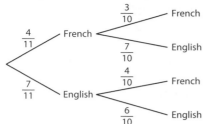

First person   Second person

Probability of one French and one English speaker
$= \frac{4}{11} \times \frac{7}{10} + \frac{7}{11} \times \frac{4}{10} = 0.509\ldots = 50.9\ldots\%$

*1 mark for correct first set of branches with probabilities correct;
1 mark for correct second set of branches with probabilities
correct; 1 mark for adding the probabilities of the two correct
sets of branches (allow mark if probabilities are incorrect);
1 mark for showing probability of 50.9(…)%. Total 4 marks.*

Page 111, Conditional probability 1

1. a $\frac{8}{200}$

1 mark for correct answer or equivalent e.g. $\frac{1}{25}$, 0.04

b 76 + 26 = 102 didn't buy a burger.
So probability $= \frac{18+4}{102} = \frac{22}{102}$

*1 mark for a denominator of 102; 1 mark for fully correct
answer or equivalent e.g. $\frac{11}{51}$*

2. a $\frac{35}{150}$

1 mark for correct answer or equivalent e.g. $\frac{7}{30}$

b 51 study German.
So probability $= \frac{17}{51}$

*1 mark for a denominator of 51; 1 mark for fully correct
answer or equivalent e.g. $\frac{1}{3}$*

3.

Coin\Dice	Even number	Odd number
Heads	**27**	23
Tails	24	**26**

*1 mark for 27 or 26 correctly placed; 1 mark for both
correctly placed.*

Page 112, Conditional probability 2

1. a $0.5 \times 0.7 + 0.5 \times 0.4 = 0.35 + 0.2 = 0.55$

*1 mark for $0.5 \times 0.7 + 0.5 \times 0.4$; 1 mark for correct answer or
equivalent e.g. $\frac{55}{100}, \frac{11}{20}$*

b Probability of missing 2nd penalty = 1 − 0.55 = 0.45
(or $0.5 \times 0.3 + 0.5 \times 0.6 = 0.45$)
So P(score 1st given miss 2nd) $= \frac{0.5 \times 0.3}{0.45} = \frac{15}{45}$

*1 mark for P(miss 2nd penalty) = 1 − your answer to part a;
1 mark for correct $\frac{0.5 \times 0.3}{P(missing\ 2nd\ penalty)}$; 1 mark for correct
final answer or equivalent e.g. $\frac{1}{3}$. Total 3 marks.*

2. P(A given B) $= \frac{P(A\ and\ B)}{P(B)}$

$0.45 = \frac{0.375}{P(B)}$

$P(B) = 0.375 \div 0.45 = \frac{5}{6}$

$P(not\ B) = 1 - \frac{5}{6} = \frac{1}{6}$

*1 mark for attempt to use conditional probability formula;
1 mark for 0.375 ÷ 0.45; 1 mark for 1 − P(B); 1 mark for
correct final answer or equivalent e.g. 0.1$\dot{6}$. Total 4 marks.*

3. Let 4x be the number of red balls.
Then 5x is the number of blue balls and the total
number is 9x
Construct a tree diagram:

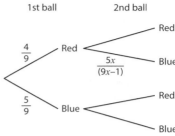

1st ball   2nd ball

P(red then blue) $= \frac{4}{9} \times \frac{5x}{9x - 1} = \frac{40}{159}$
$159x = 18(9x - 1)$; $18 = 3x$; $x = 6$
So 4x = 24
The number of red balls was 24

*1 mark for attempt to construct a tree diagram with correct
probabilities used; 1 mark for $\frac{4}{9} \times$ something $= \frac{40}{159}$ or
$\frac{40}{159} \div \frac{4}{9}$; 1 mark for $\frac{30}{53}$ or for attempt to solve an equation
in terms of unknown total number of balls or red balls;
1 mark for correct final answer of 24. Total 4 marks.
Full marks can be awarded if a correct answer is given
without the use of a diagram.*

Page 113, Set notation

1.

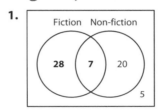

*1 mark for 28 in correct position; 1 mark for 7 in correct
position.*

2.

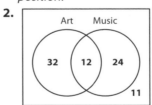

*1 mark for each number placed in correct position. Total
4 marks.*

3. a {2, 3, 6, 7, 9, 10, 12}   **b** {10, 12, 17, 18}
1 mark for each correct answer.

4. a

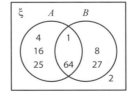

*1 mark for 4, 16 and 25 correctly placed; 1 mark for 1 and
64 correctly placed; 1 mark for 8 and 27 correctly placed;
1 mark for 2 correctly placed. Total 4 marks.*

b {1, 64}
1 mark for fully correct.

Page 114, Probability from Venn diagrams

1. a

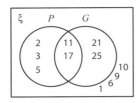

*1 mark for 2, 3 and 5 correctly placed; **1 mark** for 11 and 17 correctly placed; **1 mark** for 21 and 25 correctly placed; **1 mark** for 1, 6, 9 and 10 correctly placed. Total 4 marks.*

b i $\frac{2}{11}$ **ii** $\frac{7}{11}$ **iii** $\frac{3}{11}$

1 mark for each correct answer.

2. a Total customers = 88

Total for not apples = $11 + 8 + 14 = 33$

So probability = $\frac{33}{88}$

*1 mark for denominator of 88; **1 mark** for fully correct answer or equivalent e.g. $\frac{3}{8}$, 0.375*

b Bananas = $8 + 12 + 13 + 14 = 47$

So probability = $\frac{13 + 12}{47} = \frac{25}{47}$

*1 mark for denominator of 47; **1 mark** for fully correct answer.*

3. a Construct a Venn diagram:

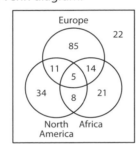

$\text{P(Europe)} = \frac{85 + 11 + 5 + 14}{200} = \frac{115}{200}$

*1 mark for attempt to draw an appropriate Venn diagram i.e. 3 intersecting circles inside a square/rectangle; **1 mark** for 85 in 'Europe only' or for at least 6 of the 8 entries correctly placed on the Venn diagram; **1 mark** for numerator of 115; **1 mark** for correct answer or equivalent e.g. $\frac{23}{40}$, 0.575. Total 4 marks.*

Full marks can be awarded if a correct answer is given without the use of a diagram.

b North America = $34 + 11 + 5 + 8 = 58$

North America and Africa = $5 + 8$

So probability = $\frac{13}{58}$

*1 mark for denominator of 58; **1 mark** for fully correct answer.*

Practice exam paper guided answers

For further practice and support, see the page reference after each guided answer.

Paper 1 (Non-calculator)

1. $1 - \frac{2}{5} = \frac{3}{5}$

$\frac{1}{8} \times \frac{3}{5} = \frac{3}{40}$

$\frac{3}{40} + \frac{2}{5} = \frac{3}{40} + \frac{16}{40} = \frac{19}{40}$

*1 mark for $\frac{1}{8} \times \frac{3}{5}$; **1 mark** for adding answer to $\frac{2}{5}$; **1 mark** for correct answer. Total 3 marks.*

See page 5, Adding & subtracting fractions and page 6, Multiplying & dividing fractions

2. a −3 is the first missing number since it must occur more than once.

The mean is 7, so the total of all the numbers is
$7 \times 7 = 49$

Other missing number is
$49 - (-3 - 3 + 1 + 4 + 7 + 32) = 11$

1 mark for each missing number.

b Range = $32 - (-3) = 35$

Median = 4

1 mark for each correct answer.

c Mode is unsuitable as it gives the lowest value in the list.

Mean is unsuitable as 32 is an outlier.

Median is the best choice as it doesn't use outliers.

*1 mark for mentioning outliers; **1 mark** for correct answer and reason.*

See page 96, Averages and spread

3. Percentage increase in price for large vs. small

$= \frac{(90 - 75)}{75} \times 100\% = \frac{15}{75} \times 100\% = 20\%$

The number of sweets increases by 35% and the cost increases by 20%, so the large bag is better value.

*1 mark for an attempt to find the % increase in the price e.g. $\frac{(90 - 75)}{75} \times 100\%$; **1 mark** for 20%; **1 mark** for comparison with correct conclusion i.e. large bag is better value. Total 3 marks.*

See page 58, Percentage change

4. 1st graph: $y = x^2$; 2nd graph: $y = \frac{1}{x}$

3rd graph: $y = x$; 4th graph: $y = x^3$

*1 mark for any two equations matched to the correct graphs; **1 mark** if all correct.*

See page 38, Cubic and reciprocal graphs

5. Difference in number of 'parts' = $7 - 2 = 5$

5 parts = 90 cm; 1 part = $90 \div 5 = 18$ cm

Length of wood = total number of parts × 18

$= (2 + 7) \times 18 = 9 \times 18 = 162$ cm

*1 mark for 5 parts = 90 cm; **1 mark** for $9 \times (90 \div 5)$ or equivalent; **1 mark** for correct answer. Total 3 marks.*

See page 57, Harder ratio problems

6.

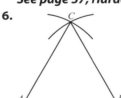

*1 mark for attempt to draw two construction arcs positioned as shown or a different orientation; **1 mark** for fully correct triangle including construction arcs.*

See page 79, Constructing triangles

7. $(2 \times 10^{-4}) \times (3 \times 10^3)^2 = (2 \times 10^{-4}) \times (9 \times 10^6)$

$= 18 \times 10^2 = 1.8 \times 10^3$

*1 mark for correct first step i.e. $(3 \times 10^3)^2 = 9 \times 10^6$; **1 mark** for correct second step e.g. $(2 \times 10^{-4}) \times$ your (9×10^6) (= 18×10^2); **1 mark** for correct final answer in standard form. Total 3 marks.*

See page 14, Calculating with standard form

8. a $168 = 2 \times 2 \times 2 \times 3 \times 7$

1 mark *for prime factor tree (or equivalent) with at least one correct product pair seen;* ***1 mark*** *for correct final answer or equivalent e.g.* $2^3 \times 3 \times 7$

b $168 \times 441 = (2^3 \times 3 \times 7) \times (3^2 \times 7^2)$
$\qquad\qquad\quad = (2 \times 3 \times 7)^3 = 42^3$
$\qquad\qquad n = 42$

1 mark *for* $(2 \times 3 \times 7)^3$; ***1 mark*** *for correct final answer.*

See page 11, Prime factor decomposition

9. Let the number of catfish be x

$\dfrac{12}{x} = \dfrac{6}{20}$

$x = \dfrac{20 \times 12}{6} = 40$

The estimated number of catfish in the lake is 40

1 mark *for proportion used (e.g.* $\frac{6}{20}$ *or* $\frac{6}{12}$ *seen);* ***1 mark*** *for* $\frac{20 \times 12}{6}$; ***1 mark*** *for correct answer. Total 3 marks.*

See page 95, Capture-recapture method

10. $3\frac{2}{3} \times 2\frac{1}{4} \div 2\frac{1}{2} = \frac{11}{3} \times \frac{9}{4} \times \frac{2}{5} = \frac{11}{1} \times \frac{3}{2} \times \frac{1}{5} = \frac{33}{10} = 3\frac{3}{10}$

1 mark *for any of the three mixed numbers correctly converted to an improper fraction;* ***1 mark*** *for attempt to cancel common factors or for* $\frac{33}{10}$ *or equivalent e.g.* $\frac{198}{60}$; ***1 mark*** *for correct final answer as a mixed number in its simplest form. Total 3 marks.*

See page 6, Multiplying & dividing fractions

11. $3x - 13 + y = x + 5$ and $y + x + 5 = 3y - 6$

Simplifying: $2x + y = 18$ (1) and $x - 2y = -11$ (2)

$2 \times$ (1) + (2): $5x = 25; x = 5$

Substituting $x = 5$ into (1) gives $2 \times 5 + y = 18; y = 8$

1 mark *for forming a correct equation (can be unsimplified);* ***1 mark*** *for forming two correct simplified equations;* ***1 mark*** *for attempt to eliminate one variable to achieve* $x = \dots$ *or* $y = \dots$; ***1 mark*** *for either x or y correct;* ***1 mark*** *for fully correct. Total 5 marks.*

See page 22, Linear simultaneous equations

12. $(\sin 45°)^2 : (\cos 30°)^2 : (\tan 60°)^2 = \left(\frac{\sqrt{2}}{2}\right)^2 : \left(\frac{\sqrt{3}}{2}\right)^2 : (\sqrt{3})^2$
$\qquad\qquad\qquad\qquad\qquad\qquad\qquad = \frac{2}{4} : \frac{3}{4} : 3 = 2 : 3 : 12$

This is in the form $a : b : c$ where a, b and c are integers. Therefore, Steven is wrong.

1 mark *for* $\frac{1}{\sqrt{2}}$ *or* $\left(\frac{\sqrt{2}}{2}\right)$ *or* $\frac{\sqrt{3}}{2}$ *or* $\sqrt{3}$; ***1 mark*** *for attempt to work out each square or to multiply each part of ratio by 4;* ***1 mark*** *for correct final answer with justification. Total 3 marks.*

See page 86, Exact values of sin, cos, tan

13. a All quadratics are parabolas which have one turning point.

1 mark *for 'It is a quadratic' or 'It is a parabola' etc.*

b $x^2 - 10x + 7 = (x - 5)^2 - 25 + 7 = (x - 5)^2 - 18$

Minimum when $x = 5$ and $y = -18$

Coordinates of turning point = $(5, -18)$

1 mark *for completing the square i.e.* $(x - 5)^2 - 25 + 7$ *or* $(x - 5)^2 - 18$; ***1 mark*** *for correct final coordinates.*

See page 28, Completing the square

14. a Consider a rhombus $PQRS$ and let the intersection of the diagonals be C

All sides of a rhombus are equal, so

$PQ = SR = PS = QR$

Also, as the diagonals bisect each other, $PC = CR$ and $QC = CS$

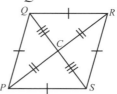

All four triangles have the same sides (SSS). Therefore, all four triangles are congruent.

1 mark *for* $PQ = SR = PS = QR$; ***1 mark*** *for* $PC = CR$ *and* $QC = CS$; ***1 mark*** *for fully justified conclusion e.g. SSS, so congruent. Total 3 marks.*

b From part **a**, all four triangles are congruent, so angle $PCS =$ angle $SCR =$ angle $RCQ =$ angle QCP

However, angles at a point add up to 360°, so each is a right angle.

Therefore, the diagonals are perpendicular.

1 mark *for using part* ***a*** *to deduce that angles at intersection are equal;* ***1 mark*** *for fully justified conclusion e.g. angles at intersection all 90°, so diagonals are perpendicular.*

See page 72, Congruent shapes

15. $\dfrac{1 + \sqrt{2}}{3\sqrt{5}} \times \dfrac{\sqrt{5}}{\sqrt{5}} = \dfrac{\sqrt{5} + \sqrt{10}}{15}$

1 mark *for multiplying both numerator and denominator by* $\sqrt{5}$ *(or* $3\sqrt{5}$*);* ***1 mark*** *for correct final answer (must be simplified).*

See page 9, Surds

16. Area of triangle = 25, so $\frac{1}{2} \times OA \times 5 = 25$

Therefore, $OA = 10$ and coordinates of A are $(10, 0)$.

Gradient of $l_1 = -5 \div 10 = -\frac{1}{2}$

Gradient of $l_2 = -1 \div -\frac{1}{2} = 2$ since the lines are perpendicular.

$\dfrac{16 - 7}{7 - a} = 2; 9 = 14 - 2a; a = 2.5$

1 mark *for* $\frac{1}{2} \times OA \times 5 = 25$ *(or for* $OA = 10$*);* ***1 mark*** *for gradient of* $l_1 = -5 \div 10 \left(= -\frac{1}{2}\right)$; ***1 mark*** *for gradient of* $l_2 = -1 \div$ *gradient of* $l_1 (= 2)$; ***1 mark*** *for final answer of* $a = 2.5$. *Total 4 marks.*

See page 19, Perpendicular lines

17. Write 4 and 8 as powers of 2

$(2^2)^2 \times (2^3)^2 = \dfrac{1}{2^x}$

$\qquad 2^4 \times 2^6 = 2^{-x}$

$\qquad\qquad 2^{10} = 2^{-x}$

$\qquad\qquad\quad x = -10$

1 mark *for attempt to use base of 2 i.e. either* $(2^2)^2$ *or* $(2^3)^2$ *seen;* ***1 mark*** *for power rule correctly used i.e. either* 2^4 *or* 2^6 *seen or for addition rule used correctly i.e. either* 2^{10} *or* $10 = -x$ *seen;* ***1 mark*** *for correct final answer. Total 3 marks.*

See page 10, Index notation

18. a $10 \times 3 = 30$ students
1 mark for 10×3; 1 mark for correct final answer.

b i

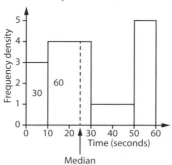

Total area of bars
$= (10 \times 3) + (20 \times 4) + (20 \times 1) + (10 \times 5) = 180$
$180 \div 2 = 90$ students
$(10 \times 3) + [(\text{median} - 10) \times 4)] = 90$
Median $- 10 = 15$
Estimate of median = 25 seconds
1 mark for attempt to find total area of the bars (= 180); 1 mark for dividing by 2 (= 90); 1 mark for attempt to show that required point is where area of 2nd bar is 60 (can be shown on diagram); 1 mark for correct answer of 25. Total 4 marks.

ii It is based on class intervals only, not actual times.
1 mark for correct answer e.g. the histogram does not show individual times etc.

See page 105, Histograms

19. a $\frac{1}{f(x)}$ is the reciprocal of f(x), not the inverse.
1 mark for identifying $\frac{1}{f(x)}$ as the reciprocal of f(x) or for explanation of how the inverse can be found e.g. change the subject to x etc.

b Let $y = \frac{1-x}{2x+4}$
$y(2x + 4) = 1 - x$
$2xy + 4y = 1 - x$
$2xy + x = 1 - 4y$
$x(2y + 1) = 1 - 4y$
$x = \frac{1-4y}{2y+1}$
$f^{-1}(x) = \frac{1-4x}{2x+1}$
1 mark for setting y = f(x) and attempting to change the subject to x; 1 mark for $\frac{1-4y}{2y+1}$; 1 mark for final correct answer. Total 3 marks.

See page 54, Inverse functions

20. a Convert km/h to m/s.
$8 \, \text{km/h} = \frac{8 \times 1000}{60 \times 60} \, \text{m/s}$
$= \frac{20}{9} \, \text{m/s} = 2.\dot{2} \, \text{m/s}$
$2.5 > 2.\dot{2}$, so Jordan is faster.
1 mark for correct calculation for conversion; 1 mark for clear comparison of correct figures with correct conclusion.

Alternative solution:
Convert m/s to km/h.
$2.5 \, \text{m/s} = \frac{2.5 \times 60 \times 60}{1000} \, \text{km/h} = 9 \, \text{km/h}$
1 mark for correct calculation for conversion; 1 mark for clear comparison of correct figures with correct conclusion.

b Distance = 8500 m = 8.5 km
$2.5 \, \text{m/s} = \frac{2.5 \times 60 \times 60}{1000} \, \text{km/h} = 9 \, \text{km/h}$
Combined speed of runners = 8 km/h + 9 km/h
$= 17 \, \text{km/h}$

Time = $8.5 \div 17 = 0.5$ hours = 30 minutes
The runners will pass each other after 30 minutes.
1 mark for attempt to combine speeds i.e. 8 + 9 or $2.5 + 2.\dot{2}$; 1 mark for dividing total distance by combined speeds or for answer of 0.5; 1 mark for correct answer of 30 minutes. Total 3 marks.

c Riley's speed is 8 km/h = 4 km per 30 minutes.
The runners meet 4 km from point A
*1 mark for attempt to convert 8 km/h to km per your time from part **b** (or 2.5 m/s to m per your time from part **b**); 1 mark for correct answer including units i.e. 4 km or 4000 m.*

See page 61, Compound measures

21. a $(a^b + 1)(a^b - 1) = a^{2b} - ab + ab - 1 = a^{2b} - 1$
1 mark for attempt to expand; 1 mark for correct, simplified answer.

b $a^{2b} - 1 = (a^b + 1)(a^b - 1)$
As a and b are both integers greater than 1, $a^b - 1$ and $a^b + 1$ are distinct positive integers greater than 1, so $a^{2b} - 1$ has two distinct factors both greater than 1. Therefore, $a^{2b} - 1$ cannot be prime.
1 mark for $a^{2b} - 1 = (a^b + 1)(a^b - 1)$; 1 mark for explanation about factors; 1 mark for correct conclusion. Total 3 marks.

See page 23, Expanding brackets

Paper 2 (Calculator)

1. a $0.865 < x \le 0.875$
1 mark for 0.865 or 0.875 at correct end of an error interval; 1 mark for fully correct.

b $7 \le y < 8$
1 mark for 7 or 8 at correct end of an error interval; 1 mark for fully correct.

See page 2, Rounding & truncation

2. Original price $\times 0.77 = £48.77$
So, original price $= \frac{48.77}{0.77} = £63.34$ (to 2 dp)
This is not £59.99, so the sign is incorrect.
1 mark for using 0.77 as a multiplier or for stating that £48.77 = 77%; 1 mark for $\frac{48.77}{0.77}$ or equivalent; 1 mark for correct conclusion with correct reason. Total 3 marks. Note that there are alternative methods.

See page 59, Using multipliers

3. Class 3A has a greater median, so their scores are higher on average.
Class 3B has a lower range, so their scores are more consistent.
1 mark for comparing medians in context e.g. 'Average scores lower for 3B'; 1 mark for comparing ranges in context e.g. '3A are less consistent'.

See page 96, Averages and spread

4. $12\,742\,000 \, \text{m} = 1.2742 \times 10^7$
$1.429\,84 \times 10^8 = 14.2984 \times 10^7$
Comparing the numbers written as multiples of the same power of 10 shows the diameter of Jupiter is closer to 10 times ($14.2984 \div 1.2742$) the diameter of Earth, not 1000 times. Sebastian is wrong.
1 mark for converting first number to standard form; 1 mark for comparing numbers; 1 mark for correct conclusion and reason. Total 3 marks. Note that there are alternative methods.

See page 13, Standard form

5. 4 hours and 20 minutes $= 4\frac{1}{3}$ hours

Speed $= 440 \div 4\frac{1}{3} = 101.538\ldots = 101.5$ km/h to 1 dp

1 mark *for converting 20 minutes to $\frac{1}{3}$ hours;* ***1 mark*** *for dividing distance by time;* ***1 mark*** *for correct answer to 1 dp. Total 3 marks.*

See page 61, Compound measures

6. $25\% = \frac{1}{4}$ (= white)

$\frac{1}{4} + \frac{1}{6} = \frac{3}{12} + \frac{2}{12} = \frac{5}{12}$

$1 - \frac{5}{12} = \frac{7}{12}$ (= green)

Ratio red : green $= \frac{2}{12} : \frac{7}{12} = 2:7$

1 mark *for converting percentage and fraction to same form;* ***1 mark*** *for adding and then subtracting from 1;* ***1 mark*** *for correct answer in correct order. Total 3 marks.*

See page 57, Harder ratio problems

7. Volume $= \pi r^2 h$

$1000 = \pi r^3$

$r = \sqrt[3]{\frac{1000}{\pi}} = 6.827\ldots = 6.8$ cm to 1 dp

1 mark *for attempt to use πr^3;* ***1 mark*** *for $\sqrt[3]{\frac{1000}{\pi}}$ (= 6.827…);* ***1 mark*** *for 6.8. Total 3 marks.*

See page 76, Prisms and cylinders

8. a $PQ:QR = 5:3 = 20:12$

$QR:RS = 4:7 = 12:21$

Therefore, $PQ:QR:RS = 20:12:21$

1 mark *for finding a common multiple of 3 and 4 e.g. 12, 24 (can be seen in a bar model);* ***1 mark*** *for correct answer or equivalent e.g. 40:24:42*

b $20 + 12 + 21 = 53$

$PQ:PS = 20:53 = 10:26.5$

Distance $PS = 26.5$ cm

1 mark *for attempt to use ratio $PQ:PQ + QR + RS$;* ***1 mark*** *for correct answer of 26.5 cm.*

See page 57, Harder ratio problems

9. a The differences are 4, 10, 16, 22 and 28 i.e. increasing by 6

The next two differences are 34 and 40

The next two terms are 121 and 161

1 mark *for 121 and 161 both correct.*

b Half the 2nd difference = 3

Use $3n^2$: 3, 12, 27, 48, 75, …

Subtracting from the original sequence:

4, –1, –6, –11, –16, …

This has differences of –5

nth term is $-5n + 9$

Hence, sequence is $3n^2 - 5n + 9$

1 mark *for $3n^2$;* ***1 mark*** *for either –5n or 9 or for subtracting from original sequence and attempting to find formula for this difference,* ***1 mark*** *for fully correct. Total 3 marks.*

See page 50, Quadratic sequences

10. Mass of silver per cm³ $= 10.49 \times 0.925 = 9.70325$ g

Mass of nickel per cm³ $= 9.908 \times 0.075 = 0.7431$ g

Density (= total mass per cm³) $= 9.70325 + 0.7431$

$= 10.44635 = 10.45$ g/cm³

1 mark *for either 10.49 × 0.925 (= 9.70325) or 9.908 × 0.075 (= 0.7431);* ***1 mark*** *for adding masses (= 10.446 35);* ***1 mark*** *for correct answer to 2 dp. Total 3 marks.*

See page 61, Compound measures

11. Initially, Celine has $3x$, Dean has $2x$ and Eileen has $5x$

Later, Celine has $3x$, Dean has $2x + 4$ and Eileen has $5x - 5$

Celine and Dean now have the same number of marshmallows, so $3x = 2x + 4$; $x = 4$

Therefore, Celine started with 12, Dean started with 8 and Eileen started with 20

1 mark *for an attempt to use algebra e.g. 3x or equivalent seen;* ***1 mark*** *for solving an equation;* ***1 mark*** *for correct final answer. Total 3 marks.*

Note that solutions based on trial-and-error methods score a maximum of 2 marks.

See page 57, Harder ratio problems

12. a $(x - 1)(x - 2)(x - 3)$

$= (x^2 - 3x + 2)(x - 3)$

$= x^3 - 3x^2 + 2x - 3x^2 + 9x - 6$

$= x^3 - 6x^2 + 11x - 6$

1 mark *for $x^2 - 3x + 2$ or $x^2 - 5x + 6$;* ***1 mark*** *for any three correct terms in final answer;* ***1 mark*** *for fully correct. Total 3 marks.*

b $n^4 - 6n^3 + 11n^2 - 6n = n(n^3 - 6n^2 + 11n - 6)$

$= n(n - 1)(n - 2)(n - 3)$ from part **a**

If n is even, then you have a multiple of 2

If n is odd, then $n - 1$ is even, so you have a multiple of 2

$n^4 - 6n^3 + 11n^2 - 6n$ is always a multiple of 2

Therefore, it is always even.

1 mark *for factorising;* ***1 mark*** *for consider n even and n odd with clear conclusion or explaining that, since it is a product of consecutive integers, one of them is even so product is even.*

See page 23, Expanding brackets and page 24, Factorising 1

13. $x = 0.\dot{7}0\dot{2}$

$1000x = 702.\dot{7}0\dot{2}$

Subtracting x from $1000x$ gives $999x = 702$

$x = \frac{702}{999} = \frac{26}{37}$

1 mark *for attempt to find 1000x,* ***1 mark*** *for subtracting your two equations;* ***1 mark*** *for fully correct. Total 3 marks.*

See page 8, Recurring decimals

14. a He has gone wrong on line 3. If the product of two expressions is negative, then one of the expressions must be positive. Chad's are both negative.

1 mark *for identifying line 3 (accept mention of line 4, as long as line 3 is also identified);* ***1 mark*** *for clear explanation e.g. both cannot be negative.*

b $12x^2 + x - 6 < 0$

$(4x + 3)(3x - 2) < 0$

Critical values are $x = -\frac{3}{4}$ and $x = \frac{2}{3}$

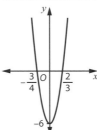

Solution is $-\frac{3}{4} < x < \frac{2}{3}$

1 mark *for correctly factorising or equivalent e.g. quadratic formula, or for both $-\frac{3}{4}$ and $\frac{2}{3}$ correct;* ***1 mark*** *for correct final inequality.*

See page 35, Quadratic inequalities

15. a $26 \times 10 \times 10 \times 10 \times 10 \times 10 = 2\,600\,000$
1 mark for correct product; 1 mark for correct final answer (or equivalent).
b $26 \times 10 \times 9 \times 8 \times 7 \times 25 = 3\,276\,000$
1 mark for $26 \times 10 \times 9 \times 8 \times 7 \times 25$; 1 mark for correct final answer.
See page 107, Outcomes and possibility spaces

16. $80 \times 0.75 = 60$ and $120 \times 0.75 = 90$
Medium trapezium has height $0.75h$ and parallel sides of length 60 and 90
Area of medium trapezium
$= \frac{1}{2} \times (60 + 90) \times 0.75h = 56.25h$
$0.75h \times 0.5 = 0.375h$, $60 \times 0.5 = 30$ and $90 \times 0.5 = 45$
Small trapezium has height $0.375h$ and parallel sides of length 30 and 45
Area of small trapezium
$= \frac{1}{2} \times (30 + 45) \times 0.375h = 14.0625h$
$56.25h - 14.0625h = 4050$
$42.1875h = 4050$
$h = 4050 \div 42.1875 = 96\,cm$
1 mark for $0.75h$ or 60 or 90; 1 mark for $0.5 \times$ your $0.75h$ $(= 0.375h)$ or $0.5 \times$ your 60 $(= 30)$ or $0.5 \times$ your 90 $(= 45)$; 1 mark for attempt to use $\frac{1}{2} \times$ (sum of parallel sides) $\times$ height for any trapezium; 1 mark for subtracting area of small trapezium from area of medium trapezium; 1 mark for correct answer of 96 cm. Total 5 marks.
Note that there are alternative methods.
See page 74, Area and perimeter

17.

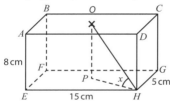

$PH^2 = 7.5^2 + 2.5^2 = 62.5$ (Pythagoras)
So $PH = \sqrt{62.5}$ $(= 7.90569\ldots)$
$\tan x = \frac{8}{\sqrt{62.5}}$ $(= 1.0119\ldots)$
$x = 45.3397\ldots = 45.3°$ to 1 dp
1 mark for $7.5^2 + 2.5^2$ $(= 62.5)$; 1 mark for $PH = 7.90569\ldots$; 1 mark for $\tan x = \frac{8}{PH}$; 1 mark for correct answer to 1 dp. Total 4 marks.
See page 88, Trigonometry in 3D

18. Consider an unknown angle (ABC) in a semicircle as shown. Let $\angle BAC = x$ and let $\angle BCA = y$

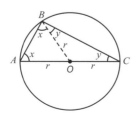

Let the radius of the circle be r
Then $OC = OA = OB = r$
As the base angles of an isosceles triangle are equal,
$\angle OBA = x$ and $\angle OBC = y$
So, $\angle ACB = x + y$

Now, as the angles in a triangle add up to 180°,
$x + y + x + y = 180°$
$2x + 2y = 180°$
$2(x + y) = 180°$
$x + y = 90°$
Therefore, the angle in a semicircle is a right angle.
1 mark for clear use of isosceles triangles to identify angle OCA ($= x$) or angle OCB ($= y$); 1 mark for $ACB = x + y$; 1 mark for $x + y + x + y = 180$; 1 mark for fully correct proof. Total 4 marks.
See page 66, Triangles & quadrilaterals

19. a i {3, 5, 7, 11, 13, 15, 17, 19}
   ii {1, 7, 9, 11, 17, 19}
1 mark for each correct answer.
b P(A given B) $= \frac{\text{P(A and B)}}{\text{P(B)}} = \frac{3}{7}$
1 mark for conditional probability seen or implied; 1 mark for correct answer or equivalent.
See page 114, Probability from Venn diagrams

20.

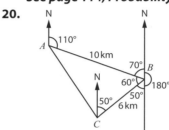

Angle $ABC = 110° - 50° = 60°$ (alternate angles)
Using the cosine rule,
$AC^2 = 10^2 + 6^2 - 2 \times 10 \times 6 \times \cos 60° = 76$
$AC = \sqrt{76}$ $(= 2\sqrt{19} = 8.717\ldots)$
Using the sine rule,
$\frac{\sin ACB}{10} = \frac{\sin 60°}{AC}$
$\sin ACB = \frac{10 \sin 60°}{AC} = \frac{5\sqrt{57}}{38}$ $(= 0.993\ldots)$
Angle $ACB = 83.4132\ldots°$ to 1 dp
Bearing of B from $C = 050°$ (alternate angles)
Bearing of A from $C = 360 - ($angle $ACB - 50)$
$= 326.6°$ to 1 dp
1 mark for 70, 60 or 50 (can be shown on diagram); 1 mark for use of cosine rule to find AC; 1 mark for use of sine rule to find ACB or BAC; 1 mark for correct value of ACB, BAC or AC; 1 mark for correct final bearing. Total 5 marks.
See page 85, Bearings

21. a

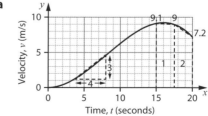

Acceleration = gradient of tangent
$\approx 3 \div 4 = 0.75\,m/s^2$
1 mark for drawing a line of correct slope on the graph; 1 mark for attempt to find gradient of your line; 1 mark for answer between 0.7 and 0.8. Total 3 marks.

b i Width of each strip = 2.5

Area of 1st trapezium = $\frac{1}{2} \times (9.1 + 9.0) \times 2.5$

= 22.625

Area of 2nd trapezium = $\frac{1}{2} \times (9.0 + 7.2) \times 2.5$

= 20.25

Total area = 22.625 + 20.25 = 43 (to 2 sf)

***1 mark** for using strips of width 2.5; **1 mark** for using correct formula for the area of either trapezium or for area of 1st trapezium between 22 and 23 or for area of 2nd trapezium between 20 and 21; **1 mark** for correct final answer between 42 and 44. Total 3 marks.*

ii Distance travelled between 15 and 20 seconds

***1 mark** for 'distance'.*

See page 44, Simple kinematic graphs

Paper 3 (Calculator)

1. $s = ut + \frac{1}{2}at^2$

$s - ut = \frac{1}{2}at^2$

$2(s - ut) = at^2$

$a = \frac{2(s - ut)}{t^2}$

***1 mark** for attempt to rearrange to a = … ; **1 mark** for correct final answer.*

See page 32, Rearranging formulae

2.

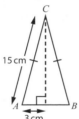

Base of right-angled triangle = $\frac{6}{2}$ = 3

$\cos CAB = \frac{3}{15}$

$CAB = \cos^{-1}\left(\frac{3}{15}\right)$ = 78.5° to 1 dp

***1 mark** for $\cos CAB = \frac{3}{15}$; **1 mark** for taking the inverse (= 78.46…); **1 mark** for correct answer to 1 dp. Total 3 marks.*

See page 83, Trigonometry 1

3. Let width be x, then length is $2x$

Area = $x \times 2x = 2x^2$

$2x^2 = 20$; $x^2 = 10$; $x = \sqrt{10}$

Length = $2 \times \sqrt{10} = 6.32$ cm to 3 sf

***1 mark** for algebraic representations for length and width; **1 mark** for setting expression for area equal to 20 and attempting to solve; **1 mark** for finding length; **1 mark** for correct answer (accept unrounded or different rounding). Total 4 marks.*

See page 74, Area and perimeter

4. a $2x - 5 \le 7 - x$; $3x - 5 \le 7$; $3x \le 12$; $x \le 4$

***1 mark** for a correct algebraic step; **1 mark** for final answer of $x \le 4$. (Note the inequality symbol must be used in final answer.)*

b

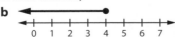

***1 mark** for number line with solid circle at 4 with line in the direction shown.*

c $-1.5 < 3n \le 9$

$-0.5 < n \le 3$

Integer values for n are 0, 1, 2 and 3

***1 mark** for $-0.5 < n \le 3$ or equivalent, e.g. $n > -0.5$ and $n \le 3$; **1 mark** for correct final answer.*

See page 20, Linear inequalities

5. As both numbers are even, you can call them $2m$ and $2n$ where n and m are integers.

Then the product is $2m \times 2n = 4mn$

This is a multiple of 4, so the product of the numbers is divisible by 4, as required.

***1 mark** for use of $2m$ or $2n$ for either even number; **1 mark** for $4mn$; **1 mark** for clear conclusion. Total 3 marks.*

See page 55, Algebraic proof

6. Enlargement, scale factor 2, from centre of enlargement (–4, 4)

***1 mark** for enlargement; **1 mark** for scale factor 2; **1 mark** for (–4, 4). Total 3 marks.*

See page 71, Enlargement

7. Multiplier for 3% increase is 1.03

Let the original amount be x

$x \times 1.03 = £711.22$

$x = £711.22 \div 1.03 = £690.50$

The original amount was £690.50

***1 mark** for $x \times 1.03 = £711.22$ or equivalent; **1 mark** for correct final answer.*

See page 60, Growth and depreciation

8.

Length (x cm)	Frequency	Midpoint	Frequency × midpoint
$0 < x \le 10$	8	5	40
$10 < x \le 20$	3	15	45
$20 < x \le 30$	y	25	$25y$
$30 < x \le 40$	15	35	525
$40 < x \le 50$	3	45	135
	$29 + y$		$745 + 25y$

From the table, $25.5 = \frac{745 + 25y}{29 + y}$

$739.5 + 25.5y = 745 + 25y$

$0.5y = 5.5$

$y = 11$

***1 mark** for using midpoints and multiplying by frequencies; **1 mark** for 25.5 = 4th column total ÷ 2nd column total; **1 mark** for attempt to rearrange to $y = …$; **1 mark** for correct final answer. Total 4 marks.*

See page 97, Grouped data

9. $\frac{3}{8}$ of the parcels are medium.

$\frac{5}{8}$ of the parcels are large.

$\frac{1}{3}$ of the medium parcels are 1st class.

$\frac{1}{3} \times \frac{3}{8} = \frac{3}{24} \left(= \frac{1}{8}\right)$

$\frac{3}{5}$ of the large parcels are 1st class.

$\frac{3}{5} \times \frac{5}{8} = \frac{15}{40} \left(= \frac{3}{8}\right)$

$\frac{1}{8} + \frac{3}{8} = \frac{4}{8} = \frac{1}{2}$

$\frac{1}{2}$ of the parcels are 1st class.

***1 mark** for $\frac{3}{8}$ or $\frac{5}{8}$; **1 mark** for $\frac{1}{3}$ or $\frac{3}{5}$; **1 mark** for $\frac{1}{3} \times \frac{3}{8}$ $\left(= \frac{3}{24} = \frac{1}{8}\right)$ or $\frac{3}{5} \times \frac{5}{8}$ $\left(= \frac{15}{40} = \frac{3}{8}\right)$; **1 mark** for correct final answer. Total 4 marks.*

See page 57, Harder ratio problems

10. Using line BC to form a right-angled triangle,

Base of triangle $= \dfrac{5\sqrt{2} - 3\sqrt{2}}{2} = \sqrt{2}$

Height of triangle $= \dfrac{2\sqrt{2}}{2} = \sqrt{2}$

$BC^2 = \sqrt{2}^2 + \sqrt{2}^2 = 4$

$BC = 2$

Length of $ABCDEF = 3\sqrt{2} + 2 \times 2 = 4 + 3\sqrt{2}\,\text{m}$

1 mark for attempt to find base or height of right-angled triangle ($= \sqrt{2}$); 1 mark for attempt to use Pythagoras to find BC ($= 2$); 1 mark for adding your five lengths; 1 mark for correct answer. Total 4 marks.

See page 82, Pythagoras' theorem

11.

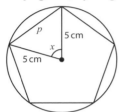

$x = 360° \div 5 = 72°$ (Angles at a point sum to $360°$.)

Using the cosine rule,

$p^2 = 5^2 + 5^2 - 2 \times 5 \times 5 \times \cos 72°$

$p = 5.8778\ldots = 5.9\,\text{cm}$ to 1 dp

1 mark for $360 \div 5$ ($= 72$); 1 mark for attempt to use the cosine rule (or for $p^2 = 34.54\ldots$); 1 mark for correct answer to 1 dp. Total 3 marks. Note that there are alternative methods.

See page 89, Sine and cosine rules

12. The 1st team has the higher median (3 vs 2), so they score more goals per game on average. The 2nd team has a greater interquartile range (3 vs 2.5), so they are less consistent.

1 mark for comparison using medians; 1 mark for comparison using IQR.

See page 103, Box plots

13. $p = \dfrac{c}{q^2}$ and $q = dr$, where c and d are constants.

Therefore, $p = \dfrac{k}{r^2}$, where k is a constant.

When $q = \dfrac{1}{3}$, $p = 36$ and $r = \dfrac{2}{9}$

Therefore, $36 = \dfrac{k}{\left(\frac{2}{9}\right)^2}$

$k = 36\left(\dfrac{4}{81}\right) = \dfrac{16}{9}$

$p = \dfrac{16}{9r^2}$

1 mark for either $p = \dfrac{c}{q^2}$ or $q = dr$ or equivalent; 1 mark for combining your two equations; 1 mark for substituting to find value of k; 1 mark for correct final answer. Total 4 marks.

Note that you also score the marks for working out two constants first and combining at the end.

See page 63, Direct & inverse proportion 2

14. Even though the products do not share a common prime factor, N and M are still both divisible by 1, so Jools is wrong.

1 mark for considering 1 as a factor or for observing that the products do not share a common prime factor; 1 mark for full explanation and statement that Jools is wrong.

See page 11, Prime factor decomposition

15. $\dfrac{3}{2x-1} - \dfrac{1}{3-x} = \dfrac{3(3-x) - (2x-1)}{(2x-1)(3-x)} = \dfrac{9 - 3x - 2x + 1}{(2x-1)(3-x)}$

$\qquad = \dfrac{10 - 5x}{(2x-1)(3-x)} = \dfrac{5(2-x)}{(2x-1)(3-x)}$

1 mark for attempt to change to common denominator; 1 mark for expanding and simplifying numerator; 1 mark for correct final answer. Total 3 marks.

See page 31, Algebraic fractions 3

16. a Let $f(x) = 3x^3 + x^2 - 3x - 5$

$f(1) = 3 \times 1^3 + 1^2 - 3 \times 1 - 5 = -4$

$f(1.5) = 3 \times 1.5^3 + 1.5^2 - 3 \times 1.5 - 5 = 2.875$

Change of sign, so root lies in interval $1 < x < 1.5$

1 mark for calculating $f(1)$ and $f(1.5)$; 1 mark for correct values and correct conclusion (change of sign).

b $3x^3 + x^2 - 3x - 5 = 0$

$3x^3 = 3x - x^2 + 5$

$x^3 = \dfrac{3x - x^2 + 5}{3}$

$x = \sqrt[3]{\dfrac{3x - x^2 + 5}{3}}$

1 mark for any correct algebraic step; 1 mark for fully correct.

c $x_0 = 1.5$

$x_1 = \sqrt[3]{\dfrac{3 \times 1.5 - 1.5^2 + 5}{3}} = 1.34195\ldots$

$x_2 = 1.34041\ldots$

$x_3 = 1.34038\ldots$

$x_4 = 1.34038\ldots$

Solution is $x = 1.3404$ to 4 dp.

1 mark for attempt to substitute $x = 1.5$ into iteration formula (or for $x = 1.34195\ldots$); 1 mark for two correct values; 1 mark for correct answer to 4 dp. Total 3 marks.

See page 52, Iteration 2

17. a The period is the number of degrees after which the graph repeats itself.

1 mark for explanation.

b

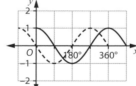

1 mark for correct answer.

c $y = 1 - \cos x$

1 mark for $-f(x)$; 1 mark for correct answer (also accept $1 - f(x)$).

See page 41, Trigonometric graphs and page 43, Graph transformations 2

18. a Substituting the coordinates gives

$(-4)^2 + 3^2 = 16 + 9 = 25$

Therefore, A lies on the circle.

1 mark for correct substitution and explanation.

b

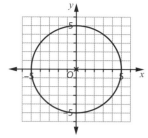

1 mark for circle drawn; 1 mark for radius 5 and centre O

c The angle in a semicircle is a right angle (circle theorem). Either AC or BC is the diameter.

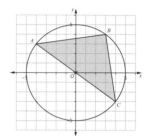 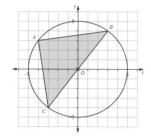

By symmetry, the possible coordinates of C are $(4, -3)$ and $(-3, -4)$.

1 mark for stating the correct circle theorem; 1 mark for each correct pair of coordinates. Total 3 marks.

See page 40, Equation of a circle and page 68, Circle theorems 1

19. $5x + y = 10 \Rightarrow y = 10 - 5x$

Substituting for y in the other equation gives

$10x(10 - 5x) = -48$

$100x - 50x^2 = -48$

$50x^2 - 100x - 48 = 0$

$25x^2 - 50x - 24 = 0$

$(5x - 12)(5x + 2) = 0$

$x = \frac{12}{5}$ or $x = -\frac{2}{5}$

When $x = \frac{12}{5}$, $y = 10 - 5\left(\frac{12}{5}\right) = -2$

When $x = -\frac{2}{5}$, $y = 10 - 5\left(-\frac{2}{5}\right) = 12$

1 mark for rearranging the linear equation to make y (or x) the subject and substituting into the non-linear equation; 1 mark for expanding the brackets; 1 mark for rearranging the quadratic to make equal to 0; 1 mark for finding the two values of x; 1 mark for finding the corresponding values of y. Total 5 marks.

See page 36, Non-linear simultaneous equations

20. a

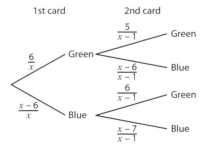

1 mark for either branch correct; 1 mark for both correct.

b $\frac{6}{x} \times \frac{5}{x-1} = \frac{1}{42}$

$6 \times 5 \times 42 = x(x - 1)$

$x^2 - x - 1260 = 0$

$(x + 35)(x - 36) = 0$

$x = -35$ or $x = 36$

$x > 0 \Rightarrow x = 36$

1 mark for attempt to form an equation with denominators x and $x - 1$ both seen; 1 mark for attempt to form a quadratic equation (= 0); 1 mark for factorising (or equivalent method e.g. quadratic formula) and solving; 1 mark for correct final answer (negative solution does not need to be seen). Total 4 marks.

See page 110, Tree diagrams

21. $\vec{AB} = \vec{AO} + \vec{OB} = \mathbf{b} - \mathbf{a}$

$\vec{OC} = 3\vec{AB} = 3(\mathbf{b} - \mathbf{a})$

$\vec{AN} = \frac{2}{5}(\mathbf{b} - \mathbf{a})$

$\vec{NC} = \vec{NA} + \vec{AO} + \vec{OC} = -\frac{2}{5}(\mathbf{b} - \mathbf{a}) - \mathbf{a} + 3(\mathbf{b} - \mathbf{a})$

$\qquad = -\frac{18}{5}\mathbf{a} + \frac{13}{5}\mathbf{b}$

$\vec{OP} = t\vec{OB} = t\mathbf{b}$ for some constant, t

Also, $\vec{OP} = \vec{OA} + \vec{AN} + \vec{NP}$

$\qquad = \mathbf{a} + \frac{2}{5}(\mathbf{b} - \mathbf{a}) + \frac{1}{k+1}\vec{NC}$

$\qquad = \mathbf{a} + \frac{2}{5}(\mathbf{b} - \mathbf{a}) + \frac{1}{k+1}\left(-\frac{18}{5}\mathbf{a} + \frac{13}{5}\mathbf{b}\right)$

Equating expressions for $\vec{OP}$,

$t\mathbf{b} = \mathbf{a} + \frac{2}{5}(\mathbf{b} - \mathbf{a}) + \frac{1}{k+1}\left(-\frac{18}{5}\mathbf{a} + \frac{13}{5}\mathbf{b}\right)$

Comparing coefficients for $\mathbf{a}$,

$0 = 1 - \frac{2}{5} - \frac{18}{5(k+1)}$

$\frac{3}{5} = \frac{18}{5(k+1)}$

$k + 1 = 6$

$k = 5$

1 mark for $\vec{OC} = 3(\mathbf{b} - \mathbf{a})$; 1 mark for attempt to find $\vec{NC}$ or $\vec{PC}$; 1 mark for finding two separate expressions for $\vec{OP}$ (or equivalent) and for equating coefficients; 1 mark for correct final answer. Total 4 marks.

See page 93, Vectors 2

My notes

My notes

My notes

My notes

My notes

OXFORD
UNIVERSITY PRESS

Great Clarendon Street, Oxford, OX2 6DP, United Kingdom

Oxford University Press is a department of the University of Oxford.

It furthers the University's objective of excellence in research, scholarship, and education by publishing worldwide. Oxford is a registered trade mark of Oxford University Press in the UK and in certain other countries

© Oxford University Press 2020

The moral rights of the authors have been asserted

First published in 2020

All rights reserved. No part of this publication may be reproduced, stored in a retrieval system, or transmitted, in any form or by any means, without the prior permission in writing of Oxford University Press, or as expressly permitted by law, by licence or under terms agreed with the appropriate reprographics rights organization. Enquiries concerning reproduction outside the scope of the above should be sent to the Rights Department, Oxford University Press, at the address above.

You must not circulate this work in any other form and you must impose this same condition on any acquirer

British Library Cataloguing in Publication Data
Data available

978-1-38-200652-1

10 9 8 7 6 5 4 3 2 1

Paper used in the production of this book is a natural, recyclable product made from wood grown in sustainable forests.

The manufacturing process conforms to the environmental regulations of the country of origin.

Printed in the United Kingdom by Bell and Bain Ltd, Glasgow

Acknowledgements
Authors: Paul Hunt and Jemma Sherwood
Series Editor: Naomi Bartholomew-Millar
Editorial team: Dom Holdsworth and Rosie Day
With thanks to Katie Wood, Karen Gordon and Rachel Phillipson for their contributions.

The publisher would like to thank the following for permission to use copyright material:

Cover illustrations: Cristina Romero Palma / Shutterstock, Rachael Arnott / Shutterstock

Artwork: QBS Media Services Inc.

Although we have made every effort to trace and contact all copyright holders before publication this has not been possible in all cases. If notified, the publisher will rectify any errors or omissions at the earliest opportunity.

Links to third party websites are provided by Oxford in good faith and for information only. Oxford disclaims any responsibility for the materials contained in any third party website referenced in this work.